THE Second FIELD
Book of Country Queries

THE Second FIELD
Book of
Country Queries

Edited by
VALERIE PORTER

PELHAM BOOKS
Stephen Greene Press

PELHAM BOOKS/STEPHEN GREENE PRESS

Published by the Penguin Group
27 Wrights Lane, London W8 5TZ, England
Viking Penguin Inc., 40 West 23rd Street, New York, New York 10010, USA
The Stephen Greene Press Inc., 15 Muzzey Street, Lexington, Massachusetts 02173,
USA
Penguin Books Australia Ltd, Ringwood, Victoria, Australia
Penguin Books Canada Ltd, 2801 John Street, Markham, Ontario, Canada L3R 1B4
Penguin Books (NZ) Ltd, 182–190 Wairau Road, Auckland 10, New Zealand

Penguin Books Ltd, Registered Offices: Harmondsworth, Middlesex, England

First published 1989

Photoset in 10 on 12 point Linotron Bembo by Wilmaset, Birkenhead, Wirral

Printed and bound in Great Britain by Richard Clay Ltd, Bungay, Suffolk

British Library Cataloguing in Publication Data
Porter, Val, *1942–*
The Field book of country queries II.
1. Great Britain. Countryside
I. Title   II. The Field
941'.009'734

ISBN 0 7207 1862 7

Contents

CONTENTS

Introduction

THE FIELD was first published in 1853, when it described itself as
THE FIELD ILLUSTRATED, OR COUNTRY GENTLE-MAN'S NEWSPAPER. The very title, even in the abbreviated
form, immediately brings to mind a wellbred country gentleman of
property and means whose main interests are perhaps in the sport he
finds in the countryside. The title was carefully chosen: 'field' carries
implications of agriculture, hunting, racing, sport, battle, open
country and general areas of interest. Thus in one word it embraced
most of the subjects covered by the paper.

To a large extent, the earlier reader of *THE FIELD* was indeed a
country gentleman who enjoyed riding to hounds and shooting, but
his interests were in fact much wider than field sports and farming.
He enjoyed a broad range of sports, from angling and archery to
rowing and yachting and, in later periods, croquet, cricket, tennis,
cycling, motoring and golf. He also enjoyed gambling, and ample
column inches were devoted to the turf and coursing as well as the
chase.

But *THE FIELD* sought to cover far more than the sporting and
rural connotations suggested by its title and many of its numerous
pages of very small print were devoted to global, or at least imperial,
matters as well as home and provincial news. It was a genuine
newspaper, collecting information from around the world and
presenting it in a lively style supported by some very persuasive and
well written leading articles and editorial comments.

For most of the first century of *THE FIELD*'s existence, England
(and *THE FIELD* was very much an English paper) seemed to be at
war somewhere in the world, and the kind of man who subscribed
to *THE FIELD* was very likely to have a military background, or to
send a son or two to fight for his country. Those who remained at
home could play soldiers by reading the very detailed intelligence
reports and despatches from the front, and a nation of frustrated

armchair generals and admirals could devise their own tactics for defeating the enemy with the aid of the maps and opinions published each week in *THE FIELD*.

Sunday, September 9, 1854
To the Public in General, and Advertisers in particular.
THE FIELD
ILLUSTRATED;
Or, EVERY GENTLEMAN'S NEWSPAPER

Having obtained an extensive circulation amongst the Aristocracy, Gentry, and Monied Classes in this country and its dependencies, and in Europe and America, is the best medium of Advertising.

From the Stamp Returns, published on April 5, 1854, it appears, that during the two years, 1852 and 1853, the number of Stamps supplied to each of the under-mentioned Newspapers gave them an average sale as follows:

FIELD	4,409	Express	2,235
Morning Herald	4,021	Leader	2,140
Daily News	3,910	Herapath's Journal	2,066
Guardian	3,904	John Bull	2,020
Economist	3,837	Globe	1,926
British Banner	3,798	Weekly News	1,709
Record	3,736	United Service Gazette	1,708
Watchman	3,681	Railway Times	1,641
Nonconformist	2,987	Atlas	1,479
Spectator	2,856	Standard	1,456
St James's Chronicle	2,844	Naval & Military	
Morning Post	2,652	Gazette	1,313
Sun	2,539	Patriot	1,304
Morning Chronicle	2,364	Gardeners' & Farmers'	
Britannia	2,329	Journal	752

Very often the gentleman reader owned a substantial country house and estate, though very often too he kept a London residence and carried out most of his business in the city, much like the commuter of today, so that his outlook tended to be cosmopolitan rather than parochial. Naturally he employed staff to carry out their duties in the house, in the garden, in the stables and kennels and on the estate.

But gradually times changed, property-holding dwindled, and the focus of his interests began to shift. Leisure time decreased, and during the 20th century the change was radical, widespread and irrevocable. There is a telling article, an extract from which appears in the final section of this book, which shows how the Great War changed the pattern of life forever: suddenly the gentleman had to make do without some of his servants and he actually had to learn some of their skills for himself, like driving a car or growing vegetables. It is perhaps at this point that THE FIELD's weekly *Answers to Correspondents*, upon which this book is based, began to reflect a change from gentleman employer to 'do-it-yourself'.

From the very first issue in January 1853, the paper relied quite heavily on its readers to stimulate discussion about all manner of subjects. Every issue had a special page of *Answers to Correspondents* (originally rather formidably headed *Notices to Correspondents*), as well as many more answers to personal queries scattered among the various regular sections devoted to, say, horticulture or agriculture. (At first, incidentally, letters from observers of nature tended to be printed under Hunting or under Shooting, as they invariably related to foxes and gamebirds.)

However, right up to the Second World War, the question prompting the answer was not printed, nor in many cases was it even indirectly indicated. Only the correspondent and the editor knew the question: the rest of the readers, intruders upon a semi-private exchange of information, simply had to try and guess what the question might have been, and frequently there were few if any clues to guide them. In this compilation of those answers, we have on the whole continued that editorial coyness and you are invited to imagine the question for yourself. Very often it has been impossible for us to be more specific anyway, though there may have been vague clues in the original publication because the answers were sometimes given under general subject headings like 'Angling', 'Canine', 'Racing' or 'Aquatics'. But the most popular headings were 'Miscellaneous' and 'Replies to Inquiries', which help not at all.

It was an important part of THE FIELD's philosophy to encourage its readers not only to ask questions but to answer those of other readers and on occasion to put THE FIELD's own experts right if necessary. Before the paper was two years old, it was acquired by new publishers and they specifically invited 'the communications of our readers'. There were, they said, 'many topics on which information is sought by some, that the experience of others can answer; let them send the inquiry for insertion, and, doubtless, it will elicit replies. Thus . . . do we hope to facilitate the communication of mutual intelligence on all country things.'

Thereafter it became the practice to publish several readers' letters among the pages of, say, *The Naturalist* (an innovation during the 1860s) or *The Country House* sections, to see if other readers might solve the questioner's problem. Even in the *Answers to Correspondents* section, there was now a note proclaiming: 'TO CORRESPONDENTS. Although Editorial answers are given in this column to some of the questions forwarded to us, it is not with the intention of suppressing discussion. If, therefore, any one dissents from the view taken by us, or can throw further light upon the subject, we shall be happy to insert his comments.'

The editors were well aware that people do like sharing their knowledge and experience, and no doubt they also bore in mind that, by never on principle answering questions through the post but only through the public pages of the paper, they offered every incentive for questioners and answerers to keep buying THE FIELD each week! But there is a deeper philosophy at work here and it is hinted at in an article in 1900 about the increase in 'spectator' sports. It was recognised that, little by little, the Englishman was becoming a voyeur, watching others taking an active part rather than playing the game himself. Participation was becoming a thing of the past. Of course, in our own time radio and television, particularly the latter, have perhaps brought this trend to a head and the very great majority of people are but armchair sportsmen, in spite of recent fashions for jogging and fitness. The attitude extends well beyond the boundaries of recreation and one begins to realise from the pages of *THE FIELD* that we are far more likely today to let 'them' do it, rather than do it ourselves, whether it is playing football or cricket, or making sure the buses keep running . . .

The 19th-century country gentleman, privileged no doubt, could find time for what one might call trivial pursuits like worrying about matters of etiquette or watching wildlife. As an amateur observer, he has left us an invaluable treasury of information on the natural world, whether his interest was sparked by concern for his field sports or whether he was a true lover of all nature for its own sake. He also had time to have an inquiring mind on all matters and to broaden his horizons with travel and literature, though admittedly there was very little about the appreciation of art in *THE*

FIELD, except for social visits to the theatre and the opera house. He had a boyish passion for toys – new guns, pills and potions, contraptions, gimmicks and patented inventions. And, of course, there was so much that *was* new and exciting: it was a great age of discovery.

One can glean a considerable feel for the period just from the choice of the correspondents' subjects, the attitudes revealed by the answers, and the manner and style in which the answers were given, and it is hoped that, as well as being practically informed and entertained by those answers, you will also gain a little insight into the social and moral changes which have crept over our society in the last 135 years or so. Here and there brief extracts from leading articles have been included to help build up the period picture.

The wheel turns. Some of the matters which concern us today were equally of concern a century or more ago and it comes as something of a shock to read, for example, a diatribe against intensive farming and the loss of wildlife in the time of our great grandparents.

Today we still thirst healthily for knowledge and are just as eager to look back to the experience and wisdom of old as forward to the fast-developing technology which both intrigues and alarms us. The response to *THE FIELD Book of Country Queries* we published in 1987 was unexpectedly enthusiastic and in this second book we have had a chance to include some of the gems which lack of space forced out of the first book, and have also had more time to continue browsing through some seven thousand dusty back numbers of *THE FIELD* (yes, one issue a week since 1853!). It is an enjoyable and distracting occupation because there are so many intriguing articles, comments, illustrations and advertisements scattered between the *Answers*: not only does the eye wander but also the mind sets off tangentially to meander down unimaginable pathways while countless trains of thought steam off on journeys to unknown destinations. The past gives one a perspective on the present.

True to the philosophy of the paper's editors, our first book sparked off all sorts of responses from its readers. For example, one *Answer* had stated that fly-paper 'did not survive the Second World War and the advent of DDT'. That answer was given in the early 1970s. Not so! A reader in Herefordshire wrote to say that his village shop had never stopped stocking and selling sticky fly-paper and still did so (it was now made by such technically advanced companies as Rentokil). A 1937 item on coracles at Cenarth excited a radio interviewer who told us that the very same place still boasted

HEADINGS LISTED
IN THE INDEX, 1853

AGRICULTURE
ANGLING
ANSWERS TO
  CORRESPONDENTS
ARCHERY
BIRTHS, MARRIAGES
  AND DEATHS
THE CHASE
CHESS
COURSING
CRICKET
FOREIGN AND
  COLONIAL
  INTELLIGENCE
FREEMANSONRY AND
  MASONIC
  INTELLIGENCE
HOME NEWS
HORTICULTURAL
  INTELLIGENCE
HUNTING FIXTURES
  AND RUNS
IRELAND (NEWS FROM)
LAW INTELLIGENCE
LIFE OF A RACEHORSE
MARKETS
MEDICAL
METROPOLITAN
  INTELLIGENCE
MILITARY
  INTELLIGENCE
MISCELLANEOUS
NAVAL INTELLIGENCE
NEWS FROM THE
  ARCTIC EXPEDITION
NEWS OF THE WEEK

NOTICES OF BOOKS
OUR LETTER BAG
PARLIAMENTARY
  INTELLIGENCE
POLICE INTELLIGENCE
POULTRY
PROVINCIAL
  INTELLIGENCE
RACES
RACING
RAILWAYS AND
  TELEGRAPHS
ROWING FIXTURES
SCOTLAND
  (NEWS FROM)
SHOOTING
SPORTING
  (MISCELLANEOUS)
THEATRES AND
  AMUSEMENTS
UNIVERSITY AND
  CLERICAL
WEATHER
WORK AND WAGES
YEOMANRY AND
  MILITIA
YACHTING – REGATTAS
YACHTING – THE
  ROYAL CLUBS
YACHT CLUBS NOT
  UNDER ROYAL
  PATRONAGE
YACHTING
  MISCELLANEA
YACHTING
  ILLUSTRATIONS

coracles today. Many people thanked the book for solving their own practical problems, though others disagreed with suggested remedies and put forward better ideas. It is by this sharing of experience that the human gains wisdom, and we have the added advantage over other creatures that, being able to read, we can absorb the knowledge of people we shall never meet, and of people and indeed whole cultures long since dead.

Finally, we have printed the *Answers* with very little comment as to their validity or efficacy, because that is how the original reader of *THE FIELD* accepted them. Occasionally there is an observation from the editor, set in italics and enclosed in square brackets. We make no claim at all to having tried out every remedy and must warn you that in some cases the practices recommended have long since been condemned as ineffectual or even dangerous. Arsenic, lead and other toxic substances were commonly employed in the past, for example, and DDT, the miracle dust, was once the answer for every pest until it was banned because of its infinite persistence. Even today, the aerosol sprays we take for granted are now suspected of causing quite serious environmental damage. No doubt many of the chemicals and medicines recommended today will one day prove to be just as inappropriate or even harmful as some of those of the past. So bear in mind that we learn something new every day and what seemed good once might be a very bad thing now. In many cases the date of an *Answer* has been indicated to serve as a gentle warning as well as an interesting historical note, or else the language betrays the period. However, we can take no responsibility at all for any results of carrying out advice given long ago. Laws change, too, and you should be aware of them. Be prudent.

On the other hand, many of the forgotten secret remedies of the past are of great value today and our own scientists are admitting that the herbalists and witches of old really did know a thing or two about curing people with plant extracts in some cases.

There *is* plenty of sound practical advice in the *Answers* printed in the following pages, but perhaps above all the book should be seen as an interesting entertainment and a historical record of a changing society, and perhaps too a source of inspiration.

Valerie Porter
1988

The Country House

🐝 The Fabric of the House

DATING

Dating a House by its Handmade Bricks

Bricks, by their shape, consistency, size and sometimes makers'
marks, can give clues to the date of a house or building, in
conjunction with other architectural and structural materials and
facts. Bricks and brick-making were introduced into England by the
Romans but the signs are only in mounds of building remains. Their
successors – Danes, Saxons, Norsemen and Normans – did not use
bricks. A precise date for the reappearance of bricks cannot be given
but they began to be imported from north Germany in the early 15th
century; apparently the native manufacture of bricks started in the
middle of the century, encouraged by Henry VI. These were used in
the building of Eton College (1440). Bricks were at first baked or
fired in clamps and they contained ash, which gives clues to their
dating. Later, bricks were fired in kilns and, although at first varying
in size and thickness, eventually became standardised at 9 ins x 4.5
ins x 3 ins. Clays differ in colour and bricks can be identified with
certain areas. *The History of English Brickwork* by W. Frost (1928)
may be of interest.

Georgian or Queen Anne?

A typical Queen Anne house has a gable with flowing curves and
round-headed door and windows. In the later Georgian styles a
prominent key stone was placed at the top of these openings. The
style became more plain and devoid of decoration. Sash windows
were used in the Queen Anne period but the date of introduction is
uncertain. In the Regency period windows were more often square
than the previous oblong type. Another feature was that the upper

8

storey windows came to have the upper sash only half the depth of the lower one. Quite a number of details of this kind appeared and it was rather in this way than in any fundamental change of design that differences occurred. As buildings, the essentials of the two periods have much in common. Indeed unless a house is dated or has some outstanding characteristic feature to mark it, even the experts find it difficult to say exactly where it comes in the Queen Anne – Georgian period.

CHIMNEYS AND FIREPLACES
Clinker

The formation of clinker in your multi-fuel Windhanger Stove would be related to the types of fuel being burnt and probably uneven combustion. We would suspect mixtures of soft coal, coal dust and unseasoned and/or resinous wood, which would tend to lead to rather sticky mixtures of poorly vaporised tars, resins etc. Unfavourable weather affecting temperatures of air supply, chimney, etc. could aggravate the problem. A possible solution is to add a sprinkling of salt (cheap agricultural salt will do) when adding wood. Check flues and chimney for smooth passage of gases and smoke. Obviously, the cheaper grades of fuel would contribute to clinker. It is also unwise to use such a stove for the disposal of damp rubbish, kitchen or household waste.

Church Heating System

It would be quite safe to use antifreeze in the electrically heated and pump-circulated water heating system of your local church. An anti-freeze based on ethylene glycol would be suitable and can be obtained with a corrosion inhibitor (sodium nitrate, or benzoate) added. You can use one of the products marketed by most of the oil companies through garages, motor factors or central heating firms. The amount needed will be proportionate to the water capacity of the system and ambient temperature to be maintained.

Sparky Logs

It is not easy to prevent some logs from throwing out sparks and chips or shreds of burning wood entirely. This usually occurs when coniferous wood (pine, larch, fir etc.) is burnt. These woods contain small knots of resinous wood and nodes of resins, which 'pop' under heat. The simplest way to check the sparking is to sprinkle salt lightly on the logs when they have begun to burn and repeat when fresh logs are added. As a further insurance, place a fine-mesh fireguard in front of the fire. We suspect you are burning rather green logs: sparking is less pronounced from seasoned wood, cut and stored in an airy place for a year or so before use. It helps if the logs are cut in small, chunky pieces and are added with the bark facing inwards. Feed a wood fire from the back, placing fresh logs more or less behind those already burning.

Fireplace Design

A fireplace should be designed to give smooth, swift passage to smoke and hot gases: the fireback should lean forward and a cold air pocket behind the chimney or fireplace breast should be avoided. For this purpose it would be necessary to fill in some of the space created above the sheet-metal you have used to block off the old flue when attempting to restrict the opening at the throat of the chimney (a sound method of reducing the draught created by your hearth fire). Otherwise there will be eddies and a mixture of cold and hot air and gases conducive to downdraughts. This fill-in could be done with sheet metal. The alternative is to fit a fireclay back, which would have to be a tall one, and a canopy with an underlip which restricts the opening, through which the smokes goes, to 6–9 in. A factor which may impair the drawing of a fireplace is that an outside wall could be more exposed and thus slow to warm, and this could affect performance after lighting due to the presence of cold air. The position of the chimney pot or exit in relationship to surrounding buildings, trees etc., may be too low and liable to be affected by air currents and turbulences in certain weather conditions; this can be mitigated by fitting louvred pots which have baffles that stop downdraughts.

Two Chimney Sweeps

The danger with leaving the resinous deposit made by burning wood on the inside of your small chimney is that the cakey matter burns fiercely and stubbornly should it catch fire and can be extremely hazardous – more so than the ordinary deposit of soot from a coal fire. There is, apparently, no easy way of dislodging it except by scraping. If you find the space too small, the best way is to have a piece of steel made to fit just inside the chimney, fastened to ropes at each end; lower this from the pot, and with two people, one holding the rope at the fireside end, the other at the pot end, work the steel plate carefully up and down to dislodge the caked matter. This is only practical where the chimney is reasonably smooth-sided. In rough chimneys there is a danger of dislodging stones and mortar. Otherwise, the alternative is to burn a smokeless fuel for a season with a view to drying out the deposit and rendering it more amenable to ordinary sweeping. The trouble generally arises from the burning of insufficiently seasoned wood containing sap.

WALLS
Brighter Bricks

The methods of brightening your cottage's sand-faced bricks, while keeping the bricks in their natural state, depend on what is wearing the brick. If it is a patina of greenish colour imparted by the growth of algae, moss and lichens, you can clear this by wetting thoroughly with a solution of ordinary domestic bleach (1 part to 25 parts water) applied as a drenching spray on a dry, dull day. If weathering has dulled the brick, then mechanical treatment will be necessary such as scouring with a wire brush (an electric appliance or drill with a suitable head is best) or rubbing with a carborundum stone. Sand-blasting with quartz or carborundum grit is a matter for professionals. Afterwards, the brick could usefully be painted with a silicone water-repellent paint.

Mixing Limewash

There are several ways of preparing limewash for external application so that it will not flake. A very good country way is to place a bushel measure of quick-lime and 20 lb of tallow in a rainwater barrel or cask, and slake it with hot water. Cover it with sack-cloth to enclose the steam, and when cool, run it through a sieve and then apply it. You should add enough water to give a creamy painting consistency. A more modern alternative is to add 1 part Portland cement to 3 parts lime and mix it well while it is dry, then add the water to give a creamy consistency and it is ready for application. To give a pink colour, you can add Venetian red or a household dye.

Reed and Plaster

The perfect condition of the reeds you found bedding the plaster on the walls of your house built in 1787 is of much interest. It is not highly exceptional, however, for work of this kind to be uncovered where the building has been kept in good repair and protection from the weather. There are at least three factors which have contributed to the excellent state of preservation in which you found the reeds. Firstly the fact that the reeds themselves contain a relatively high content of silica – a durable element; secondly the use of a lime plaster, itself a good preservative, and thirdly the use of reeds properly ripened and dried, under conditions of construction where the weather, damp and agents of decomposition had no access.

ROOF

Moss on Tiles

Moss and lichen are likely to do only superficial harm on stone roofing tiles by causing very gradual crumbling of the stone to fine dust. But the tiles usually accumulate a 'soil' of stone dust and dirt, which may eventually house other plants and insects, which are more damaging. Then moisture is held, and constant freezing and thawing may accelerate erosion of the tiles. Moss and lichen growths can be quelled by spraying with a tar oil wash at 10% concentration, repeating occasionally. Do this when the roof is dry and ensure that the first rain-water after spraying goes to waste.

To Fireproof Thatch [1954]

A straightforward method of fire-proofing thatch and straw-walled buildings is to spray them with a solution of $\frac{1}{2}$ lb boric acid and 4 lb of ammonium phosphate in 5 gallons of water. This quantity should treat 80–120 sq yards, according to the degree of fire-resistance desired. The intent must be to coat the straw with the solution as far and as deeply as possible and allow it to dry in. Much depends upon the fineness of the spray used and the force behind it. Any run-off of the solution should be avoided, and if there is difficulty in wetting the straw at first attempt it would be helpful to add a wetting agent or spreader and then follow with a second spraying when the first is dry. It does not give 100% immunity from fire but it does make the straw fire-resistant and very difficult to ignite. There would have to be a secondary source of heat to set the underlying straw alight. There are proprietary fire-proofing materials available, based on asbestos, but these would presumably prove too expensive for the purpose of a straw-walled farm building.

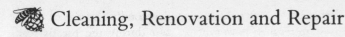 Cleaning, Renovation and Repair

STAINS
Blueberry Marks

To remove blueberry stains from clothing, first sponge well with cold, soft water. Follow this by sponging with glycerine using a small-pored plastic sponge. Leave for an hour and then apply a liquid dry cleaner based on carbon tetrachloride. If the dark staining still persists, a bleach such as hydrogen peroxide may have to be used. Much depends on the nature of the cloth and application needs care.

Coffee

If the coffee stain on the lamb's wool pullover is recent, moisten it and sponge with a solution of borax ($\frac{1}{2}$ oz to $\frac{1}{2}$ pint of tepid water); rinse and wash with a cold-water woollen detergent.

Puppy Puddles

It is difficult to restore faded patches where a puppy has made puddles on a carpet after the carpet has dried. However, try carefully moistening the damaged areas with a solution of 1 tablespoonful of white vinegar, 3 tablespoonsful of soft water and 1 teaspoonful of liquid detergent. Leave for about 15 minutes, rinse well and sponge dry. When dry it may be possible to touch up colour with a cold-water dye solution; use a camel hair brush and part the tufts to moisten along the strands.

Spilt Tea

To remove tea stains from a Wilton carpet, sponge lightly with a clean cloth wrung out in warm water to which a little sodium bicarbonate has been added ($\frac{1}{2}$ teaspoon per quart). Finish by sponging with warm water only, work lightly, and then allow to dry. If tea with milk was spilt, use a detergent solution or a carpet shampoo. To deal with stains from hot tea spilt on a leather-topped coffee table, professionals would use British Museum Leather Dressing to clean and preserve the leather and this should help you. It is usually available ready-made from leather shops or from craft shops specialising in leatherwork, or it can be made up as follows. Dissolve $\frac{1}{2}$ oz white beeswax in 11 oz hexane; add 7 oz anhydrous lanolin, stir and mix well, then add 1 fl oz of cedar oil. Hexane is highly inflammable: keep clear of naked lights and do not smoke while mixing. Use the mixture to rub sparingly into the leather; polish after about two days with a soft cloth. Another good stain remover for leather is trichloroethane, sometimes sold as Genkilene in craft or do-it-yourself shops. Alternatively, if the staining cannot be satisfactorily removed, paint the leather with a coating of polyurethane leather paint, usually marketed for shoes in various colours.

Vegetable Stains on Fingers

Vegetable stains can be removed from the fingers by soaking them for a few minutes in warm water to which a little lemon juice has been added (about a teaspoonful to a pint of water) and then rubbing; or by rubbing the stains with the skin of lemon or banana. The hands should be oiled afterwards with a skin lotion or cream.

LEATHER AND SKINS
A Very Old Stuffed Tiger's Head

Provided that the hair of the tiger's head and skin is still firmly anchored and the skin itself has suffered no deterioration, you can best clean the head by first removing all loose dust and detritus, carefully lifting it with a vacuum cleaner fitted with a small nozzle. The fur can be further cleaned by shampooing with a dry powder shampoo, applied to the fur, and then removed with the vacuum cleaner, or with a sudsy solution of a detergent suitable for wool (such as Stergene or Dreft) applied with a plastic sponge, rinsed off with clear soft water, and then dried in the shade on a warm day or with a hair-dryer. You can use a comb to facilitate the work. The eyes, teeth etc. can be wiped with a damp cloth dipped in detergent if necessary. There is no need for fresh preservative treatment but see that the head is dry before re-hanging. You may have to watch for moth and insect activity in the warmer months but the application of a household insecticide about the base should prevent this.

Stuffed Stag's Head

Assuming that the stag's head has been prepared by a competent taxidermist to preserve the hide and skin against deterioration by bacteria, insects and fungi, the most promising method of protecting it against weathering by rain, frost, snow and sun would be to apply a clear water-repellent silicone solution to all exposed areas. It can be applied by spray or brush and allowed to dry. An alternative is a clear organic wood preservative. You would probably have to renew annually. As the head is an organic substance, even the bones and antlers would eventually be subject to change and some decomposition.

Moulting Deerskin

The shedding of hair in your deerskin rug is unlikely to be due to any lack of care (unless moths are in it) but may be caused by some fault in the curing of the skin. Either it was left too long between being taken from the animal and cured, or the method used may not have been the most suitable. Normally, it is desirable that skins should be stretched, scraped and treated with a preservative containing alum in order to ensure that the hair is held fast. To a lesser degree, the condition of the animal at the time of the year it was skinned may have some effect, but the hair should not be lost in huge quantities if curing was prompt and properly done. If you could find out from the supplier what method was followed, it might be possible to improve matters by re-curing, so the skin will retain what hair is left. It would entail removing any backing, restretching the skin on a frame, treating with an alum preservative solution, and re-drying. Whether the skin will stand up to this or not could only be decided by expert visual examination.

Salty Sheepskin

It is probable that the sheepskin you bought last summer, which now becomes wet on damp days and dries leaving salt grains on the surface, has been cured by salting and the salt absorbs moisture from a damp atmosphere. The next time it happens, stretch the skin on a board, wool side down, and scrape it free of salt and any loose shreds of membrane. Cover with a dressing of 2 oz of carbonate of soda, 4 oz of dry powder soap, 3 oz of powdered alum, well mixed together, and rub in for a few minutes. Leave covered with the dressing for a week, rubbing the powder in and stirring it about daily, with the skin in a dry, warm room. Then shake off the powder, which may be kept for future use if desired. Any further treatment will depend on the use to which the skin is put. If it is to be a rug, it needs only working a little with the hands to flex it, and then backing with a lining.

To Soften a Sheepskin

It is not clear whether the sheepskin has been simply air-cured or chemically cured. You will have to restore suppleness by sponging on the flesh side with a solution of $\frac{1}{2}$ gallon of hot water, poured over $\frac{1}{2}$ lb of powered alum and 2 oz plain salt, well stirred, and allowed to cool to lukewarmness. Leave overnight, or until the skin is soft enough to be worked and be flexible. You may have to repeat the sponging in the morning. Allow to dry without losing flexibility, and smear liberally with an animal fat (lard, lanoline, tallow, etc.), working this into the skin with your hands and a flat stick or flat rib bone. Then remove the skin from the frame and continue to work the fat into the tissue by kneading, hand pressure and folding, until it is rendered thoroughly supple. Remove excess fat with a scraper, clean up the wool side with fine veneer sawdust or oatmeal, applied to reach the base of the wool and subsequently vacuumed out. The skin should then he ready for making up and lining.

Leather Rifle Sling

Presumably the rifle sling has been made from animal hide, probably oil-dressed. Provided it has not become brittle with age, it should be possible to restore some flexibility by dressing it with castor oil or pure lanolin. For a first application, apply mixed with about 30% alcohol or methylated spirit, painted on, which should help penetration, followed 24 hours later with just castor oil or lanolin which has been warmed (to about 100–120°F). As the leather becomes more flexible, repeat. When flexibility has been restored, wipe off surplus oil and use a wax leather dressing for a finish, as used for saddlery. If the buckles are hard to use because the leather has hardened to them, the oil dressing should go some way to freeing them. Remove dirt from the metal with steel wool, slightly moistened with a releasing oil such as 3-in-1, which will clean and polish the metal and help to free the movement of the buckle parts. If they are brass, you can polish later with a brass polish. Rotted stitching could be picked out and replaced using saddler's thread and a fine needle, and if necessary the thread can be stained with brown boot polish.

Raising a Toe Cap

Presumably the dent in the toe cap of a brogue shoe means that the stiffener or former of the toe cap beneath the leather has been depressed. Use a wooden or metal shoe shaper – a hinged wooden former with holes in it at strategic points which take shaped metal 'buttons' which can be pressed up against the parts of the shoe needing correction or expansion. The shaper is furnished with a screwed metal rod and angled piece of metal; when turned by the handle, a cross-piece at the top of the rod, the two halves of the wooden former are forced apart and pressure is brought to bear on the dented area. You can buy a former from a shoe-maker or good department store. A more economical alternative is to crumple small pieces of newspaper and pack these into the toe area of the shoe with a wooden rammer (the handle end of a hammer will do). Do this methodically and as you fill in the toe space the dent should yield. Keep a hand and fingers over the toe cap to feel the effect. The dented area may be weakened and susceptible to depression again.

TEXTILES
Dyeing a Panama Hat

You can dye your panama hat to a neutral brown or green for use when fishing by using one of the aniline dyes normally sold for dresses etc. We suggest you put the hat on a block, or stuff it with crumpled newspaper and paint the solution on. Use a dilute solution, and make a trial patch on the underside before doing the whole. Alternatively, you can use a wood dye and this would have some insect repellent effect.

Sooty Satin

Soot is formed of fine carbon particles which are not easy to shift. However, first go over the fabric with a carbon tetrachloride dry cleaner on a fine-pored sponge, using a picking (not rubbing) action to lift off the staining. It will clear the grease and should lighten the stain fairly well. If this is not enough, dab the stained patches and cover immediately with fuller's earth or fine French chalk, leave overnight, and brush off: this should draw out more of the soot. For bad stains that persist use a bleach, such as hydrogen peroxide (20 vols), but this may impair the colour of the satin. There is a chemical available to neutralise the burnt smell.

To Waterproof an Oilskin

The old traditional mixtures of linseed oil or tar derivatives are not as effective or as easy to apply as modern proprietary brands of synthetic waterproofers obtainable from good ironmongers or from firms handling camping and outdoor activity equipment. Try a good tent-maker.

Yellow Lace

Provided that the condition of the old lace garments is sound, the safest home treatment is to soak them overnight in soft or distilled water in which borax has been dissolved (1 level tablespoonful per gallon). Then wash in a warm, sudsy solution of pure soap flakes, rinse in clear warm water and dry. Delicate pieces of lace can best be dried on clean, white blotting paper. If the yellowing is very bad, then a mild bleaching agent may be added to the water – but test a piece separately first. The safest bleach would be sodium hypochlorite in the form of Milton: stronger bleaches may weaken the lace fabric. When dry, store in blue tissue paper (never white) and opaque plastic bags or containers. Light must be excluded.

PAPER AND PICTURES
Gilt Frame

To restore discoloured gilt picture frames, add to 1 pint of water sufficient flowers of sulphur to give a golden colour (about ½ oz) and about 1 lb of bruised onions. Boil together until the onions are soft; strain off the liquid and, when cold, use to wash the frames with a soft brush. This will not, however, restore gilt where it has been worn away by chemical action and the remedy can be only of limited effect.

Stuck Pages

To unstick the glazed pages of a book stuck together by dampness will need care, patience and a certain amount of skill and dexterity. With a thin knife blade or metal paper knife (preferably stainless steel, bronze or rustless material), gently insert the blade between the sheets and play steam from the spout of a kettle along the opening to soften the adhesion. Free the pages by manipulating the knife blade, gently turning it to and fro and giving the steam time to work. You may find it a tedious business but any attempt to hurry will tear or spoil the paper surfaces. The freed pages will then have to be dried: excess moisture can be dabbed up with blotting paper, without pressing. Allow the pages to air-dry, keeping them apart if necessary with paper 'spells' or toothpicks at the bases.

Waterproofing Wallpaper

To waterproof ordinary wallpaper already in place on a wall, spray or brush with a silicone solution from a good builders' merchant or decorators' store. The wallpaper must be in good condition and you may have to apply two coats if it is very absorbent. It should be suitable where wallpaper is subject to splashing, as in a bathroom or kitchen. Alternatively you could paint the paper with a polyurethane varnish giving a matt finish.

WOOD
Scorched Mahogany

So much depends on the extent of the damage. If the wood is actually 'scorched' in a manner that has removed some of the surface, then the only really satisfactory way is to repolish. If the marks are just surface blemishes, then there are various ways of dealing with them. One quite good method is to simmer a pint of linseed oil for 10 minutes, add $\frac{1}{4}$ pint of turpentine; dab on frequently with a soft rag, then polish. Hot dish marks respond to light rubbing with a piece of flannel dampened with spirits of camphor or essence of peppermint. Allow to harden, then polish. If the colour has been removed in the process it will be necessary to

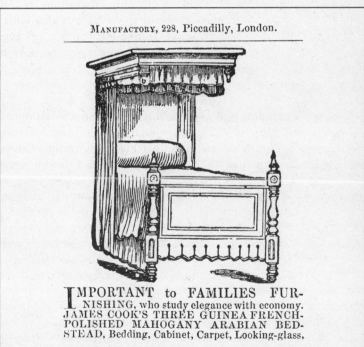

MANUFACTORY, 228, Piccadilly, London.

IMPORTANT to FAMILIES FUR-NISHING, who study elegance with economy. JAMES COOK'S THREE GUINEA FRENCH-POLISHED MAHOGANY ARABIAN BED-STEAD, Bedding, Cabinet, Carpet, Looking-glass,

stain to the original colour, and then proceed with polishing. Beeswax in turpentine is as good as anything, or a proprietary polish of mahogany colour.

Oak Panel Restoration

Dulling and blackening of old 17th-century oak panelling is most likely traceable to the use of linseed oil and/or beeswax in polishing the wood. You can remove much of this and the absorbed dirt by rubbing down with a mixture of equal parts by volume of raw linseed oil, vinegar and turpentine and $\frac{1}{4}$ part of methylated spirit, well shaken and mixed together. Apply with a soft cloth. Finally, wipe down with a cloth pad moistened with turpentine, and dry. Use fine steel wool to remove sticky parts or to smooth the surface. You can then repolish with linseed oil, rubbing it into the wood vigorously with a cloth, daily for 3–4 weeks, to form a tough, hard finish which will be resistant to damp and household damage. Or more simply you can coat the wood with a modern polyurethane varnish for a hardened surface resistant to knocks and stains.

GLASS AND STONE
Waterproofing a Glass Vase

The simplest and cheapest remedy for a Bristol glass vase with a hemline crack in the flat base would be to clean and dry the internal surface well and then paint with a solution of sodium silicate (water-glass) using 1 part to 3 parts water by volume. Allow to dry thoroughly and repeat two or three times. A small amount of the chemical should be available at a good chemist and it seems unnecessary to buy large amounts of the branded products. An alternative would be to paint the base inside with a polyurethane clear varnish and let this dry hard before use. A third alternative is to use a polythene lining bag to hold the water when using the vase.

Marble

Marble is a porous and absorbent stone and needs cleaning with great care. It acquires a patina from exposure which should not be lightly destroyed. First dust with a feather duster to remove loose dirt. Then wash with warm soft water or distilled water – no soaps, pastes or cleaning agents should be used. Treat a small area at a time and blot this dry before treating other parts so that no dirty water can lodge or further stain the stone. Use a soft nylon brush for washing and a fine-pored sponge to blot the dirty water. Add a few drops of household ammonia to each gallon of water. If the dirt has become ingrained and is greasy, soften it with a solution of methylene chloride or a paint remover containing this. Apply it with a brush with a dabbing action and work the dirt out. Use in an open, well-aired space. More stubborn stains should yield to a cloth well moistened with acetone, benzene or clear petrol.

Marble Polish

The best polishing agent for marble is fine marble dust, or failing that fine pumice. It is worth putting the marble on a good sheet of stout paper or polythene when buffing it so that the marble dust can be collected for use in polishing. A superfine finish is obtained by buffing with a cloth buffing wheel or disc and powdered jeweller's rouge.

Oil on Tarmac

Scrape off as much free oil as possible, using a piece of wood, hardboard or stout cardboard which can then be discarded. Cover the oil patch with a thin layer of fine sawdust or a mixture of sawdust and ground limestone and leave for 24 hours before scraping and brushing off. Then scrub with a commercial detergent or use an oil solvent (such as that used at garages for cleaning their floors, and obtainable from them) or a proprietary floor cleaner from a builders' merchant. Wash down with clean water afterwards. There is a limit to what can be done on an asphalt or tarmac surface as some of the oil may have penetrated the surface and may require burning out; then the surface cover will need replacing with new bitumen-asphalt material. Burning needs a certain amount of care and skill, confining the heat to the damaged area. Small areas could be treated with a blowlamp.

Encrustation in Lavatory

The build-up of encrustations at water-level in your lavatories may be caused by salts other than those of calcium, not removed in the water-softening process. If you find that a liquid lavatory-bowl cleaner fails to soften and remove the deposits, use a solution of spirits of salt (1 part by volume hydrochloric acid to 9 parts water); wear rubber gloves and apply with a coarse plastic sponge. It might be informative to have the water of the flush analysed to see just exactly what salts are present and your local water authority may be willing to do this, free of charge.

METAL

Brass Church Memorial

To remove the varnish or lacquer from a brass memorial tablet, apply a modern varnish and paint remover – first to soften the varnish and then remove with wads of cottonwool or a cloth. If it is very dirty, wash it down with a solution of 1 part of household ammonia to 9 parts water; rinse with clear water and dry well. To repolish, use a long-term brass polish applied carefully with a soft cloth. Around the lettering you may find it easiest to fold the cloth over a flat wooden blade or stick. The retaining of the black lettering may be a little troublesome. If in good condition, you could preserve it by covering with masking tape while removing the varnish. Some slight damage may be done, however, and the simplest remedy would be to retrace the lettering with Black Japan, a paint sold for use on metals.

A Very Weathered Sundial

It is possible that the sundial is made of bronze, an alloy of copper and tin, if it has been cast. If of copper it is likely that discoloration from weathering will be bluish-green. However, it is most likely to be made of brass, an alloy of copper and zinc. In any case, first wash with a solution of a tablespoonful of household ammonia in a pint of tepid water to remove surface dirt, grease or oil. Rinse thoroughly in clear water. Then prepare a solution of 2 tablespoonsful of vinegar and one heaped teaspoonful of salt in a pint of water; apply with a sponge, then rinse thoroughly with soft rainwater or distilled water. Allow to dry, polish with a brass polish and then protect with a coat of clear polyurethane varnish or lacquer.

Weathered Bronze

To clean weathered bronze plaques and wreaths set in stone, try a chrome cleansing solution as sold for cars. This comes in the form of a pinkish, cream-like solution. Paint it on the bronze, allow a few minutes to penetrate the grime, then wipe and rub off with cloths. For the creviced and curlicued bits, use a brush (about the texture and firmness of a shoe-polishing brush). You may have to repeat where badly stained. Wipe over with 3-in-1 oil or a brass lacquer.

Bronze Sculpture

An accumulation of dust in the crevices of a piece of sculpture can be easily dealt with by using a fairly stiff fibre brush, like a toothbrush.

If this is not effective, use a brass wire brush – but never an iron or steel wire brush.

Bronze Chinese Vase

We would certainly not advise using an old toothbrush to clean your heavily chased and ornamented old Chinese vase: it is liable to scratch a valuable article. If a brush is used, it should be a special plate brush with long bristles. We would suggest that you do not try complete cleaning, as there may be a patina acquired by age which it would be a pity to destroy. Wash the article in soft warm water (rainwater if possible) with plenty of soap. Rub with a flannel and if there are indentations that a flannel will not reach, use a soft brush and move about gently. Wash well in clean water to remove any soap and then dry in hot sawdust. It is probable that polishing will not be necessary, but if it is, all that should be required is a rub with a chamois leather of soft quality, and then finish off with a silk handkerchief.

Burnishing Mitt

A burnisher or burnishing mitt is made from chain steel interlaced with chamois leather and is used for cleaning bits, stirrups and other metalware used with horses and their harness. It is used to remove any encrustations or fouling of the metal by rubbing hard. It leaves the metal surface smooth and clean.

Copper Coal-scuttle

If the coal-scuttle has merely been neglected from being outside so long, cleaning off the grey and green will be simple. Wash off all removable surface dirt with warm water and soap, using a roughish flannel but not a scrubbing brush or anything likely to damage the surface. Then apply a paste of well powdered chalk and methylated spirit. Rub this preparation on and leave until the spirit evaporates and the chalk is left dry. Remove, and polish with crocus powder or fine chalk. If the scuttle has been suffering from long neglect, it may be necessary to use a powerful solvent. A weak solution of oxalic acid may be safely applied, using a piece of woollen material and wearing gloves. This will remove the tarnish. Wash, dry and polish with whiting or fine chalk. Any spots of damp through exposure outdoors can be removed by chalk and spirits of turpentine. Finally, apply a good brass polish. All this may need much effort, especially if the article has been subjected to much exposure.

Tinned Copper Saucepans

Copper saucepans are traditionally valued for the evenness with which they transmit heat to the food being cooked. Copper, however, in direct contact with many foods, especially soups, sauces, stews etc., reacts adversely to acids in the foods, with the formation of salts such as sulphates, and this makes the food objectionable in taste and palatability as well as in colour; mild, perhaps, in effect but unwholesome. Lining copper saucepans with tin (an inert metal) prevents this, and tin-lined copper pans are often preferred by lovers of good cooking. The pans do need careful cleaning, and when the lining wears thin and the red of copper shows through they should be retinned by a tinsmith (the chef in a hotel will know one). You can, of course, usually boil water in copper kettles and utensils, and unlined copper pans are considered best for sugar boiling.

Rusty Antique Golf Clubs

To remove rust from antique golf-club heads, first remove all loose surface rust by brushing with an old toothbrush or scrubbing brush with nylon or plastic fibre bristles. Then either use a solution of oxalic acid ($2\frac{1}{4}$ oz oxalic acid carefully dissolved in $1\frac{1}{4}$ pints of water to make a 9% solution), soak the metal heads (but not the wood or shaft) and remove released rust with a synthetic plastic sponge, then wash thoroughly in clean warm water and dry. Alternatively you can try one of the proprietary rust removers used commercially in car repairs, which would be simpler and less hazardous to use. After cleaning and drying, protect with a coating of clear lacquer, vaseline, graphite oil or microcrystalline wax.

Wrought Iron Lamp Standard

There are two ways of restoring your rusty-looking lamp standard to give it a dull black finish. First clean off all grease by washing in benzine or soapless detergent, using a wire brush and emery paper to remove the rust. Then dip in a 10% solution of potassium bichromate, allow to dry in the open air and then hold over a glowing, sootless fire for 2 minutes. Repeat the dipping in potassium bichromate, drying and heating until the desired shade is obtained. The second way is to clean off rust and grease, then coat thinly with linseed oil varnish; burn this off over a charcoal fire (it will flame off); repeat this treatment until the iron is black; then wipe with a dry rag; heat again moderately, and rub with a rag saturated in linseed oil varnish.

Ormolu

Ormolu is a type of brass for castings and is usually made of copper, zinc and tin. It was much used for ornamenting French furniture and also for cheap jewellery under the name of mosaic gold. To clean ormolu, scrub with soap and water to which a little ammonia has been added. Rinse well with clean water.

To Clean Pewter

Pewter is an alloy of tin and lead (or sometimes antimony). To clean, first wash it in hot water with a modern detergent. If the pewter is very black, take 8 oz of the finest silver sand and ½ oz of the salts of tartar, moisten with water in a dish and apply this with a soft wool rag, working carefully as it is abrasive. Then finish by polishing with a soft cloth dipped in precipitated chalk. Alternatively, when the blackening is even and largely the result of neglect, make a paste of powdered rottenstone, soft soap and turpentine; or rottenstone with equal parts turpentine and linseed oil, mixed together. Apply by rubbing, and then wash over, and finally polish with sifted whitening or precipitated chalk. For deep persistent stains, try boiling the utensils in water to which a good quantity of hay has been added. Or dip a damp cloth pad in a little powdered pumice, rinsing thoroughly afterwards. More unorthodox, for internal stains put a little denture-cleaning powder in the pot, fill with water and leave overnight, then rinse. For paint splashes, try silver sand moistened with turpentine, but if this does not work a paint stripper will be necessary: wash well afterwards and use silver sand (this time moistened in methylated spirit) to restore the surface, but keep the rubbing down to a minimum. Then finish with powdered chalk, whiting or crocus powder moistened with methylated spirit. Wash off, dry, and then polish well with a soft duster.

Re-silvering a Clock Dial

First, the dial must be thoroughly cleaned, by washing with a grease-removing detergent. Second, heat it by careful manipulation over an alcohol (methylated spirits) lamp, or by dipping into hot water, to a temperature sufficient to melt black sealing wax, which is rubbed over the face to fill in engraving or figures. Take a flat piece of pumice stone, pulverised powdered pumice, and water, and work to grind off the wax until the metal is exposed on all facets.

Finish by rubbing along the grain with Blue-stone or Water of Ayr Stone, and finally with pulverised pumice and water on a muslin pad. Rinse thoroughly, and dry carefully; lay on a clean board, and with a pad of fine muslin gently rub with fine salt. When the surface has been evenly salted, use a fresh pad of fine muslin and silvering paste to rub the paste in evenly and quickly over the entire surface. Now rub with cream of tartar moistened to a thin paste on the pad until white all over. Rinse quickly with copious sluicings of water, dry rapidly either plunging into hot water, shaking off surplus and then drying over an alcohol lamp until it glistens, or with a hair dryer. Finally cover with a suitable hard spirit varnish or clear polyurethane varnish.

Whiting Powder

Whitening or whiting is simply finely ground or powdered chalk (calcium carbonate). It is alkaline, which means it neutralises any traces of acid, etc., from fingermarks for instance, and also mildly abrasive, though not unduly so; so it does make a useful material for making cloths with which to clean silver. It is still available, and can be bought in packets from decorators' stores; for it is sometimes used for making a whitewash. It is also sold by shops catering for metal craftsmen and do-it-yourself stores. An alternative is jeweller's rouge, a finely abrasive reddish powder, usually sold by jewellers.

SHELL

Coral

It is not clear from your letter what type of coral you are interested in, whether those commercially exploited or those chiefly gathered for their collector interest. The kinds generally gathered for their commercial appeal, such as the red coral of Naples Bay and other Mediterranean localities, or the black coral of the Persian Gulf etc., are not usually given any specially significant treatment to preserve their colour. They are cut, ground and polished and otherwise worked up for jewellery etc., but their colour depends primarily upon the choice of the original material. In as much as coral is the product of living organisms, and the sea itself tends to lend sheen and tone to their colouring, almost all corals tend to lose some lustre and tone when taken from their native element. Inferior corals may be dyed but this is easily detected by the expert.

Shiny Seashells

To clean seashells and preserve them, brush with a soft brush dipped in a 50% solution of Isopropyl alcohol (obtainable from a good chemist) and then paint or spray with polyurethane varnish to give a hard, glossy, clear finish. It should halt the tendency of shells to flake, though this is something of an ageing problem and possibly a reaction to atmospheric conditions. Alternatively, use a microcrystalline wax for a polished finish: apply with soft cloths, as you would a wax polish.

Mother-of-pearl and Tortoiseshell Sewing Box

To cut through and remove the residues of oft-applied furniture polish, apply methylated spirit carefully, on soft cloth or cotton-wool pads, discarding the pads as they discolour. If the mother-of-pearl is very dirty, make a paste of precipitated whiting with a little water and rub with this; allow to dry then brush off. Fasten any loosened pieces with an epoxy-resin glue. Later, carefully wash the whole surface of the box with a little sudsy soap and water, and mop up to dry quickly. When dry, you can repolish with microcrystalline wax (Cosmolloid 80H).

To Polish Tortoiseshell

Start with fine powdered rottenstone with a little linseed oil, neatsfoot oil or lanolin and a soft cotton pad; dip the pad in the oil or grease, then in the rottenstone, and work to promote a smooth surface on the shell. When it is brighter and more or less scratchless, work again, this time polishing with jeweller's rouge, and finally finish with a soft chamois leather. It requires firm but gentle working and may take a long time to restore the original colour and gloss. An occasional rubbing with sweet oil or liquid polish will keep the surface from becoming too dry.

SPECIALS
Cleaning a Meerschaum Pipe

Meerschaum is the German name given to natural hydrated magnesium silicate, which is esteemed for pipe making as it is held to give a cool smoke and is easy to handle. It is usually waxed and polished after carving and shaping, and the brown staining that occurs in use is fostered. As far as cleaning is concerned, the bowl and stem are kept clean of deposits with a soft pipe cleaner and materials normally used in clearing pipes. The bowl of the pipe should not be scraped with hard metal. Any stains or deposits round the rim of the bowl can be removed with a pad of fine steel wool. The outer bowl should be polished occasionally with the palm and fingers moistened with a little carnauba wax to enhance the polish and then rubbed with a soft cloth.

Fumigating a Horse-drawn Caravan (1948)

Most forms of bugs, lice, mosquitoes, houseflies, woodlice, etc., likely to be found in a caravan are now readily destroyed by the use of an insecticide containing DDT (Dichloro-diphenyltrichloro-ethane). DDT is now put up in various forms. For your purpose you should choose a DDT insecticide specified for household use. You can get it in powder form for application as a dust; in liquid form for application as a spray; and in 'aerosol bomb' packaging for use as a mist spray. The latter form should be particularly useful for your purpose. The value of DDT lies in the fact that its lethal effect persists for some time, and yet in the dosages advised it is completely harmless to humans or animals.

[*Editor's note: Of course, DDT is now in disgrace for just that persistent quality and is no longer available.*]

🐚 Antiques and Collecting

Ancient Brasses

The old original brasses, now very rare and expensive, were fretted out of sheet metal by the aid of a chisel and file. Their characteristic is that the uneven nature of handwork is evident, and no two are exactly alike. Possibly, however, you wish to know how to distinguish a brass cast, shall we say, up to the early years of this century, from one produced from the same moulds in recent years for sale in antique shops. Well, this can only be done by the look and feel of the two. Get the two types together and the difference is evident. The old ones were made of a better quality brass that took a brighter polish. Their finish is much better, the new ones often being crude. The old ones will generally have been in use, and the signs of wear mark them. Some reproductions are well finished, however, and are quite useful in a collection until they can be replaced by the genuine article.

Baculumarianism

There is no correct or authenticated name for a collector of walking sticks, though no doubt such a person could quite reasonably and logically be called a baculumary and the hobby baculumarianism. The terms are derived from the Latin *baculum* – a staff. Some may prefer a bacilliumary and bacilliumarianism, from *bacillium*, Latin for a rod, but this derivation has been drawn upon medically to describe the rod-like bacteria, *bacilli*, and is less valid.

Clocks by Wicksteed

After an exhaustive search we have traced Edward Wicksteed, strangely enough, in an American book on clocks. One of his clocks, dated 1781 and made in London, has also been traced. It is an excellent example of good workmanship, but no other information has been discovered about the maker. Your clock, therefore, might date from the latter part of the 18th century or the early part of the 19th. A number of clocks then seem to have been taken overseas by settlers, including to South Africa where you reside.

Coins (1860)

The coins are not scarce, and present nothing peculiar. The two English coins are of Charles II and William III, and are called 'five-guinea pieces', and the third is a Portuguese coin. They are worth no more than the value of the gold.

Coin Balances

In the 18th and 19th centuries, firms dealing with a large number of gold or silver coins generally had the means of weighing them, for clipping the coins was often done, thus reducing their value. Jewellers and dealers in coins used these balances too. Balances of many types were on the market until the introduction of the serrated instead of plain edges to coins reduced the clipping. Some were small and intended for the pocket. Those intended for testing guineas and half-guineas in circulation were in use between the reigns of Charles II and George III.

Token Coin

From your description of a copper coin the size of a halfpenny, with the date 1693 or '83, scales on one side and two lions on their hind legs holding a flag, this is not an official coin of the Realm, but a special token coin. During the Commonwealth period there was no authorised copper coinage, and traders found it very inconvenient to give small change. To overcome this problem, many issued a token coin which they would redeem at the value it was intended to be. The issue continued during the reign of Charles II. The scales often appeared on such trader's tokens. In the 18th century a vast number of token pennies and halfpennies were struck. Some were of artistic design and are still found in excellent condition. With the issue of official copper coinage in 1797, it was made illegal to issue any more copper tokens. These coins are not valuable unless in first-class condition and with some other special merit; for instance of an issue where few have survived.

Izaak Walton Chests

There must be a fair number of these 'Izaak Walton' chests about – oak coffers with the initials 'I.W.' chiselled on them – for a new one turns up every decade or so. Probably few, if any of them, date from Walton's day. There seems to have been a mild spate of them which were made about the end of the 18th and beginning of the 19th century, judging from the style of carving. Probably they are not fakes, but simply the result of a fashion among anglers at some period.

Keyless Watches

There is no definite date for the introduction of keyless pocket watches nor records as to who was responsible for introducing them. The first keyless watches were made in the latter part of the 19th century from a commercial point of view, but in the early years of the 20th century first-class English lever watches were still made with keys. The keyless watch appears to have come into special favour in America, and a large export trade was built up, mainly with cheap watches. The war of 1914–18 brought the wrist-watch into general favour, when keyless watches supplied by the Army Ordnance services became standard.

Lion's Head and Ring

For countless centuries the lion has held high rank in many forms of ornamentation and has occurred in both heraldic and purely orna-mental fashion. Parts of the lion, such as the head, are used without the body quite extensively and the design of the head with the ring in its mouth goes back at least to the Middle Ages and Renaissance. It was much used as a handle or knocker on doors, and in Italian cities old examples are still to be seen. There is such a knocker in the cathedral at Mainz. Among the Greeks and Romans, the lion was looked upon as a guardian of springs, temples, entrances etc. The head with a ring came into use at entrances and was sometimes placed low enough for use as a fastening for a horse. It may even be possible that this was the reason for using the ring with the head in such positions. In Sienna such lion heads with rings can be seen among the vast number of rings of various types for fastening horses. The old tradition as a symbol of guardianship might well account for the design being carried on in the case of andirons, as the fireside was looked upon as a family sanctuary.

Loving Cup

Your saltglaze stoneware loving cup with greyhound handles and impressed Doulton & Co., Limited, Lambeth, was made after 1 January 1899, when Mr Henry Lewis Doulton converted the business he inherited two years before from his father, Sir Henry Doulton, into a limited company. Fulham, just over 4 miles across the Thames from Lambeth, was the home of the London stoneware manufacture from the end of the 17th to the close of the 18th century and it was there that John Doulton served an apprenticeship till he founded the famous stoneware pottery at Lambeth in 1815. The decorative motifs you describe, of smoking and drinking 'Tobies', a stag, boar or fox hunt, hounds, windmill, etc., can all be traced back in one form or another to the cups and jugs of early Nottingham, Fulham or Brampton ware. You will note that the date of the loving cup about coincides with that of the outbreak of the South African war and the arrival there of 'dukes' sons, cooks' sons, sons of a belted earl'.

Mother-of-pearl Shapes

During the 19th century there was a vogue for carved and decoratively engraved mother-of-pearl pieces, such as the 'shapes' about 1/10 in thick and up to 3 in x 1 in in area that you describe. The more intricately ornamented and engraved pieces were often made up as brooches and pieces of jewellery. They were also used for inlays in small pieces of furniture and were employed in the decoration of Christmas and commemorative cards, Victorian valentines, and to embellish the old type of photographs mounted on stiff board. Flattish pieces were often made up as purses with snap fastenings, or to decorate knife handles and souvenirs from holiday resorts. And, of course, they were used for highly individual and decorative buttons. As pieces of Victoriana, they are claiming new interest, especially among antique collectors.

Silver Birds

[I have two pairs of silver birds, partridges and pheasants, which I believe to be French. The poise and expression in their eyes is exceptional. The wings are hinged and underneath each is the mark '3B'. They have no silver stamp.]

It has been established that birds such as you describe were made in Japan and China long ago, their use apparently being for incense burners. A model in the South Kensington Museum shows that the Japanese well understood the modelling of birds. It seems clear that the idea of sporting bird models came from the Oriental productions imported into this country in the early 19th century. Without close inspection it is, of course, not possible to suggest the origin of the birds in your possession, but the indications are that they are most probably German and not French productions. The marks you mention cannot be identified, and so do not assist in tracing their origin. However, the fact that there are no silver markings strengthens the case for German origin. French silver has always been rigorously marked. On the other hand, German silver is frequently below the English standard and not marked. The lifelike expression is mentioned in accounts of the Japanese birds.

Victorian Pots

Glazed earthenware pots (such as your 3½ in-high jar bearing an illustration of a battle scene and the words 'The fall of Sebastopol, 8th Sept. 1855') are well known and sought by collectors. In general, they came into use in early Victorian times. At first they were plain and intended to contain a variety of items like toilet ointments, pastes and, in particular, bear's grease which was in use at the time as a hair dressing for men. The practice of illustrations on pot lids grew and these are much in demand if in good condition. Favourite scenes were Shakespearian and nautical and military to commemorate battles.

Victorian Tie-pins (1957)

These pins were very fashionable at one time and were of a variety of designs. Sporting people favoured heads of dogs, foxes, crossed whips; others used family crests. Later, gold coins were the vogue; others had a variety of stones inset, from diamonds to semi-precious stones, possibly picked up as souvenirs. Rings were often used, too, just below the knot, and sometimes a neck scarf was pulled through a ring without a knot. Usually, items such as tie-pins were rarely sold, but were retained in families as personal effects. As time went on the sentimental value faded out, and when the demand for gold increased during wartime, quite a number of old pins came on the market. We regret we do not know of a book on Victorian tie-pins, and the subject seems to have been neglected in articles on old-time jewellery. As few people appear to have interested themselves in the matter, it should offer considerable opportunities for a collector.

 Making Things

HANDICRAFTS
Aran Sweaters

The earliest known datable Aran sweater was bought in Dublin in 1936. Patons of Alloa have a sweater which has a tag dating it to 1906 but with no evidence to support the date. There is no literary or pictorial evidence of the Aran sweater as we now know it before the 1930s. It seems likely that the sweaters of Aran were simply a local version of the seamen's sweaters which were developed all round the British Isles in the middle of the 19th century. It is known that the knitters of Aran were helped by ladies in London, who sent them wool and encouraged them in the development of their designs. Most of the Aran stitches can be found in early Victorian books printed for ladies. The popularity of 'Aran style' dates from the production of the film *Man of Aran* in 1934, when cinema ushers were dressed as Aran fishermen. The Paton sweater is in an oatmeal-coloured, undyed wool. The wool is harsh, the sweater small and its shape quite unlike Aran sweaters today.

Brass-rubbing

This is a simple process and the materials are few. Use tough, thin paper. The material for doing the rubbing is known as heelball. This is actually a mixture of wax and lampblack, and is used as a polishing material by shoemakers. It can be obtained from an art shop. Permission must be obtained for brass rubbing in churches. The procedure is simple, but needs care. Wipe the brass over to remove dust and any dirt. Cover the brass with the paper. Start at the top and carefully rub the heelball over bit by bit until the whole is done. Be sure to keep the paper in position. With practice and the right touch, a good representation of the design on the brass will result.

Bushman's Lamp (1870)

First get an old tin pannikin, condemned by the loss of its handle, called a 'mogo pint pot'. 'Mogo' in the blacks' language means without horns – a polled beast being described by them as a mogo bullock. Fill the pot half full with clay rammed tight down, then take a bit of stick the size and shape of a lead pencil, the length of the depth of the pannikin; twist round this a bit of rag 4 or 5 times, in the same way that ribbons are wound; fix this in the centre of the clay in the pot, fill up with fat, and when lighted it will burn with a clear bright flame.

Curing Sponges

The best method of cleaning and curing natural sea sponges is: After gathering, place the sponges in clean, clear water (in large tubs on board boats, in small ponds or crawls ashore) until the soft parts of the sponge tissue have rotted. The sponge skeletons are then taken out and the rotted tissue squeezed and washed out by rinsing thoroughly in clear sea-water. The cleaned sponges are then strung up and air-dried. If it is desired to bleach them and render very clean, the sponges may be placed in dilute ($7\frac{1}{2}$–10%) hydrochloric acid until effervescence ceases, then washed well in clear water; immersed in a 2% permanganate of potash solution for 10 minutes, squeezed, and steeped in very dilute sulphuric acid (5%) for a few minutes until white, and then washed out very well in clear water. This treatment gives a white or near-white sponge but is not strictly essential with the dark coloured sponges. Wool sponges are generally harvested most, but turkey toilet and turkey caps are the finest and most esteemed.

Dubbin

Warm together 50 parts by weight of tallow, 40 parts of neatsfoot oil, 9 parts of paraffin wax and 1 part aluminium stearate, and stir until thoroughly mixed. Pour into containers and cool.

Fat Soap

Melt and clarify beef or mutton fat by straining through muslin and put into a basin to cool. To each $3\frac{1}{2}$ lb of fat (which must be salt-free) a solution of $\frac{1}{2}$ lb sodium hydroxide (caustic soda) and $1\frac{1}{2}$ pints of water is needed; stir the two together with a wooden stick in an earthenware vessel; it heats up, and it will then have to be set aside to cool. When the fat is lukewarm and the soda solution (lye) is also lukewarm, pour the lye slowly into the fat, still stirring, and continue until well creamed together (about a minute). Then pour the mixture into moulds, or a wooden box lined with stout damp cloth (calico or linen) about 4 in deep, and place in a warm place, such as a kitchen, to set. It can be cut into bars in a day or so, and should be stored in a dry place for a month to harden before use.

Flower Drying

There are a number of ways of drying flowers with powders to retain their colour, which are more successful than air-drying. The simplest is to use dry, fine sand from a builders' merchant. Suspend the flowers head-down in a tall jar, box or cardboard container. Carefully add sand to surround completely the flower heads and stalks without distorting them. Use a funnel or cone of strong paper to direct the sand. Place the flower heads as close as possible without touching. Another powder often used is fine powdered borax, which is useful for the more delicate and fine flowers. The flowers can also be laid horizontally in a box on a layer of the drying material with more being added to cover them.

Flower Essences

Unfortunately there is no simple way of extracting the perfume from verbena, scented geranium and similar aromatic plants. Where the essential oils are largely in the foliage and stems, they are extracted by distillation, and this entails having a still with a coil. The foliage is then steamed and the steam and oils vaporise together to be cooled in the coil, and collected in a vessel in which they separate out. Much material is needed to yield any oil. The process is also employed for certain flowers; though the scent of certain delicate flower petals is extracted by what is termed enfleurage. Briefly, this consists of placing the petals on trays which have been lightly covered with purified fat which picks up the scent, and the essential oil is subsequently extracted by rendering and separating from the fat.

Fox's Pads

The simplest way of dealing with your fox's pad until you can get it mounted is to run a skewer or sharp coarse needle down by the bone and sift powdered alum down the hole made, repeating the process all round the bone. Or you can roll down the skin, extract the main bone and flesh and then rub with powdered alum inside.

Glycerine Leaves

Leaves can be preserved in glycerine by the water in them being replaced with glycerine through absorption. They should be picked as the autumn colour begins to show or before, since faded leaves cannot absorb liquid. Woody stems should be split to allow the glycerine to pass and should be placed in warm water beforehand to start the sap circulating. For the solution add 2 parts boiling water to 1 part glycerine and mix well. Place the stems in the solution, while still warm, in a narrow pot, so that they are covered, about 4 in deep. Depending on the type of leaf, the absorption can take between 2 days and 3 weeks. When drops of glycerine form on the leaves, enough has been absorbed and the stems should be removed and excess oil wiped off. If the leaves begin to droop, turn the spray upside down so that the glycerine will reach the top. With long branches, the whole branch is submerged in equal quantities of glycerine and water in a long, flat container.

Moleskin Gloves

You would need from 12–20 mole skins to make a pair of gloves, according to size and whether gauntleted or not. For a pram cover, lined on the underside, you would need from 50–70 skins, according to size. Much will depend upon the state of the skins and the cutting needed. If they have been simply air-dried you will have to have them properly cured and flexed. This is really a taxidermist's work, but your furrier could advise you best as to the state he needs the skins to be in.

Papier Mâché from Stamps (1860)

We do not believe that there is any truth in the assertion that old postage stamps are used for making papier mâché. They are worth little or nothing for that purpose – certainly not so much as the cost of carriage. There is no doubt, however, that spurious stamps, made from those previously used, have been selling in London at twopence a dozen.

'Paste' Stones

'Paste' is a form of flint glass of unusually high density. The material is often known in the trade as 'strass' and is prepared with the greatest care for imitation jewels. It is difficult to say what the composition of paste is, as there are many types, but the basic materials of the best paste are as follows: 300 parts by weight of the best powdered quartz; 470 parts of red lead; 163 parts of purified potash; 22 parts of borax; 1 part of white arsenic. These are subjected to very high temperatures, and the resulting product is colourless as used for imitation diamonds. When imitation of other stones is required the colouring is done with metallic oxides. This basic flint glass, as it is sometimes called, is transparent and very highly reflective.

Rabbit Skins

If you do not want to use aluminium potassium sulphate to cure fresh rabbit skins, boil together 1 lb soft soap, 2½ lb whiting and a pint of water and stir in 2 oz powdered chloride of lime. Allow to cool and, when nearly cold, add 1 oz tincture of musk. Dress the skins with this, tacked flat on a board, and allow to dry. Then treat to make flexible and soft.

Rose-petal Beads

The petals are separated from the flowers and dried on trays in the warm air of a shady place, out of direct sun, until well dried but not crisped. The petals are then rolled on a steel darning needle or similar thin rod, and fastened with a little vegetable gum. The size and shape of the bead can be altered by cutting the petals to suit. The base of the petal is inside the bead. If the petals are not limp enough to be rolled, they can be mist-sprayed with a little rose oil or perfume.

Sawdust Briquettes

Use equal parts by volume of sawdust and coal dust, mixed with glue-water (old-fashioned cake of joiner's Scotch glue, dissolved in hot water at 2–4 oz per gallon), to make a mixture that adheres and can be shaped into balls. Allow to dry on a clean surface in a shed or room. The coal dust or fine slack is really needed to give burning quality. An alternative recipe (though the briquettes will burn rather quickly) is 10 parts by volume of sawdust to 1 part Portland cement, mixed with water to an adherent mass which can then be shaped and dried. Or you could heat tar, pitch or crude oil until it thins and runs easily; then stir in sawdust to make a stiff, semi-dry mixture (about 1 part 'binder' to 10–15 parts sawdust by volume), then mould to shape. A simple mould is a short length of 3-in drainpipe or metal steel tubing, with a hardwood stump or rod that fits fairly tightly. Fill the tubing with the chosen sawdust mixture to about 8 in; compress with the wood billet, and push it out, to dry off.

Shell-case Gong (1916)

Possessors of empty shell cases who are not mechanically inclined may have wondered to what use such war relics could be put. Messrs Fredk. Sage and Co. Ltd., of 58 to 62, Gray's Inn-road, London, W.C., have hit upon the plan of fitting up these shells as dinner gongs. The whole stand and ring support can be made of any hard wood, such as mahogany, walnut or oak, polished to match existing furniture, with brass fittings and ornaments oxidised to a selected colour.

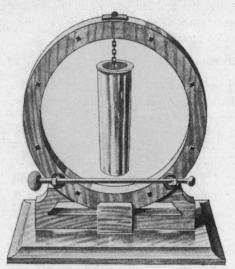

Shell-case gong

Shepherd's Crook

A ram's horn can be prepared for use as the handle to a shepherd's crook by first removing the bony core and any flesh or skin within the horn. Pull this out with pliers or drill and screw in a coarse-threaded coach bolt or screw which can be held in a vice so as to pull the whole inside loose. To ease the core, immerse the horn in hot water and try when cool. Scrape out any loose material from the inner sides of the horn; and then dress with a disinfecting solution and swab. If there is a bony core, scrape it free of flesh after boiling and treat with disinfectant. The horn should then be thoroughly washed either in strong soda water or a hot soapy water, well scrubbed to remove dirt and dried. Obviously it is helpful if the horn has a good crook shape naturally. If it has to be shaped or bent, it will need to be softened in hot water until reasonably pliable and then bent and left until cold. There is a limit to what can be done. The outside of the horn can be scraped with a piece of broken glass or steel scraper, sand-papered and finally finished with fine glass paper, and polished. The end of the chosen stick then needs to be shaped with a knife and rasp to fit well into the interior of the horn, as tight a fit as possible. The surfaces inside the horn and on the stick should then be coated with an epoxy-resin adhesive, the horn and stick brought together and left overnight to set completely. Then the joining can be smoothed and covered with a thin band of silver or other preferred metal.

Skeleton Leaves

Immerse your holly and ivy leaves in cold water and leave them until the epidermis or top skin rots, then remove them from the water. Place them flat on a board and scrape off the rotted epidermis carefully with a bone spatula or the back of a knife. Wash the skeleton leaves, dry them and press them between blotting paper or newspaper. You can speed up this process by placing the leaves in a solution of a tablespoon of washing soda in 2 or 3 pints of water and simmering for an hour or two until the skin parts readily from the vein skeleton on gentle scraping. Then wash the leaves and dry and press as above. Magnolia, holly, laurel and tough evergreen leaves are best. Ivy may need careful handling as it is softer.

Soap from Soap Ends

Shred the nub ends of old bars of soap on a cheese grater, or chop up fine with a flat-bladed decorator's scraper, into a container such as a large, clean, tinned-fruit can. Add a little warm water to make an adhesive mass and stand in a warm room for 3 or 4 days. This should give you a very stiff, well mixed mass which can be 'spooned' into a container or mould. For the mould, use a short length of plastic $2\frac{1}{2}$-in pipe, or an empty washing-up liquid container with base and conical top cut off. Then you need a stout, round billet of wood that fits just inside the mould. Place the filled container on a flat, hard, level surface and compress the soap mixture as tightly and firmly as possible to remove all air. (The mould can usefully be drilled with

$\frac{1}{16}$-in holes about an inch apart.) Leave compressed for 4–7 days, either by a weight on the wooden plunger or placing the contraption in a joiner's cramp. You should then be able to extrude the cylinder of soap by means of the wooden plunger. Cut it into suitable round pieces and place on clean paper to dry and harden further, for about 6–8 weeks. Hardness depends on being rather slow and patient in the making. Caustic soda is sometimes recommended as a hardener but gives a harsher soap and is not the safest of materials to have about.

Tanning

The tanning of animal hides and skins is a different process from curing, as it largely concerns the conversion of the skin into durable leather. Curing concerns the preservation of skins, often with the hair on, and usually to give a flexible, soft skin. Fresh skins and skins cured by drying or salting are put through pre-tanning processes which destroy the epidermis, loosen the hair for removal and are subjected to sweating and a process known as liming. They may be split into two or more layers, if thick, and de-limed. Tanning, or conversion into leather, entails soaking the hides in liquids containing tannic acid or other agents such as mineral salts which harden the tissues, render the hide impervious to putrescence and give it the hard-wearing qualities we associate with leather. Originally, leather was made by vegetable tanning, using the bark of trees, shrubs and plant materials rich in tannins, especially oak bark or oak galls boiled in rainwater to make the tanning liquor, and tanning was done in pits, wooden vats or drums. Today, various mineral salts are used for chrome tanning, alum tanning etc. Tanning with oil gives soft skins such as chamois, and synthetic tannins have been developed. After tanning, the leather may be dried and dressed, and treated for specific purposes. It can be softened, beaten, rolled, coloured or dyed, waterproofed or polished. We hope this brief explanation will help you and be of interest to your Chinese friend.

Tobacco Cured in Treacle

To obtain a dark, brownish black twist, damp the dried leaves so they may be straightened and flattened, then make up a solution of stick liquorice dissolved in hot water with honey or black treacle to a thin syrupy consistency. Actual proportions are not important and may be regulated to personal preferences, though an ounce of stick liquorice to a pint of water should be about right (using hot water to speed solution). Then paint each leaf with the solution, placing one on top of the other, using only sufficient solution to be taken up by the leaf without any likelihood of oozing. The next step is to compress the leaves; you can use an old letter press, or place them inside a stout box with an inside-fitting lid and place weights on the lid, or you can roll the leaves and bind tightly with twine. Leaves are then left under compression for 3–6 months, or longer. The tobacco can then be sliced and is ready for smoking.

White Oil Embrocation

The white oil embrocation used at the turn of the century both for humans and horses is probably an emulsion of oil and turpentine, with vinegar and egg, of which there are several versions with small differences. One is as follows: to a cupful ($\frac{1}{2}$ pint) of vinegar, add a cupful of the natural oil of turpentine, a shredded square of camphor and 1 egg, and shake up thoroughly to a white, creamy liquid.

Woad Dye

Making the blue dye from woad (*Isatis tinctoria*) is rather a time-taking and messy business. You either strip the leaves from the standing stems, or cut the plants down while in full leaf. The leaves or plants are laid on trays, hurdles or aerated surfaces to wither and dry in the sun. They are then ground to a pasty aggregate. When commercially produced, this was done in a woad mill beneath revolving wooden rollers. You could simulate the process by pounding the withered leaves with a wooden pestle in a wooden bowl, no doubt. The pasty mass is made up into small balls and left to dry under cover for a fortnight, after which the balls are ground up and fermented for some weeks under warm conditions (65–70°F). The resultant mass is well stirred and mixed, and made into round cakes and dried. The dye is made by soaking the cakes in water and then fixed by adding lime-water. Commercial woad-making ceased in England about 1930.

Wood for Carving

As soon as possible, both ends of your billet of hornbeam should be sealed with a clear waterproof varnish to prevent the rapid evaporation from the actual end surface of the wood which is the chief cause of the end-cracking you want to avoid. Small patches of bark, at irregular intervals and amounting in all to about a quarter of the total bark surface, should then be sliced off all along the circumference of the billet. It should then be stored upright in a dry but cool place, away from direct sun and artificial heat but exposed to a free circulation of air, for a year. The rest of the bark should then be removed and the billet left for a further year under the same conditions as before. This seasoning ought to make the billet remain stable and free from cracking, provided it is not placed near a fire nor in a centrally heated room.

THINGS TO DRINK
Apfelsaft

The simplest way of preparing *Apfelsaft* or fresh unfermented apple juice in the home is to grate, shred finely or mash the apples and press immediately through muslin cloth and a fruit-press. Given sufficient strength, you can press the juice out through 2–3 folds of muslin by hand. Each pound of apples yields about ½ pint of juice. On the Continent the usual method of home preparation is to pass the apples through a mill and then a press similar to those used in cider manufacture. Small hand presses for the extraction of juice can be obtained. One is a barrel of oak staves, with a pressure plate and screw attachment which compresses the fruit; the juice is collected at the base. An alternative is a small secondhand cider press from a country auction. Nowadays the simplest way of making apple juice is to use an electric juice extractor: the fruit is fed in at the top, macerated by high speed cutters and the juice separated for collection at the base. The fresh juice can be filtered into bottles and pasteurised or sterilised at once.

Cider Recipe

A very good dry cider can be made as follows. Lay out sour, fully ripe apples for about 3 weeks to become mellow and then place them in a wooden tub and pound once to pulp. Press out the juice, either through a cider press or a muslin bag, and keep in a collecting vessel at 60–65°F until the sediment has settled and bubbles begin to break through to the surface. Pour off the liquid into a cask, filling to the brim, and bung up tightly. Store in a cool place for 6–7 months, then strain off and bottle. If a sparkling cider is desired, bottle before fermentation ceases, and wire down the corks. For a sweet cider, cut the apples (windfalls will do) into slices, cover with water, stir daily for 2 weeks. Strain off the liquid through muslin, heat to lukewarmness, and to each gallon add 2¾ lb of sugar and 1 oz yeast, and stir. Leave for 48 hours, then pour into casks or jars, filling to brim, and allow to ferment in temperatures of 65–70°F. When bubbling ceases, bung tight, store under cool conditions for 6 months and then bottle off.

Exploding Cider

In fermentation, carbon dioxide gas is given off. If you seal your cask, jar or bottle immediately after you have filled it with fermenting wine it will either blow its seal or burst under the pressure of the gas. To produce sparkling cider, however, it is best to bottle off the wine after the first vigorous fermentation period is past but before fermentation has completely ceased, and then wire down the corks. If you want to use a cask, then the bung must be secured against blowing. In a steady temperature where fermentation goes steadily forward, it should be possible to close down after about 3 weeks, then remove to store.

Cowslip Wine (1948)

Pour 6 gallons of cold water over 1 lb (or 1 peck) of freshly picked yellow flowers of cowslip (no stalks or green calyces to be included) and leave to stand for 48 hours. Strain. To each gallon of liquor add 3 lb sugar and boil for half an hour; add the thin yellow peel of 8 Seville oranges and 8 lemons, and when nearly cold stir in a tablespoonful of yeast. Leave to stand for 3 days, skim off and break the oranges and lemons, scooping out the pulp, into the cask, and pour in the wine. Allow to stand until fermentation or working stops, and bung tightly. Bottle in 12 months and use 3 months later.

To make cowslip mead, boil 2 lb honey in 1 gallon water for 40 minutes. Skim. In a pint of the liquor, slice a large lemon. To the remainder, add 1 gallon yellow cowslip flowers, stir well, cover and set both liquors in a warm place for 24 hours. Add lemon liquor to the cowslip wine, stir in $\frac{1}{4}$ oz yeast, stand for 4 days and then cask. Tightly bung when fermentation ceases. Leave for 6 months and then bottle and use in 2–3 months.

Dandelion Coffee

It is not difficult to make dandelion coffee at home if one has a supply of dandelions with long, thickish roots. These are washed, sliced if very thick, roasted in a moderate oven on a baking sheet until crisp and brown, and then ground through a coffee or hammer mill.

Gooseberry Champagne

Gooseberry champagne is simply home-made gooseberry wine to which brandy (whisky, sherry or Madeira) is added when the first fermentation ceases. It is then casked for 6 months, bottled and allowed to stand in the bottles for a further 6 months. This apparently gives the somewhat bubbly nature of a champagne to the wine. A recipe of 1807 is: to every gallon of water add 4 lb well-ripened gooseberries; bruise thoroughly, cover and stand for 3–4 days, stirring twice daily. Strain through a sieve, measure, and to each gallon of liquor add 3 lb loaf sugar, and to each 5 gallons add a bottle of brandy. When the cask is full, bung tight and leave to stand for 6 months; bottle and store in a cool and dark place for a further 6 months before use.

Japanese Rice Wine

It must be pointed out that the rice wines of Japan and the East are made from special types of rice, and the whole grain is used. Polished commercial rice is of no use: you would have to try a wholegrain brown rice from a health-food store. The Oriental method involves steeping the grain for 3 or 4 weeks, covered with cold water, then boiling it gently until soft and pulpy. Then it is poured to ferment in earthenware vessels, with yeast and usually flavouring essences such as flowers, fruit etc. When fermentation ceases, pour off the liquid to stand again until fermentation stops and then carefully pour off the clear liquid for casking or bottling and storing. It is difficult to give exact quantities but, roughly, there should be 8 times as much water to rice, and $\frac{1}{2}$ oz yeast per gallon of liquor. For a sweet wine, dried fruits (raisins etc.) or sugar may be added. An anglicised version is: 1 gallon water to each pound of rice, plus 2 lb raisins, $2\frac{1}{2}$ lb sugar and 2 oz yeast.

Malt for Beer

To make malt at home, obtain malting barley in the grain and place it in a suitable vessel – earthenware, copper, wooden, enamelled, but not iron. Cover well with soft rain water and allow to soak for $2\frac{1}{2}$–3 days. Strain, and spread the soaked grain on wooden trays or a clean surface, even the floor, where an even temperature of about 50°F can be assured. Leave to sprout for at least 10 days, or until the grains germinate a small rootlet, turning the grain twice each day. The small shoots are the malt and have to be separated from the rest of the grain by drying slowly, either on a stove hotplate or in a very slow oven (temperature not to exceed 180°F). When the rootlets have parted from the grains, sift them out. They should be sweet and crisp, and slightly toffee-like in taste. They may be coarsely ground to facilitate brewing.

Mangel Wurzel Wine

Clean and cut mature roots into slices. To each 4 lb, add 1 gallon water and about 1–1½ oz ginger, and boil until soft and tender. Strain off the juice and to each gallon add 3 lb sugar, ½ oz yeast (liquefied with a little of the juice before adding) and the juice of 3 good-size oranges. Place in a suitable vessel to ferment, filling to the brim and keeping topped, in a warm room for 4 or 5 weeks or until bubbling ceases. Then give a thorough stir, leave 3 days, and strain or filter off into a cask, jars or bottles. Bung tightly, and store in a cool, dark place for at least 5 months.

Mead from Old Honey

To use fermented 3-year-old honey for mead, much depends on how far fermentation has gone. If the honey has frothed but appears fairly sugary underneath, you may try pouring or removing the froth and then making up a mead as follows from the remainder. Dissolve 4–5 lb honey in 1 gallon water; add the thinly sliced peel of 2 lemons, ½ oz root ginger and 1 oz hops. Boil together for 35–45 minutes; then cool to lukewarmness and add 1 tablespoonful of brewer's yeast (1 oz) liquefied with a little of the liquor. Stir, and pour into a cask to ferment, filling to the brim and reserving a little liquor to top up from time to time. Allow to ferment in a warm room (70–80°F) until bubbling ceases, then put in ¼ oz isinglass and bung tightly. Store under cool, dry conditions and bottle off after 6 months. Much depends on the sweetness or sugars still left in the honey. If it already tastes sour and vinegary, do not waste your time with it: you could turn it into honey vinegar instead.

Oak Wine

An old recipe for oak wine uses 3½ lb honey to each gallon of water, boiled for 45 minutes. Add about 3 dozen sound and healthy oak leaves, the hot liquor being poured over the leaves, and then allow to stand for half a day or overnight until cooled to blood heat, then strain off. Add about a teaspoonful of yeast per gallon and leave to ferment in a warm room for 3 or 4 days. Then pour into a cask or jar, seal, and allow to stand for 3–6 months before use, though it would keep longer.

Spruce Beer

'Spruce' or 'Spruce Beer' is still made in Norway and Canada, and sometimes in the north of Britain. It is usually made from the Scotch fir (*Pinus sylvestris*), using the young green shoots in spring. The 'essence' is prepared by placing the shoots in a preserving pan or suitable vessel, covering with water, and boiling until the resinous flavour is extracted, the water a deep brown; then the solution is strained off, re-boiled to reduce by half, and the liquid then bottled and stored. To make the 'Spruce', dissolve 2 lb black treacle, molasses or coarse brown sugar in 1 gallon water, warming slightly; put this in a suitable cask or earthenware jar; add another gallon of cold water (spring water if available), 2 tablespoonsful of the Essence of Spruce, and ½ oz brewer's yeast, when tepid. Stir. Allow to ferment in a warm place (70°F) for a few days. When bubbling ceases, bung tight and store cool. It may be used in a week or two. For a 'white' beer, use loaf sugar or honey in place of treacle.

Valentine Cocktail

White wine is its length and skeleton, but not just from any district. Make it a Mâcon blanc and to this add one of the biggest double brandies you ever poured, a little less Kirsch, ½ pint champagne (or more economically 2 soda splits) and 4 ice cubes. Stir until you have a white foam on top, then add 1 whole clear slice from the middle of a large lemon. Pour it into a reasonably large cocktail or wine glass as soon as possible.

To Clear Home-made Wine

For great brilliance, stir in infusorial earth, using ½ oz per pint of wine, and then filter through 2 thicknesses of filter paper, topped by a 2-in layer of unmedicated cotton wool. Stipulate that you want the filter papers for wine. Or, using ¼ oz isinglass per gallon, dissolve the isinglass in a cupful of lukewarm wine, pour into the rest of the wine and filter.

Wine in Metal

Wine should not be made in vessels of aluminium, brass, copper, iron or steel since it will acquire a metallic taste. It is held that aluminium salts may cause poisoning, though to what extent is disputed. The aluminium itself may suffer discoloration and possibly some pitting. For fermenting, it is really best to use wooden vessels or casks, large glass jars or bottles, or earthenware.

KITCHEN CRAFT

To Crack Almonds

To crack almonds does require skill. Commercially, it is done by skilled crackers, using a hammer and a hard wood base. Mechanical cracking, a process similar to the use of a series of vices, is apt to produce many broken kernels. In using a hammer and anvil, the key is to hold the nut correctly so that it splits longitudinally. It is largely a question of finding the right angle of the nut to receive the blow, holding the nut upright on its end. It should not be broken from the flanks. Cracking is easier if the shells are heated slightly before cracking. If a vice is used, the nut should be placed with its sharpest or thinnest edges subject to pressure.

Annatto (1900)

Annatto is the red pulp surrounding the seeds of *Bixa orellana*. The fruit having been bruised and macerated with water, the juice is allowed to stand till the colouring matter subsides to the bottom, an operation which can be hastened by the addition of vinegar; it is then strained and the residue dried. Sometimes fermentation is allowed to take place, when an article superior for dyeing purposes is produced, but which has a disagreeable smell. Annatto is used for dyeing cloth, but it is of slight permanence. It is in the manufacture of butter and cheese that it is chiefly employed, although its value in that respect is purely a sentimental one, depending on a taste for a high coloured article. In this country flour, chalk, and other foreign substances are added to the crude article, being necessary to adapt it to its various uses.

Camping Flapjacks

Flapjacks in their simplest form are flour plus salt, mixed with a little water to form a soft dough, moulded into flat shapes or cakes and fried in hot grease, usually bacon fat. They are staple bread for hunters and trappers in Canada, and popular primarily because of the few ingredients needed and the easiness of putting them together. To a hungry man, they are very good. Like most flour breadstuffs, however, much depends on the cook; the lighter they are handled, the lighter they cook. Variations can be made, of course. Some outdoor cooks hold it vastly improves them to rub a little fat in before adding water. Milk may be used in place of water. And in boredom or extravagance, various flavourings may be added, such as currants. But the standard flapjack is just flour, plus about a dessertspoonful of salt per pound, and enough water to mix to a manageable dough; the lighter the better. Then the hot fat gives added taste, and with fried tomato and eggs, you have a meal.

To Clarify Fat

If it is fat like dripping or the contents of the chip pan after much use, melt it, pour into an earthenware basin with about a cupful of boiling water, stir, and leave to set. When cold, lift off the cake of fat, scrape the underside free of unwanted matter; and if you wish, re-melt and pour into a container to keep. If it is animal fat, such as beef or mutton, cut into ½-in squares, allow a pint of water to each pound of fat, boil gently for 3–4 hours until clear, skimming off scum as it arises, strain off and cool. If it is butter, melt, and skim off scum until clear, then carefully pour off to reject the sediment. If it is vegetable fat, proceed as for butter.

Fig and Ginger Jam

To make green fig and ginger jam, to each 5 lb clean, ripe, fresh figs add ½ pint water, 8 tablespoonsful of lemon juice and the rind and pith of 2 lemons, 2 level teaspoonsful of citric or tartaric acid, and simmer gently until the fruit is soft; then add pectin; warm and add gradually 3 lb sugar, stirring in until it is dissolved. Bring to the boil, and boil rapidly unti the jam sets, stirring only to avoid burning. The addition of ginger depends on the type used. If you use preserved ginger, add 7½ oz chopped up in a small muslin bag at simmering stage; if dried root ginger, use 2½ oz bruised, and in the muslin bag add at simmering stage; if ginger essence add 2½ oz mixed with a little hot jam first and then thoroughly stirred in.

Keeping Fish Fresh

Pack the fish in masses of ice; this is the ideal method of keeping it fresh. Or it will keep a very long time in the deepfreeze. For both these methods the fish should be kept whole. Stuffing with grass is possible but less effective.

Flead Cake

Flead is the flaky part of the pig from which lard is rendered but when making flead cake it is used as it comes from the pig and should be thick, fresh and sweet. The ingredients for this Kentish dish are 1 lb flead, 1½ lb flour, salt to taste and water to mix. The flead should be freed of all skin and veins and cut into thin flakes. Add the cut-up flead to the flour and salt and mix very thoroughly together; then add cold water, just sufficient to make into a stiff dough. Turn the dough on to a floured baking board and beat it as hard as you can with the end of a wooden rolling pin, turning over as required, working quickly, but handling as little as possible; let it rest for quarter of an hour, then beat again, and repeat the rest and beating 3 times in all. Then, after a final beating and a rest of a quarter of an hour, roll out to about 1 in thick, cut to shape and bake in a quick oven until well risen, then cool in a warm kitchen.

Fruit Vinegar

Fruit vinegars like raspberry vinegar are usually used for sauces to accompany plain puddings. They may also be used for pickling fruit. There is no reason why a fruit vinegar should not be used in place of a plain vinegar according to taste. The simplest fruit vinegars consist of fruit juices and vinegar mixed or, in other terms, an extraction of the fruit preserved in vinegar. True fruit vinegars made from the fruit juice which is allowed to ferment and sour are rather different, and are highly appreciated as the condiment to fried and savoury courses or dishes.

Goola Malacca

Goola Malacca is based on the nests of the Asian swift, at one time common throughout southern Malaya. The black sauce may have been a black bean sauce. At one time it was possible to buy the nests in various forms – as made by the birds, or dried and crushed, or packeted – and, though still marketed, they have become expensive. This product would have to be found through an Eastern importer.

Gur Molasses

There are various forms of molasses, both for the health food market and the animal-feeding market. Molasses is considered invaluable for its iron and mineral content as well as for its high calorie count; but some brands are more palatable than others. The 'gur' or 'goor' you used to obtain in India is a native-prepared crude molasses, and being made directly from the sugar cane it is probably richer in mineral salts, enzymes, etc., combined with the sweet sap, than the prepared black molasses from the sugar refineries, though it is less rich in carbohydrates. Unfortunately, gur does not seem to be offered in this country.

Haggis

Take a sheep's paunch, soak in salted water for some hours, turn inside out and wash thoroughly. Take the pluck (liver, lights, heart etc.) and wash. Cover the liver with cold water, boil for 90 minutes, adding the heart and lights after 45 minutes. Chop half the liver up coarsely; chop the other half and the rest of the pluck up finely, mixing all together; add ½ pint oatmeal, 1 lb finely chopped beef suet, 2 chopped onions, 2 tablespoonsful of salt, 1 teaspoonful of pepper, the juice of a lemon, half a grated nutmeg, and about 1½ pints stock. Place this mixture into the paunch, leaving room to allow for it to swell, and stitch up the opening. Place in gently boiling water and allow to cook for about 3 hours, pricking occasionally with a needle. Haggis may be served hot or cold, and needs neither sauce nor gravy.

Hush Puppies

Mix together 2 cups of corn meal, a teaspoon of baking soda, a teaspoon of salt, 2 tablespoonsful of flour, 1 tablespoonful of baking powder. Add 5 tablespoonsful of finely chopped onion, then 2 cups of buttermilk and an egg, amalgamated. Season with cayenne pepper, if liked. Drop by small spoonsful into boiling fat. When they are cooked, they will float. Drain on absorbent paper.

Lampreys and Freshwater Mussels

Partly fresh and partly salt water creatures, lampreys are akin to eels but they require longer cooking than eels because the flesh is not very digestible. The old fashioned way is to remove the backbone, season the fish with spices and stew it in port flavoured stock. When half cooked, put it in a pie with minced anchovies, cover with puff pastry and bake. The chief precaution you must take is to remove the two filaments in the back of the fish, which are definitely highly poisonous, before cooking. There is little interest in freshwater mussels: they are very muddy and are definitely to be termed non-edible.

Mallard

Mallard now appears in recipe books as 'Wild Duck'. It is the largest wild duck and makes the best eating. It is particularly good in the autumn, before the cold weather drives it to look for food in unfrozen salt water. Normally its diet consists of marsh plants and seeds, so its reputation for tasting fishy is undeserved. Mallard should be hung for 2 or 3 days, when the skin on the belly will begin to turn greenish. Slit open the rear end and feel around the rib cavity to loosen the guts. Pull them all out together. Remove the crop from the neck: you should be able to feel this under the skin. Roast a young duck with butter on the breast, and an onion, bayleaf and piece of orange or lemon peel should be put within. Duck should be served pink: 30 minutes in the oven for a large fat bird. Serve with an orange-based sauce such as *bigarade*; or simply by heating the juices from the pan with a little orange juice to make a gravy. The classic recipe for an old bird is to braise it with turnips: sear the bird with a chopped onion then cook in a closed casserole with 1 lb turnips and a small bunch of fresh herbs, a little stock added, for 2 hours in the oven. 'Let the roasting of the duck be as rapid as his flight.'

Margosa Oil

Margosa oil is extracted from the fruits of the deciduous tree, *Melia azadirachta*, native to the East Indies, and commonly known as the Indian lilac, neem or nemb tree. It had medical uses as an aromatic but bitter oil, in treating fevers, but it is not much used in England now. The bark of the tree is more often used, chiefly in herbal practice.

Medlar Jelly

To every 4 lb fruit, washed and cut up, add 3 pints water and 6 tablespoonsful of lemon juice (or 2 level teaspoonsful of citric or tartaric acid). Crush and simmer for at least 1 hour; strain as hot as possible through a hair sieve or butter muslin *and* a flannel bag, and add ¾ lb sugar to each pint of juice. Bring quickly to boil after adding the sugar gradually; test for setting after about 5 minutes. Remove scum, and pot hot, sealing airtight.

To Sour Milk

If the milk is pasteurised, it does not sour naturally and therefore does not make a good curd. A curd of a kind can be obtained by adding a starter such as rennet (1 small teaspoonful to 1 pint warm milk) and then straining, but you will probably try this only once. The best curd comes from souring non-pasteurised milk, as fresh as can be obtained. Keep it in a warm room temperature (65–75°F) until it forms curds, which can then be strained. Ideally, the quicker the milk sours, the better, and the best starter is a spoonful of sour milk from a previous souring. But one of the commercial starters could be used and would be obtainable from a good dairy.

Drying Mushrooms

To dry horse mushrooms, first wipe with a dry cloth, peel off the skin, and lay on sheets of parchment paper in quite a cool oven, turning occasionally. When quite dry, they will have shrivelled considerably, and may be kept in paper bags hung in a dry, cool place. Only perfect mushrooms should be dried. Any that are shedding spores, or which are infested by maggots, should be discarded. To use, place in a cold gravy, sauce or milk, bring gradually to the simmer, and they will plump up and can be cooked to the stage desired.

Storing Nuts

Hazel nuts, cob and filbert, should be gathered when the nuts turn brown or fall out of their cups. Dry them on trays or on a floor and, when the shells are dry, pack in containers, boxes or tins. For keeping, the best method is to layer them in dry sand – put ½ in sand in the base of the container, cover with a layer of nuts, sprinkle over enough sand to cover, then sprinkle lightly with cooking salt. Repeat until the container is full, finishing with another ½-in layer of sand at the top. Place in a cool, dry place. English nuts contain more moisture than those grown in warmer regions, and some shrinkage of the kernels will occur if kept too long.

In the case of walnuts, remove the green husk or outer casing. As a rule, only those from which the green husk will split and come away easily are likely to be ripe nuts worth keeping. If the nuts have been blown down prematurely, the husk is difficult to remove and the kernels themselves are likely to be rather immature. Fallen nuts gathered in October should be ripe enough. After removing the husks, clean the kernels by removing all traces of soft fibre or threads with a stiff-bristled or wire brush. Put the nuts in a tub with coarse sharp sand and water and churn with a stiff broom until more or less clean of tender greenish husk. Then dry the nuts and store in sand with a light sprinkling of salt, and keep in a cool place.

Preparing Oatmeal

Commercially, oats are prepared for oatmeal by (a) cleaning to remove dirt, weeds, seeds etc.; (b) subjecting to hot steam to kill undesirable enzymes; (c) kiln drying and then dehusking by abrasion on stones through a mill, or by impact. The chaff and kernels can then be separated and the oats treated further – either ground for meal, or cut into pinhead oatmeal, or crushed and flattened through rollers. The husk or chaff of oats is not so readily removed as that of, say, wheat. Passing the oats first through a mill (a coffee grinder mill or one of the Scandinavian cereal mills) set to coarse grind would break the chaff and release the oat grain to enable separation by sifting. Then grind the oats to the consistency desired. They should be ripe and dry before grinding.

Pease Pudding

Tie a pint of split peas in a cloth, leaving them room to swell but no more. Place in a pan of cold water, and boil for just half an hour until tender, but not watery. If swelling directions are followed with care, all will be well. Turn out of the cloth, rub through a sieve into a basin, then add ¼ lb butter. Season with salt and white pepper. Bind with 3 egg yolks and 1 whole egg. Lightly flour a pudding cloth which you put in a small round-bottomed basin, pour in the mixture, tie the cloth and boil the pudding for an hour in a pan of boiling water. Turn from the cloth on to a serving dish. The pudding is ideal with pork.

Pheasant Stuffed with Woodcock

Mince the woodcock. Add an ounce or so of breadcrumbs to the mince. Moisten with a little brandy or cream, and include a little shredded suet. Proceed then as for roasting stuffed pheasant. This is not a usual stuffing for a pheasant.

Sucking Pig

After killing, the pig should be immersed in cold water for about 15 minutes, then plunged into boiling water for 2 or 3 minutes. When taken out, all the hair should be removed as quickly as possible by pulling and scraping. When the skin has been dressed, slit underneath down the belly and remove the entrails and organs; clean out the nostrils, ears and mouth; wash thoroughly in cold water and then wipe dry very well. Remove the feet at the first joint, leaving skin to wrap over and seal. To roast: prepare a forcemeat or sage-and-onion stuffing and pack this inside the pig, sealing the opening with a needle and thread. Brush the pig all over with melted butter or salad oil and wrap in greased paper. Bake or roast in a good oven for 2½–3 hours, basting well. Half an hour before it is likely to be ready, remove the paper wrapping and brush again with butter, salad oil or thick cream, and put back to brown and crisp. Serve with apple sauce. It is usually served with the head cut off and halved;

then the carcase is split down the middle, laid open on the serving dish, with one half of the head at each end.

Thin Pikelets

Measure into a mixing bowl 3 cups of flour. Mix in nearly 2 cups of milk, 2 eggs that have been beaten until light and 2 oz castor sugar. In the small amount of milk saved from the 2 cups, dissolve a teaspoonful of carbonate of soda and mix this in with the other ingredients. Add 2 teaspoonsful of cream of tartar. Grease a girdle and put the mixture on in careful spoonfuls, seeing that the mixture is well spread out so as to make the pikelets thin. When they have risen, turn and cook on the other side.

Plum Cake (1860)

Half a dozen recipes for making plum cake may be found in every cookery book, and as your taste does not seem very easily suited, we would advise you to consult your own authority, and try each in succession.

Popcorn (1959)

American popcorn is usually made from special varieties of the maize or sweet corn plant, *Zea mays*. It can be grown in this country if the seeds are sown early under glass and the seedlings transplanted later out-of-doors. The popcorn varieties, developed in America, are not as a rule available in this country. You can, of course, make popcorn from the ripe seeds of other varieties, such as golden bantam, Kortland's golden maize etc. Seeds of varieties usually grown for corn on the cob are offered by several firms. The seeds can be popped, but the difficulty lies in bringing the crop to the necessary full ripeness in our climate.

Potted Trout, Eels and Herrings (1861)

Cut off the heads, tails and fins (and if the fish are large, that is about $\frac{1}{2}$ lb, the back-bone) and scale and trim the fish. Clean them by wiping, but use no water. Salt them inside and out. Lay them on a sloping stone or slate, to cause them to drain. If for immediate use, let them remain in salt for 1 hour; if for keeping some time, 2 or 3 hours. Wipe them again, quite dry. Sprinkle them well, inside and out, with the mixture. Lay them in a dish to be baked side by side, the backs uppermost. Cover well with fresh butter, place a cover over the whole to confine the steam, and do not let the dish touch the bottom of the oven, but place a few pieces of crockery under it, or the bottom layer will be burned. Let them stew in a slow oven for 2, 3 or 4 hours, until the bones are dissolved; drain off the butter and remove the fish into potting-mugs; press them well down and pour fresh clarified butter over them. If trout are cooked according to the above mode, 'Culex' will find them 'tasty' and an agreeable dish for the breakfast-table, or for dispatching to distant friends. The following is the mixture: 6 teaspoonsful of ground black pepper, 6 do. allspice, 4 do. mace, 2 do. cloves, 2 do. nutmeg, 1 do. cayenne; or to keep it fresh and pungent, one half of the above quantities may be kept in a phial well corked. When used, but not before, add to it an equal quantity of salt. [The Secretary of the Ryedale Anglers' Club]

Rowan Jam (1900)

The berries of the mountain ash or rowan tree are certainly not poisonous, but we cannot say whether they would make good jam. Some kind of conserve is still made from them in parts of Scotland. Formerly, if not at the present time, a fermented beverage was prepared from the juice, and Evelyn says that 'ale and beer brewed with these berries, being ripe, is an incomparable drink familiar in Wales'.

Soft Cheeses from Normandy (1887)

The soft cheeses sent from Normandy are not made from cream, but from new milk, or new milk which has been slightly skimmed. They are the Camembert, Livarot, Neufchâtel, and Bondon, all of which are ripened varieties, and all will keep a considerable time. There is a little cheese made of milk and cream, which is sent over new; but this will not keep very long.

Turkish Delight

Turkish Delight is made from wheat starch dissolved in hot water, and flavoured with otto of roses, lemon, vanilla, mastic, etc.; the process requires skill and can hardly be simulated in the kitchen, even if the proper ingredients were forthcoming. The nearest recipe we can give you is: Put 1 lb granulated sugar with 1 gill of water in a saucepan and heat to 240°F; add $\frac{1}{4}$ teaspoonful tartaric acid, and stand on one side for a moment. Measure 5 gills of water; use a little of this to blend 3 oz cornflour with 7 oz icing sugar, and when smooth, boil the remainder of the water, and pour it into the blended cornflour and icing sugar, stirring to prevent lumpiness. Return to the saucepan and boil, stirring and beating vigorously until clear and thick. Now add the sugar syrup gradually, beating it in; boil together for 20–30 minutes, and when transparent and of a pale straw colour, add 2 oz honey, and stir in, then flavouring (lemon extract, or vanilla etc.) and a few drops of rose water. Pour half the boiling mixture into a buttered tin; colour the remainder to rose or pink, and pour on top of the first lot; stand aside until cold. Then take a sharp knife, dip in icing sugar and cut the mixture into squares; place each square into icing sugar, coating liberally, and leave overnight in the sugar; then pack in airtight tin, liberally dusted with icing sugar.

Wedding Cake Wood

The type of wood likely to be most suitable for a box in which to cook a wedding cake slowly at relatively low temperatures would be a seasoned hardwood – ash, sycamore, elm, thorn, even oak – rather than a resinous softwood. For the haybox technique, it is less important; even a tea chest, suitably lined and insulated, would do.

What is Yoghourt? (1952)

It is strange that many dictionaries omit yoghourt, since the product has been known through travellers to this country from Turkey since the early 17th century. The word is derived from the Turkish, and has been variously spelt as youghourt, yogurd, yogurt, yooghort, yahourt, yaghourt, yughard, yaourt and there are probably other variations. The most acceptable pronunciation seems to be yo-girt or yo-gourt (as in 'go' and 'gourd'). It is simply milk fermented by a beneficial bacterium – *lactobaccillus bulgaricus*. It is a common method of preserving milk in hot countries such as those around the eastern Mediterranean, where it may otherwise quickly go bad.

CURING, PICKLING AND SMOKING
Curing Pig Meat

To each stone (14 lb) of meat allow 1 lb common salt, 1 oz saltpetre, 6 oz moist brown sugar and $\frac{3}{4}$ pint vinegar. Remove backbone and ribs from the flitches; cut off the feet, the shoulders and hams, removing the head of the thigh bones. Sprinkle the meat well with salt and lay on sloping boards or bench for 24 hours to empty blood vessels etc. Wipe clean with a cloth. Mix the salt and saltpetre and rub very thoroughly into the meat, with particular care around the bones. Place the pieces rind side down in the bath; spread on top with the sugar and leave for 3 days, and pour over the vinegar. Bathe

the meat with the pickle several times daily, turning over every other day. Bacon will take 10–14 days to cure; hams and shoulder 3–4 weeks. When taken out, cover with muslin and hang in a dry place. A galvanised bath is not ideal for the purpose, and it is better to use a wooden trough or unchipped enamel-ware.

Soused Herrings

Wash and scale the herrings, cut off the heads, remove the backbones after splitting open, and roll up tightly. Place the rolled-up fish in a pie-dish in which there is a layer of thinly sliced onions, season to taste with salt and pepper, and cover with vinegar and a little water. Bake in a slow oven for about an hour. The term soused is also sometimes applied to herrings pickled in salt. Bismarck herrings are refinements of simple salting and worth trying with freshwater fish of similar size. You scale, behead, clean and take out the backbone of the small-sized fish. Soak them in brine ($\frac{1}{2}$ lb salt to 3 pints water) for 4 hours; then take out, cover with vinegar, and leave for 14 hours. Roll up each fish around a tablespoonful of sliced onion, pack in jars with a slice of lemon, cover with cold, spiced white wine vinegar, seal airtight, and they will keep.

Kippers

To 'kipper' herrings at home is rather troublesome. You split and gut fresh, plump herrings, opening them flat; rub with a mixture of equal parts by weight Jamaica pepper and salt; leave 24 hours; drain and wipe; stretch on sticks, and then smoke. To smoke the fish you need a smoking chamber. This can be constructed from an open-ended wood box or barrel, resting on 2 parallel lines of bricks, with a sheet of iron below the opening, just large enough to leave open spaces at each side for smoke to enter and ascend through the chamber. The fish are hung in the chamber from rods placed across and a damp sack is used to cover the top. A fire is made below, between the bricks, and fed with hardwood sawdust, oak or ash or juniper. The sawdust is allowed to smoulder, the draught being manipulated with the sack at the top. Smoking takes 24–72 hours, according to flavour desired. If the fish are wanted to keep for more than 1–2 weeks, it is wise to cure them more fully before smoking. After the salt–pepper treatment, rub with a mixture of $\frac{1}{2}$ lb salt, $1\frac{1}{2}$ oz natural brown sugar and $\frac{1}{2}$ oz saltpetre, and repeat for 3–4 days, and then smoke.

Smoked Mussels

Smoking mussels must be looked upon as an experiment. After cleansing, remove the beard, as for cooking. They may be laid on wire mesh and smoked for 3 days with hardwood (oak or juniper) sawdust on a charcoal-initiated fire. The Abu Smoker is generally used with special sawdust and a smoking ingredient for a short period, and the fish is usually for early consumption.

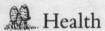 Health

Cholera Under the Microscope (1854)

There are few large towns in which some one or more persons have not microscopes of modern construction, with objective powers up to 500 linear. Where cholera has broken out in any locality I suggest this test: Get a few sheets of glass 6 in square, thin, but as level as can be obtained; let a glazier run his diamond in parallel lines 1 in apart from top to bottom of these pieces of glass, so as to make it easy to break off, when wanted, slides of 6 in long by 1 in. Place these sheets of glass so ruled, some in rooms where there are cholera patients, others in the cleft of sticks, projecting into the air outside the windows of houses in infected localities. Take a broad camel-hair pencil and lightly wash over these glasses with a solution of glycerine and distilled water, 1 part of the former to 3 of the latter; leave them for 12 hours; now remove them, break the said glasses up where ruled with the diamond, and submit the slides to the best microscope investigation; let it be seen whether in any given number there is, amid the dust, insects, etc., anything, *however minute*, of a *fungoid* appearance. If so, let some of the *ejecta* and *disjecta* from the choleraic patients be submitted to the same ocular test, and ascertain whether anything of the like character can be found in these. If this be the case, I say you have gained a step, and a step on which I would have men of real science take their first stand in the endeavour to trace out the actual something productive of choleraic symptoms. Let anyone take a piece of glass or two prepared as above, and, by means of cleft sticks, put them up in gardens and in fields, only for a few hours, even on a still day, and I think the result will surprise him, for it reveals secrets in the air few suspect. I would have the experiment made by night as well as by day; we have yet much to learn of the effect of night air in the propagation of corrupting influences. I think the moon has had much laid to its charge which with justice it should have shared with smaller lights, at least with the time both most reign. [Investigator]

Healthy Cottages (1860)

While such things are happening here, there, or everywhere, every year, it is a matter of no small consequence to ascertain the conditions on which our labouring population may be well housed – as a matter of business, and not of mere charity; that is, under the steady, natural laws of society, and not the fluctuating influence of human sensibilities, which have always more calls upon them than they can meet. When it is ascertained that it answers to labourers to pay from £3–£6 rent, rather than have sickness in the house, and that they may have for that rent good dwellings of from 4–6 rooms, or equivalent attachments, there will be a manifest decrease in the sickness and mortality of the country. [Miss Martineau]

Eyebrows (1861)

Can any of the readers of THE FIELD tell me of a remedy to prevent eyebrows and lashes falling off after an illness? [Rover] [*Editor's note: This heartfelt plea went unanswered*]

Hydrophobia: All in the Mind? (1898)

People talk as if the contest was between those who identify hydrophobia with tetanus, and those who maintain the distinctness of the two diseases; or between those who say that hydrophobia is caused by anxiety and terror of mind, and those who contend that the cause of the distress is physical rather than mental. Nothing can be further from the truth, if it is contended that these are the only theories antagonistic to the hypothesis of a specific virus. Those who talk of hydrophobia being a form of tetanus must either be ignorant of medical definitions, or must be using the word tetanus in a metaphorical and analogical sense, as equivalent to any very violent affection of the nervous system. The other party are possessed with the idea that hydrophobia is always the result of intense mental reflection, which view Sir Thomas Watson easily demolishes by adducing the case of infants and idiots, incapable of understanding about hydrophobia. Other contagionist writers have argued, from the case of animals that have gone mad after being bitten by rabid dogs, that the imagination cannot be the cause of hydrophobia. Sir Thomas distinguishes rabies in animals from hydrophobia in man; but, anyhow, it must be remembered that children, idiots, and animals are equally possessed of a nervous system with Sir Thomas himself. He has, therefore, done nothing to refute the notion of the disease originating in the nervous system rather than in the blood. The real contest is between the only two logical issues: the one, that hydrophobia is caused by a specific virus contained in the saliva of the rabid dog; the other, that it is a purely nervous disease (nervous as opposed to mental or bodily, in the sense of body minus the nerves), resulting from the original shock, and from the attention (objectively speaking) being fixed on the bitten part, so as to produce abnormal and morbid nervous action. The story of the woman who was infected through the stitches of her gown is quoted from Hildanus – who died in 1634.

Migraine (1860)

'Firefly' is thanked for her kind attention to the question on migraine. The disease appears to be the result of a damp and variable climate. Some relief has been obtained by taking citrate or iron and quinine, and rubbing the part affected, during the paroxysms, with an anodyne oil called *Baume tranquille*, of which belladonna is the principal ingredient.

Moustache Wash (1860)

The recipes for wash for strengthening the hair appeared in Nos. 370 and 373. It is against our rule to republish the letters, but you could obtain the numbers containing them. If you wish to write to the correspondents mentioned we shall be happy to forward your letters.

Women Healers (1853)

The Female Medical College of Pennsylvania will commence its next course of lectures on 1 October. Its faculty consists of 5 male and 2 female professors – the latter regularly graduated physicians as well as the former – while the demonstrator in anatomy is also an able female physician. That many women possess extraordinary capacities for the healing art is established; that there are cases requiring medical treatment in which they are better qualified to minister to each other's needs than men can be is obvious. We trust that, whatever prejudice may exist against 'woman's right' to the ballot and to demi-pants will not be allowed to bear against her right to qualify herself for a career of eminent usefulness in the relief of suffering, and the communication to her sisters of important physiological truth. [From *New York Tribune*]

The Country Garden

 The Vegetable Garden

The Life of an Asparagus Bed

The life of a well made and well cared for asparagus bed is usually at least 50 years, often more. You say that you made your bed 31 years ago and it bore splendidly for some 25 years but has since been going back steadily and now bears shoots only as thick as matchsticks. As it is now becoming sparse, with crowns dying out, it would be better to make a new bed next year rather than attempt a regeneration of the old. Much depends, of course, upon the condition of the present crowns. From the information you give, either these are dwindling from soil rot-fungi or possibly crown gall. If the crowns only produce matchstick thick stalks, and subsequently a poor head of foliage, they cannot be building up. It is possible that the crowns have become too deep in the soil. Only examination on the spot can ascertain decisively whether the present crowns are worth keeping and encouraging. From the information you give in your letter, it would seem the better plan is to start anew, say with 3-year-old plants of the newer strains.

Big Beans

The growth of side shoots on broad-bean plants shows vigour and good culture. Whether you should suppress them or not depends on the produce you want. If you want pods and beans of exhibition quality, then break off the side stems at base, thus ensuring that the main stem and produce receive all the nutrients. If you want beans of good edible quality and the heaviest crop, leave the side stems on. They will give you a second crop, though the beans and pods will not be quite up to those on the main stem. Mulch the plants for the warm weather.

Forcing Chicory

Let your witloef chicory continue to grow until the leaves die down about the beginning of November. Then lift the roots, cut off the remaining leaves to within ½ in of the base and rub off any side growths. You can then cut the roots to a uniform length of 9–10 in by tipping the bottom ends, and store layered in sand in a cool place outdoors along a north wall, or in a cool frost-proof shed. To force, you take the roots and plant them in pots or boxes, spacing 3–4 in apart, and cover with soil with the crowns 1 in below the surface. Water carefully, and place indoors in a shed, cellar or mushroom house or under curtained greenhouse staging, covered with a pot or box inverted on top, and in a temperature of not less than 45–60°F. The crowns soon put forth the blanched leaves which are ready for cutting when 8–9 in long in about 4 weeks. By planting and bringing in the roots at intervals, a succession of leaves can be obtained.

Cucumbers in Straw Bales

Briefly, this method entails taking out planting holes in a bale of straw, wetting the straw itself to a sufficiently moist condition, planting up from the pots, and then feeding with a dilute liquid manure or solution of nitrogenous–potash fertiliser. The difficulty is to get the straw moist without being over-wetted. It is suggested that the planting stations should be of holes somewhat deeper than necessary to accommodate the plant and its soil ball, so that it can be packed around and top-dressed with good soil compost or rotted manure or vegetable compost. The straw itself should be soaked prior to planting. It is useful to use hot water, though the bale must cool off before planting. Thereafter, the plant can be top-dressed with rotted manure or compost and, when it is growing vigorously and its roots fill the soil etc. and are reaching into the straw, feeding with a dilute liquid manure can be begun. You can use a proprietary liquid or a solution of ½ oz dried blood or Chilean potash nitrate per gallon of water; or natural liquid manure made by steeping rotten dung in water and diluting to a straw colour. Feed about once a week, and in between keep the straw moist by watering as required and according to weather conditions. Four to six plants can be placed equidistant in a bale.

Garlic

If you want a crop this year, act quickly: garlic should be in the ground by the second half of March. It reacts to the length of day and every day's delay will mean a diminished crop. It makes most of its growth during the shorter early days, ripening in July when day-length diminishes again. It does not, therefore, readily develop new shoots in reaction to early snipping of young growth. The shoots are seldom used in the kitchen since to cut them would ruin the growth of the garlic bulb. Shoots and leaves are edible but a little too strong and tough in salads.

Marrows Poisoned by Gourds

There are no authentic records that cross-pollination between ornamental gourds and vegetable marrows makes marrows poisonous. All, of course, belong to the same family and genus (*Cucurbita*). The ornamental gourds usually grown are varieties of annual species – *C.maxima*, *moschata* and *Pepo* and their fruits are edible. *C.Pepo* is the species to which vegetable marrows belong. There is one species, however, *C.foetidissima*, of which the fruit is inedible, but hardly poisonous. In any case, any harmful genetical traits would be conveyed to the *seed* and not to the pulpy fruit of the cross-pollinated plant. However, pollinated plants containing many seeds, and under certain growth conditions, do tend to bitterness, but this can happen to marrows growing on their own.

Peppers – Green, Red and Yellow

[I maintain that green peppers are unripe and that the red ones are just ripe green ones. Others tell me I am wrong and that the green and red are two different varieties.]

There are several varieties of pepper (*Capsicum frutescens*) in cultivation, but they may be broadly divided into 2 types: those which are red when ripe and those which are yellow. Unripe fruits of either kind are green.

The Potato Disease (1860)

It may be of service in the growth of that valuable esculent for growers thereof to learn that a knowledge of the cause of the disease in the potato, with its certain remedy, are in the possession of a labouring man named Tovey, residing at Swansea, South Wales, who for the last 2 seasons has made experiments which fully establish the genuineness of his discovery. In February last, Matthew Moggridge, Esq., a justice of the peace, residing near Swansea, permitted a plot of ground to be planted with white rocks and early reds. Some of the potatoes underwent Tovey's process, and were consequently not planted till the middle of May. The result was successful. A number of the same kind of potatoes, unprepared, were also planted, of which the white rocks were nearly half gone, and of the early reds a great many were diseased. A similar result has been obtained in the ground of H. H. Vivian, Esq., M.P., of Singleton, near Swansea. The possessor of the secret is poor, and has no means of making it known so as to be remunerative to himself. He will undertake to show the cause of the disease if taken up by any society who would guarantee him some return therefor; and the remedy – a mixture of his own preparation – he will transmit through the post, with directions for use, on receipt of a sum in proportion to the quantity required, great cheapness being its most recommendatory feature next to its potency in removing the disease. Any communication addressed J.C.M., Post-office, Swansea, will meet with prompt attention.

Potato Eelworm

If your ground is contaminated with potato eelworm, you would be well advised to rest it from potato cropping for some years at least. The critical point is that the eelworms are in the soil, as cysts of about pinhead size, even when potatoes are not growing. These cysts are sensitive to some excretion of the roots of potatoes and other Solonaceae, and burst when excited by it, releasing the eelworms, which then invade the potato plants. By resting the ground from potatoes, the cyst numbers decline slowly and the eelworm problem becomes less severe. The process can be speeded up naturally by manuring each year with a green mustard manure crop, turned in during the early winter. There is an eelworm pesticide on the market. You can crop the land with other crops, excepting potatoes and tomatoes, of course.

Storing Potatoes (1900)

The usual and only safe way, so far as we know, of storing potatoes is to pit them in a dry place on a convenient part of the farm. They may simply be placed on the surface or in a pit 10 or 12 in deep and heaped as high as they can be built on a base 3 or 4 ft wide – no need for limiting lengths – and thatched with straw and earth, the latter and outer covering sufficiently thick to ensure safety against frost. Store the potatoes only when thoroughly dry.

Purslane

The young shoots of this Dutch vegetable are often used in salads on the Continent, and the older shoots as a pot-herb or for pickling. It is an annual and is grown from seed, sowing out-of-doors in a well drained loam soil, manured for a previous crop, in a sunny, open position, in March, in drills 12 in apart, and the plants are thinned to about 8–9 in apart in the rows. The plant is not often cultivated in Britain and you would have to approach a specialist in uncommon vegetable seeds, such as Miss Kathleen Hunter, Wheal Frances, Callestick, Truro, Cornwall.

Salade de Ble (1861)

As the corn-salad question seems not without interest to the readers of *THE FIELD* (if we may judge by the many letters we have received on the subject), it may be as well to give, once and for all, the manner of its culture in this country and on the Continent generally. The seed should be sown, broadcast, every fortnight, from the middle of July or August, to the end of October, between other vegetables, or in separate beds. The plant thrives in any soil, but of course becomes more luxuriant in well-manured ground. The seeds are to be lightly covered, and require no further care. The salad comes into use in the winter, and lasts till spring. A few plants should be left for the seed, which only ripens in the following July, and readily sows itself. Only the short leaves forming the heart of the plant should be eaten, and it is generally associated with boiled or baked beetroot, cut into thin slices, and a sauce *à la Mayonnaise*.

The Orchard

Apples from Seed (1948)

Edible apples can be produced from seeds, without grafting. That is the way all our varieties have arisen. The difficulty is that the varieties seldom come true from seed, and seedlings are often the result of cross-pollination. Only a few are really worth while propagating on for their fruit. One has to wait some years for a seedling to fruit on its own roots. The purposes of grafting are chiefly: (1) to allow seedlings to be brought into fruit more quickly when their qualities can be assessed; (2) to allow the extensive propagation of a variety with the certainty that every grafted tree will be true to type; and (3) to utilise the effect of different stocks to produce trees of the type we want, i.e. cordons, dwarf bush or pyramid trees, half-standards and standards. If your seedling apple, planted 10 years ago, has produced 2 dozen good edible fruits, there is every reason for retaining it. If the fruit has exceptional qualities, you can name it and submit to the Royal Horticultural Society for trials, provided it is not of a variety already known.

Blenheim Apple Mystery (1953)

The colouring of apples is certainly not influenced by direct sunlight alone, though the sun's rays often do influence coloration. But apples also get their colouring from the balance of their nutrition. It is well known that potash, for instance, induces brighter and more crimson tones. It is also true that warmth is a factor, and it would seem from the circumstances you relate that the principal reason for your Blenheim colouring and ripening on the north side of the tree a fortnight earlier than those on the south side lies in the more favourable environmental conditions prevailing. Possibly your house gives the added shelter and reflects some steadying degree of warmth to the near side of the tree, and again it is possible that the vigour of growth and sap flow tends to diminish earlier to the north branches, thus inducing earlier ripening.

Cider Apples (1958)

Authentic English cider is made with special cider varieties, and you get different blends – sharp, dry, sweet, etc. – according to the mixture of sweet and sour varieties of cider apples used. Some of the varieties are bitter-sweet: Chisel, Jersey, Knotted Kernel, Major, Royal Wilding. Sweet varieties include Sweet Alford, Sweet Coppin, White Jersey. Sharp or sour: Cap of Liberty, Foxwhelp, Kingston Black, Ponsford, Reinette Obry.

Ripeness of Apples

From Nature's point of view, an apple is only fully ripe when it has rotted and so afforded release to its seed. This decomposition goes on remorselessly whether the apple remains on the tree, the orchard floor or the fruit store. An apple is ripe for eating when it attains a pleasant sweetness, texture and flavour. Different varieties reach this stage at different speeds, and this influences their keeping quality. One can slow the processes of decomposition but not stop them. Retention on the tree varies with varieties, and seems to be controlled by plant hormones. Apparently, growth conditions made your tree form the abscission-retarding hormone rather strongly so that your James Grieves, normally picked in September, did not part easily until November. In this case, pick according to skin colour (it should be turning yellow) and taste. James Grieves should be eaten within a week or two of picking. Try harvesting by cutting the stalks in early October, where parting does not occur easily.

Re-rooting a Blown Apple Tree

If the tree's roots have been severely injured and severed on one side, dig out the area where they will fall when the tree is replaced, remove the severed roots, and after winching the tree back into position, replace the soil, mixed liberally with thoroughly rotted manure or compost or sedge peat, and bonemeal (about 1 lb to 4 sq yards); firm the soil well to the roots, soak the area thoroughly and stake firm. It would be helpful to prune the top growth and thin out the branches first.

Fig Ripening

To have a crop of ripened figs in England it is essential to confine the root system to an area of about 16 sq ft, and there should be a hard layer at about 2 ft down. Thin out the branches and shoots, removing any spindly growths from the base and unfruitful old branches. No manure is needed. The fruitlets which make this year's crop should be at the tips of bearing shoots. If half-grown or mummied fruits are found below these, rub them off. As the bearing shoot grows, it elongates and will strive to make a second lot of fruits above those of this year's crop carried over in embryo from last autumn, but this second lot will not ripen. Above them more tiny fruitlets will form in embryo to the tip of the shoot by autumn; preserve these, but rub off the second crop below in autumn. The embryonic tiny ones at the top of the shoot are the ones that need protection from low temperatures and frost, especially in the spring. For the winter, spread litter of straw, bracken, etc., about 1 ft thick over the roots, to be kept in place by a bough or two of spruce, or a hurdle or plastic netting. You could fix a plastic sheet to deflect the wind; even more important would be a top cover over the tree to prevent radiation, especially on clear frosty nights. This can take the form of plastic sheeting draped over the top of the plant, or small mesh netting 'tented' over the plant. If the plant is on a wall, a good idea is a simple wood framework at a slope, on which plastic sheeting or netting can be arranged to drape over the top of the plant. This checks the loss of warmth from the plant surfaces and its vicinity, sufficient to prevent the frost damage that shrivels the embryo figs.

The Future of Figs (1892)

The best figs grown in Southern California are the white varieties, which part of the State is best suited for their cultivation. Competent authorities consider that there is a great future for this industry.

Grape Vine from Seed

It is quite within the realms of possibility that your grape vine, planted 4 months ago as a grape seed in your greenhouse and now about 4 ft high, will fruit – probably beginning in its third to fifth year, though sometimes taking longer, dependent on treatment. When the leaves fall this autumn, you should shorten the single stem by at least one third its length. Next year, the topmost bud will break to continue the main stem or rod, and probably one or more side shoots will develop. The first few years should be largely devoted to building up the main rod or framework of the vine, before encouraging heavy bearing. After another year of growth, you shorten the leader again, and cut back any side shoots to the base. It is from these points that new shoots appear each year to bear fruit.

Grape Growing in Unheated Vineries (1900)

For 20 years and more I grew the finest black Hamburgh grapes in unheated vineries in Guernsey and Jersey. Muscats must have fire heat and I had pipes put in my houses for that and other purposes. If you have fire heat you can get early tomatoes, etc., none of which I care for, and the vines have now no assistance in that way until they are well started and grapes showing, my wish being to keep the grapes back, as they are not wanted until the plums, peaches, etc., are over. For many years prior to 1868 I grew Sweetwater grapes in the open against the wall of the house, and used to put the bunches in grape bags, not always with success, for the rain spoilt them. I bagged more than 100 bunches in one season. They were very delicious, but at that time grapes were grapes, and you could only buy Portugal grapes sent over in jars packed with sawdust. [F. B., Lankhills, Winchester]

More Unheated Vineries (1900)

I see in your paper, under 'Garden and Woodland', an inquiry by
'F.W.' anent growing late grapes in unheated vineries, and a note by
you inviting remarks. I have a lean-to vinery attached to my
dwelling house, near Plymouth, facing nearly due south, and with
glass at each end. In this are 9 vines – 7 black Hamburg, 1 white
Muscat of Alexandria, 1 Grizzly Fontignan. There are pipes, but as
far as I can learn they have not been used for years; and when I took
the house the result of lighting the furnace, which is below the
kitchen floor, was to produce two explosions. I have not lighted the
fire since, but each year, by careful attention, I have succeeded in
producing a very fair sample of grapes from all the vines until nearly
the end of October, by which time they have been all consumed. I
am very careful about washing the vines when dormant with soft
soap, warm water, and a very small quantity of paraffin. During the
growing season of the foliage and blossoming I give plenty of air
both day and night, plenty of water on the floors as well as air in the
swelling season, and close up everything by 5.30 p.m. in the
colouring season, keeping down all superfluous foliage. The roots
run outside in a wide border of soil, a loamy clay. I dig in a cartload
of well-rotted slaughter-house manure end of January or early in
February, with a proportion of bone-meal, wood-ashes, soot, and
some potash stimulant, and give a bit more of the latter in wet
weather during the growing season. I have a splendid promise this
year, and, with good weather in the next 2 months, expect to have as
good a crop, if not as early, as some of my neighbours, who have
more elaborate appliances and larger means. I believe in: (1) Plenty
of feeding and severe thinning; (2) plenty of air; (3) plenty of water
when swelling; (4) careful bottling of the sun heat when ripening; (5)
plenty of personal attention. I do nearly everything myself.
[H.E.H.]

Bleeding Mulberry Tree

Pruning on any extensive scale is not advised for a well established
and fairly old mulberry tree. The difficulty is that this type of tree
bleeds excessively from cuts, and the more the cuts or the greater
their extent, the more the tree would suffer. You can and should cut
out all dead, diseased and weak shoots when the leaves have fallen. If
you are going to thin the live shoots, however, it would be best to
do so by removing them to their base, and then painting the cuts
with Stockholm tar or a tree antiseptic. This cutting should not be

extensive in any one year, and should be completed before the sap begins to rise again; usually before mid-December. It would be far wiser to give the large branches carrying the bulk of the crop adequate supports with wooden props.

Nutless

Nut trees take at least 6 years to reach anything like full cropping. If some of your trees (planted 3 and 8 years ago) have borne a few nuts, then their improvement should continue henceforth. For the finest crops of large nuts, prune cobnuts and filberts and restrict their size. Without pruning and in a fairly moist or rich soil, plants would tend to make much shoot and leaf growth, with the formation of fewer twiggy laterals on which flowers and catkins are borne. In this case, towards the end of February try cutting lateral shoots back to just above well placed female flowers and then tackling the thickest shoots or branches to thin them out and open the centre of each tree.

Peaches and Garlic

There seems to be no substantiated experimental proof that garlic is an antidote or preventive of peach leaf curl. In our climate, even if you plant the garlic in January or February, it will hardly make enough growth to affect the possible infection of a tree already carrying the fungus spores. But, certainly, garlic and garlic oil are potent antiseptics. Try planting cloves or segments of garlic 3 in deep within the rooting area of the tree, but spray, too, at least for the coming year.

The Raspberry (1865)

We have been much interested in the recent correspondence between W.S. and 'Firefly' on the failure of the former's raspberry crop. On the first sight of W.S.'s opening letter we formed our own conclusions as to the cause of failure, and purposed at no distant day reverting to it, giving our opinion as to the reason why; but other subjects have prevented our doing so until now. We rather rejoice that such hindrance has been in our way, because meanwhile 'Firefly' has drawn W.S. out into giving with more distinct minuteness a description of the state and condition of his raspberry plantation, for W.S. must excuse us when we say that his first letter was *rather* ambiguous. The ideas, though apparently clear (and as they would doubtless appear to him), were, to the generality of readers, very misty indeed. As far as we ourselves are concerned, we have such large practice in finding out the meaning of the 'guess-at-half-of-it' class of correspondents, that we at once formed our own conclusions, which W.S.'s second letter only confirmed. It appears, then, that the plantation has been made 4 years, that each year the annual canes have grown both strong and stout, but have not produced that quantity of fruit that might reasonably be expected of them. The inference which seems the most rational to be drawn from this is, that the annual canes have not had justice done them in the ripening process; they have been allowed to be choked up with last year's growth until late in the season, and therefore the buds which ought to have produced flowers and fruit were consequently only half formed, immature, unfruitful. This will account for their insignificant development, and also for the after appearance of young shoots starting from the bottom, and showing fruit in their first year. There is just one more conclusion which may be arrived at – if the garden is subject to severe spring frost, this would check the flower-buds that were bursting, and so paralyse the whole plant. The raspberry delights in a dark alluvium soil, well and deeply dug, and plentifully enriched with good hotbed manure. The young canes that spring up each year should be thinned in May, and immediately the last fruit is gathered the old canes ought to be cut away. About the end of August the tops of all the young (this year's) canes could be nipped off, and they should be allowed all the sun and air they can possibly have till their leaves fall, then they may be tied up, and the ground dunged and forked over; this will finish them for the season. If after this treatment they fail to bear fruit, there's something wrong somewhere – a very safe conclusion everybody must admit.

Wild Neighbour

The only explanation for the superior fruiting of neglected raspberry canes growing wild in a neighbouring garden is that their growing conditions must be more suitable than your carefully nurtured bed – chiefly in affording a cooler root run, more moisture and no disturbance. Raspberries need an acid soil, a great deal of organic matter and no disturbance of the roots.

Protecting Strawberries

For fruiting strawberry plants the best practice is to lay clean wheat or oat straw along the rows as soon as the fruit is set and beginning to swell, fitting it under the leaves of the plants and close up to the crowns, as its purpose is to ensure a clean crop and to prevent fruit being splashed with mud when it rains. The drawbacks of strawing early as suggested are chiefly (1) the straw may serve to trap cold air on frosty nights in spring and prevent it draining away, so increasing the risk of frost damage; (2) delayed ripening since the light straw reflects the sunlight instead of absorbing it; and (3) straw insulates the blossoms from the warmth of the soil while leaving them exposed to radiation losses of heat on clear spring nights, and thus again increasing the dangers of frost damage. The disadvantages of early strawing outweigh the advantages, for frost protection can be given by simply interposing any sort of cover between the plants and the open sky, such as old curtaining, newspaper or tarred paper, or planks resting on bricks over the plants.

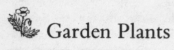 Garden Plants

PLANTS AND SHRUBS
A Tent for an Acacia

To protect an outdoor *Acacia dealbata* during the winter, enclose the plant tent-fashion with the boughs of a conifer, bound round with twine. The alternative is to make a tent framework with a tripod of canes, and to arrange sheet polythene film on this, fastened with tape or tiffany, or hessian sacking. If very exposed, it is wise to pack the tent with loose bracken, at least one third of the way up the plant. It might be wise to move the plant to a wall corner, where sheeting could be dropped over it easily. The protection is needed when temperature levels drop to round about 40–45°F.

Antagonistic Plants

There is some evidence that plants can be antagonistic in the sense that they may excrete substances that inhibit the growth of other plants in their vicinity. There is also evidence that some plants secrete or give off molecules of substances that adversely affect other plants in the near vicinity, and injure or inhibit their top growth, stem, foliage and flowers. Certain combinations of cut flowers and greenery are not compatible. It is not so much a matter of allergy as of competitive antagonism.

Chinese Lanterns

If your rapidly spreading 'garden pest' plants are growing out of doors they are probably of the species *Physalis franchetti*, commonly known as Chinese Lantern, though native to Japan. This plant and its varieties are chiefly grown for the ornamental coloured calyces enclosing the fruit. The fruit is not poisonous, but peculiarly flavoured. It is not usually used for jam. The Cape Gooseberry, which gives yellow edible fruits for dessert and preserves, is *Physalis peruviana*, var. *edulis*. This plant comes from South America and is grown under glass in this country. Your plants are hardly likely to be of this type and it is doubtful if it would be worth while making jam of their fruits.

Flower Pigments (1948)

The phenomenon of the pink flowers of your flowering currant (*Ribes sanguineum*) opening whitish when forced is a common one. It seems to be caused by the fact that the pink colour is furnished by a sap-pigment or anthocyanin, and this pigment fails when the branch is severed from the bush and is kept alive by being placed in water. Yellow, orange and red flowers owe their colour to substances known as plastids which are contained within the plant cells and, therefore, are not subject to failure in the same way as with sap pigments.

Flowering in Abundance (1967)

You ask why this is such a wonderful flowering season. In the case of shrubs and trees which flower roughly in the first half of the year (spring to June), flowering performance is largely determined by the growth made and food reserves accumulated in the previous growing season, since the plants flower on mature old wood. The 1966 season tended to favour wood growth and the formation of flower buds (especially as in many areas it was a poor blossom year). Again, a mild winter allows more flower buds to be retained (e.g. hydrangeas are favoured particularly). Finally, a spring which is not frost-ridden spares flower blossom and helps the flower parade.

Gladioli Changing Colour

The most probable cause of your home-grown stock of gladioli becoming yellow-flowered, though originally all colours except yellow, is that your soil is acid and probably loses its free lime content easily in the drainage waters. Many plants have a tendency to lose their pigment under certain soil conditions, either undue activity or the presence of an acid base in excess. There is also the point to be borne in mind that modern gladioli are highly hybridised, and to maintain a variety in its developed colours calls for repeated selection and elimination of all 'rogues'.

A Laburnum Broom

Your pink bush laburnum, which bears some yellow flowers and has a pink broom growing out of one of the branches, is plainly one of the graft-chimera *Laburnocytisus* × *adamii*, in which the genetical influence of the broom has become ascendant in the strong-growing branch. The broom tissue is usually within the laburnum, but it is not possible to predict the exact form one of these chimeras will take; they are apt to exhibit individual characteristics within the limits of their dual heredity.

Medicinal Herbs for Women Gardeners (1916)

Last week we gave particulars of a Women's Herb Growing Association which has for its object the cultivation and marketing on co-operative lines of a number of plants of medicinal value, the supply of which hitherto has come mainly from Germany and Austria. It is the crying need for drugs obtained from medicinal plants which we are now advising women gardeners to grow that has prompted this effort to organise herb-growing as an industry for women, even more than the idea of capturing trade. Prices are already going up by leaps and bounds, and unless something is done the use of the most important drugs will be only possible for the wealthy. The intention is to work a central drug farm where some of the herbs most urgently required can be grown in large quantities, but in addition to this the association, by creating machinery for the systematic collection and marketing of small quantities, will make possible the remunerative growing of herbs in small gardens or plots of large ones. Roughly speaking, 4 lb leaves, flowers, etc., are reduced to 1 lb after drying, and as the dealers buy in hundred-weights at least, it will be seen that the small grower who has only a few pounds for the market would have difficulty in disposing of her crops but for the co-operative system provided by the association. The following are some of the plants most urgently required by the dispensers:

Monkshood (*Aconitum napellus*): roots lifted in autumn.
Chamomile (*Anthemis nobilis*): flowers when ripe dried on canvas trays in hot air.
Deadly nightshade (*Atropa belladonna*): leaves for extract; roots lifted every fourth year, sliced and dried.
Thorn Apple (*Datura stramonium*): leaves, and in lesser degree, seeds.

Henbane (*Hyoscyamus niger*): terminal leaves surrounding flowering top.

Purple Foxglove (*Digitalis purpurea*): leaves, from 1–2 tons of
which may be gathered from an acre.

Fennel (*Foeniculum vulgare*): seeds.

Opium Poppy (*Papaver somniferum*): heads picked in September.

Valerian (*Valeriana officinalis*): roots sliced lengthways.

Other plants which need to be collected to meet the present need are:
balm, feverfew, dandelion, yarrow, the bark of the common
barberry, the autumn-cut branches of the common nightshade,
broom branches cut in winter and in June, henbane, sweet flag
rhizomes, and red poppy petals.

Destroying Rhododendrons

To kill rhododendrons where they are in the vicinity of other trees
or plants it is desired to preserve, the best plan is to place a pad of
cotton wool soaked in sodium chlorate solution (8 oz per gallon
water) over the cut surfaces of the shrubs, fastening in place with
insulation tape. The solution is absorbed and poisons the roots. Any
suckers which break in spring should be sprayed with the same
solution sufficiently to wet the leaves.

Roses from Seed

The hips should be allowed to remain on the plant until fully ripe,
gathered dry and then rubbed out of the capsule or pulp of the hip.
The seeds can then be sown either in a warm, sheltered border of
well drained, loamy soil in the open garden, or in shallow seed
boxes or seed pans filled with a sandy loam compost and stood in a
cold frame. The latter is better, as birds often take seeds sown in the
open. An alternative is to store the hips in layers in dry sand in a box
for the winter and rub out and sow the seed in spring. Autumn-
sown seed may germinate the following spring but germination is
rather irregular and some seeds may not germinate for a year.

Wild Irish Rose

Hips alone are hardly a conclusive character to rose identity. The
most that can be said is that the hips you sent us could be those of the
old hybrid tea varieties 'Irish Elegance' (as you suggest) and 'Irish
Fireflame'. The flowers of the former, however, are orange-red in
bud, and apricot-yellow and pink blended when open; if old and
faded, they would approach a pale yellow, yet you describe those
you have seen growing wild in County Kerry as having large, single

pale cream flowers. 'Irish Fireflame' has orange-crimson flowers. Both are scented. They are best grown as tallish bushes with little pruning. Few, if any, nurserymen offer these varieties today, and so means of comparison and knowledge of them are dying out.

Spindle Pollination

The flowers of *Euonymus europaeus* are curious in that they may be hermaphrodite (self-pollinating) or simply male or female, and consequently the tendency of a single spindle tree by itself is to fruit rather poorly. It will, no doubt, bear the attractive rosy-orange fruits in some numbers in due time, but it would certainly do this more surely and with greater prodigality if a pollinator was planted nearby – this is true of all berrying shrubs. A good pollinator would be *Euonymus hamiltonia*.

Sweet Pea Bud Drop

Even the growers and the experts are puzzled by the phenomenon of bud dropping in sweet peas. It is not a disease, not a fault of the seed, but a functional trouble. It is attributed to big changes of temperature and resultant fluctuations in the sap flow to the stems and buds. It most often occurs when night temperatures fall 10–20°F, after warm or sunny days. During the daytime, warmth and light draw water up and through the plant rapidly; then at night, the demand slackens drastically; the next day, the plant finds it hard to resume the sap flow quickly. The buds then seem to suffer a critical water shortage at a critical stage of growth, and the weakest point gives, with the bud falling.

Tulips for Sale

Tulip bulbs grown out of doors for cut flowers may be planted in rows 10–12 in apart, with 6 bulbs to the foot (2 in apart). This means you can plant up to 750–800 bulbs on your piece of ground 14 ft x 10 ft. The soil needs to be well cleaned of weeds, thoroughly dug, and, since it is heavy, it would be sensible to lay sand at the base of planting rows. A dressing of bone flour at 2 oz per 6 ft run of row would be helpful.

Non-clinging Virginia Creeper

Any drying out at the roots will check the plant's ability to cling; and young plants like yours at the foot of a wall are particularly vulnerable. Lightly fork in a dressing of 1 part by weight dried blood, 3 parts bone flour, 1 part sulphate of potash, at 4 oz per plant to the rooting area, and water it in. Top-mulch with rotted manure, compost or leaf-mould. Water liberally in any dry spell, especially in spring; and you can add a little liquid feed occasionally.

Cut Water-lilies

Most water-lily blooms make good cut flowers, especially the tropical forms, but you must cut them when they are well developed. Some water-lilies only open their flowers at night, and you would not see them open perhaps when you are up and about. Then most water-lilies open their flowers in responding to the sun, so that they open as the sun strengthens in the morning up to noon, and then close in the afternoon. So much depends on the kind of water-lily flower you cut and where you keep it. It should float in a bowl or dish of water, and receive the morning sunlight. It is best to remove the blooms from the bowl overnight and let them rest flat on a table until the morning, then replace them in the bowl.

Yams and Bananas

[Is 'yam' another name for sweet potato or for banana?]

The true yam is the tuberous-rooting plant known botanically as *Dioscorea batatas*, a native of the Philippines, though hardy even when in this country. The 'fruits' are long tubers, 2–3 ft long, which grow deep in the ground like potatoes. Other species are also grown in the tropics for food, such as *D.cayennensis*, the yellow yam, and *D.bulbifera*. The plants are twining climbers and rather ornamental. The name yam is also sometimes applied to the sweet potato, *Ipomoea batatas*, with its tuberous roots, but it is a trailer rather than a climber. The alternative name of the banana is plantain.

HEDGES AND TREES
Bark-slitting for Blossom

To encourage an almond tree which has failed to blossom for 4 years, try bark-slitting, which can be done now (June). Make an unbroken vertical cut with a sharp knife in the bark of the main stem of the tree from the junction of the lowest branch down to ground level on the north side of the tree. Paint the cut with a tree antiseptic. The full effect may not be seen for 2 years, but flower bud formation will result. If the soil is heavy and of clay, try a top-dressing of basic slag at 6 oz per sq yd.

Beheading Cupressus

Cupressus macrocarpa is unpredictable in its reaction to being cut back severely and your desire to cut a 30-ft high hedge down to 8 ft is fairly drastic for what is in fact a forest tree in free growth. The probable reaction will be for a more bushy head of growth to form from the top remaining lateral branches, gradual die-back of the lowest branches and general deterioration. In effect, you will be cutting away the most active parts of the tree. This species does not regenerate well with regrowth from lower limbs. If it must be done, the best time is in mild weather in April or May.

Fading Crab-apple Blossom (1958)

Pink, as a colour in the flowers of a crab-apple, is a sap pigment or anthocyanin, having a complex chemical structure, which may produce its tinting in varied shadings since it is sensitive to the inner chemical changes of the tree. It is particularly affected by the degree of acidity of the cell sap, and changes towards increased acidity appear to be the likely cause of the fugitiveness of the pink this year. If, as seems possible, the tree has received no special manuring or fertilising, it may be that the soil is becoming increasingly acid, and the heavy crop of fruit last year may have aggravated the nutritional resources of the soil to affect the chemical structure of the tree and its sap.

Forked Tree

There are two ways of solving the problem of water lodging in a cavity formed by the forking of tree branches, as in your copper beech. The first is to provide more or less permanent drainage by drilling a hole at an angle to the lowest point of the cavity, and insert a piece of plastic tubing (say $\frac{1}{4}$–$\frac{3}{4}$ in diameter). This would have to be carefully cut flush with the floor of the cavity, but can usefully emerge for an inch or more beyond the surface of the bark to throw water clear. The duct should be kept open. In time, the tree is likely to callus and cover the end of the tube. For the second method, syphon out the water from the cavity and dry well. Paint the inside of the cavity with a fungicidal tree paint and pruning compound (such as Arbrex), then fill the cavity with a bituminous compound of the kind usually used for repairing asphalt paths. Pack it down very firmly and finish with a surface sloped to shed rain or water draining down the bark. The danger is that a gap may open with tree movement but this type of asphalt is more flexible than cement, an alternative filling. If a gap should develop, try sealing it with a good smear of fruit-tree banding grease.

Monkey Puzzle Record

Your tree with a girth of 8 ft 10 in at a height of 4 ft above the ground is certainly large for a monkey puzzle tree and suggests a height of 70 ft or more. If your measurements are correct, it is possible that your tree is indeed the largest in Ireland. A specimen 76 ft high was recorded in Co. Waterford some years ago and your tree seems a worthy contender to it, and possibly close to 100 years old.

A Thin Privet Hedge

The only way to induce growth from the older stems low down would be to cut a proportion of them back as far as the points from which you want new growth and thin the top growth of other stems. An alternative is to nick the shoots low down just above a potential budding point or lateral, and so force growth energies into these points. All that is needed is a simple V-shaped nick into the bark.

Slow Tulip Tree

The tulip tree, *Liriodendron tulipifera*, is never in a hurry to flower, and seldom flowers before it is at the very least 20 years old. Even then, for another 10–20 years it has few, if any, flowers. Older trees provide good shows in this country. The tree belongs to North America, and although hardy needs summer warmth greater than that of Britain to hasten it to flower development. The chief reason, therefore, why your 30-year-old tree has not flowered is largely a question of age, and there is not really much to be done to quicken it to flowering, except to give dressings of bone-meal and organic matter.

Upside Down Tree (1900)

If you plant any tree upside down – e.g., the top in the ground and its roots in the light and air – it will probably die outright; but, even if its branches do root, the roots, or the stem nearest to the roots, would still throw out upright shoots as before. We presume that this is what you mean, although you have not put the question very clearly. Weeping trees are naturally only creeping or weeping branches grafted on the tops of erect growing stocks.

Garden Features and Techniques

FEATURES

Building an Incinerator

One needs a clear space under the firebars to admit draught, and there should be a chimney at one end to facilitate draught. This need only be short, and can be of galvanised metal. In essence, the incinerator is a brick bin, and is fed from the top; the ash falling through the firebars can be removed periodically for use on the garden. The incinerator should be on a south-to-north or south-west to north-east line, when built as a permanent structure.

Cover for an Iron Trellis (1887)

Unless you are too much affected by the smoke of London, we should advise you to put free-climbing and other roses on your iron trellis; say, for example, Gloire de Dijon and Felicité Perpétuelle. If the smoke is too much, try a good pear like Doyenne du Comice.

Laying Out a New Garden (1854)

To those who are laying out new gardens we would say, beware of after-thoughts, which are at once annoying, rebuking, and costly. Lay down your scheme boldly, but warily; strive to attain a good aim, based of course on what is desired and what is attainable. Having done this, let congruity of parts give the whole a consistency which may cause no regret. Do not war too much against the native character of the spot; do not attempt to carry prim and formal avenues or lines over deeply undulating surfaces. One of the first points for consideration, after fixing the sites of all structures – well considering their dependency on each other – is to plan a main perambulatory walk; and this, in small places, should be carried as near to the exterior generally as is compatible with the due preservation of privacy and the avoiding of disagreeable objects. The more such walks pursue a serpentine course, in general, the better chance will there be for the planter to give variety and to convey an idea of extent. One of our poets, of no mean celebrity, has well said:–

> 'Let not each beauty every where be spied,
> Where half the skill is decently to hide.'

Patina for New Stonework

Make a slurry of cream-like consistency using equal parts of bulk clay soil or heavy loam and cow dung, with stagnant pond water, the greener the better. Paint this liberally on to the stonework and allow it to weather naturally. This will provide a surface soil for the growth of algae and lichens associated with the ageing process and coloration of the stone. It is a little smelly but the odour soon dissipates with weathering. An alternative is to use clay soil with stagnant water and milk (in equal proportions) but it is less rapid in effect.

Water-lily Barrels

The half barrels may be sunk to their rims in any sheltered place, fully exposed to sunshine, and allowed to overflow as fresh water is added; or if they are sunk above an adjacent drain a hose-pipe may be made to act as a syphon in drawing off the surface water. Six inches of rich mud or yellow clay and cow manure will be ample rooting material for the water-lilies. An inch of fine gravel on top of the mud after planting is an advantage.

GREENHOUSE AND POTTING SHED

Crusty Pots

The white efflorescence and encrustation which develop on flower-pots are usually of salts (generally of calcium or lime) and are often due to impurities in the clay. You will see brickwork sometimes effloresce in the same way. Sometimes reactions between the soil moisture and the clay result in the deposits. They do not injure the flower-pot or weaken it materially, and normally do not greatly affect plant growth adversely. They may, however, render the pot less porous in time, and may restrict acid-loving plants like rhododendrons, strawberries, etc., and are unsightly. Removal, as you have noted, is not always easy. Copper sulphate solution ($\frac{1}{2}$ oz per gallon of water) is sometimes effective, applied with vigorous brushing. But if the pots are sterilised by (a) boiling, cooling and drying; or (b) by wetting thoroughly with 2% formaldehyde solution or $2\frac{1}{2}$% cresylic acid, covered 24 hours with damp sacks, and then thoroughly aired and dried, they will be safe to use again.

Garden Schools for Women (1916)

The following schools of gardening for women can be recommended: The Horticultural College, Studley Castle, Warwickshire; University College, Reading; Lady Woleseley's College, Glynde, Lewes. They each award their own diploma. A National Diploma in Horticulture is awarded by the Royal Horticultural Society, Vincent-square, W., to men and women who pass an examination in the Principles and Practice of Horticulture.

Greenhouse Glass

To clean greenhouse glass which has become black or green where it overlaps, wet it so that it gets soaked with a 10% solution of domestic bleach, leave it an hour or two and then scrub with a scrubbing brush dipped in a similar solution. It may need 2 applications for stubborn patches, but provided that the glass is not etched by atmospheric acids, it will become quite clean.

Potting Around the Edge

The reason for placing cuttings around the edge or rim of a clay pot is simply that the clay tends to draw the moisture from the soil, and the area nearest to the sides of the pot is usually more moist and somewhat richer in soluble plant food. In consequence, the cuttings tend to strike more easily without developing the long roots that gravitate to the pot side from the plants placed in the middle. If plastic pots are used, it is not important to plant the cuttings round the edges.

Sterilising Soil

Soil sterilisation is actually a process of partial sterilisation as completely sterile soil will not support plant life. It can be done by the use of heat or chemicals; the former is the more effective. It destroys parasitic fungi, soil-frequenting pests and eelworms, without destroying soil fertility. In fact, when properly carried out, it enhances soil fertility, by repressing the harmful soil agencies. The soil should be heated through to a temperature of 180°F but preferably not exceeding 200°F in any part. The critical temperature is 212°F. Small quantities of soil can be sterilised as follows: Place $\frac{1}{2}$ in water in a large saucepan, fill loosely with dust-dry soil sifted to remove stones. Heat rapidly until water boils, then allow to simmer for about 15 minutes. Turn the soil out at once on to a clean surface, spread out to allow excess moisture to evaporate. When sufficiently dried, it can be used.

MANURES
Hen Manure (1954)

On a weight basis, hen manure is about 4 times as rich as cow manure in nitrogen and phosphates and about the same in potash, but contains much less organic humus-forming matter. It would certainly be valuable for the garden – fruits, flowers and vegetables – but needs to be complemented by a potassic fertiliser and organic material. If you wish to use it fresh, it should be strewn and forked in at the rate of 1 hundredweight to every 25–35 sq yards, according to the vigour of the crop to follow. The higher dose is most suitable for vegetables, and needs the supplement of $\frac{1}{2}$ oz sulphate of potash per sq yard. For fruit, especially dessert, add 1 oz sulphate of potash per sq yard. It would also be more beneficial on a light soil if you could add peat at the same time; say 1 hundredweight to 40 sq yards. Surplus droppings could be composted with peat for future use as a mulch or manure. If you dried the droppings on trays in airy covered sheds, and then pulverised them to a powder, you would have a useful fertiliser for use at $\frac{1}{2}$–1 lb per sq yard in spring.

Horse Manure (1860)

Both the dung and the urine of horses are liable to decompose very rapidly; they heat, steam, and give off much ammonia and other gaseous products equally wasteful and unsanitary. Professor Gazzeri ascertained that $9\frac{1}{4}$% of the solid mass of a heap of horse dung was lost in 8 weeks. Some portion of this loss was doubtless water, but by far the greater portion of the loss was something of far more importance, as it was found at the end of that period to be less than half as valuable as manure.

Peruvian Guano and Thin Americans (1860)

There were no imports of Peruvian Guano into London last week. Prices current of guano etc.: Peruvian Guano per ton, for 30 tons, £12.5s. to £13; ditto, damaged, £10.15s. to £11; Sombrero Island Guano, £9. Thin Americans, in barrels or bags, £10.15s. to £11.5s. Bones, dust, £1 to £1.1s. per qr.; Bones, $\frac{1}{2}$-in, 19s. to £1. Blood Manure for wheat, £7.10s. per ton.

GARDEN PESTS, WEEDS AND DISEASES
Caterpillars and Cuckoos (1900)

(1) Replying to the inquiry of J.R., I may state that in the neighbourhood of Torquay I remember seeing a pair of cuckoos very active in a large gooseberry garden, so much so as not to mind my presence. The bushes were infested with caterpillars, and it seemed reasonable to suppose the birds were feeding upon them. Can any reader offer similar evidence in favour of the cuckoo? [G. Forsyth, Rose Bank, Southport]

(2) At Mosstown, Co. Westmeath, I remember counting 13 cuckoos in one kitchen garden. The owner, Capt. Fosbery, told me that he never had any gooseberries owing to caterpillars until 2 cuckoos took up their abode in the garden. As years went on, more came, the caterpillars disappeared, and there was plenty of fruit. This may interest J.R. and Mr Forsyth. There were often more than 13 in sight at once. I never saw so many cuckoos in any other garden. [Montagu Chapman]

Cabbage Root Fly

The cabbage root fly (*Delia brassica*) is a small greyish insect, like the house fly, about $\frac{1}{4}$ in long. The female places her eggs at the base of food plants (chiefly cabbage, cauliflowers and related cruciferous plants) and these hatch in a few days as small white maggots which feed on the roots and tunnel up the basal stems. Infested plants should be lifted with roots and soil and burnt; the soil should then be disturbed to expose any brown pupae to birds. As an alternative to insecticide you should aim to prevent the flies having access to the plants. One way is to cover the ground with Hortopaper, a brown mulching paper marketed by Donaldson Paper Sales of Upminster: insert transplants through cross-slits or holes and put in position when the soil is moist. The mulch blocks insect attacks, suppresses weeds and promotes a good growing medium; being biodegradable it eventually disappears naturally to humus. Another possibility is to cover the transplants with a very light polypropylene sheeting marketed by Greenspear Products of Cannock. This excludes insects, but permits ventilation, with access by light and rain, and promotes a weatherproof microclimate favourable for plants.

Clubbing Cures (1900)

Your cabbage roots are affected by a disease called 'clubbing', the most destructive disease to which the cabbage tribe is subject. It is supposed to be caused by one or more kinds of insects laying their eggs in the young roots or stems. Lime, wood ashes, soot, common salt and nitrate of soda have all been recommended as preventatives. A total change of soil should be made if possible, sowing and growing the cabbage on fresh land. Dip the roots and stems of the young seedlings, before planting, in a creamy mixture of fresh soot and water.

Club-root (1969)

If the root rot which has caused total failure of all your cauliflowers, brussels sprouts and cabbages is club-root, in which the roots of brassicas and cruciferous plants are much swollen and distorted, drastic long-term action is needed. The cause is a slime fungus, *Plasmodiophora brassicae*. The spores contaminate the soil, which should be rested for 3 years from cropping with susceptible plants of the cruciferae. All the cabbage tribe, radish, turnip, wallflowers, and weeds such as mustard and charlock, should be rooted out. The soil should be limed to bring to near neutrality (pH 6.5–7.0). Good subsoil drainage should be promoted, and if the soil is clayey or heavy, work in gypsum ($\frac{1}{2}$ lb per sq yard). Improve humus by organic manuring.

Convolvulus (1956)

The most successful way of eradicating bindweed among soft fruits is to destroy the young growing shoots as they appear in spring, and repeat through a summer. It can be done mechanically when there is time to go over the ground with a sharp hoe or by hand-weeding every few days, but chemical treatment is more effective in inhibiting regeneration and injuring the roots. Use a selective weedkiller based on 2,4:D or on 2,4,5-T: paint the solution on the young shoots and foliage when freshly unfolded, at double strength. If the shoots have grown longish, a good technique is to gather the tips of several growing near together, and without parting them from the roots, bundle into a jam jar, and half fill with weed-killing solution. Leave overnight and then treat another batch. The stuff is absorbed into the system of the whole plant.

Earwig Trap

Earwigs entering lettuces come chiefly from crevices in the soil, walls, fences and rubbish. Deter them by applying a soil insecticide. Much can also be done by trapping: put small pots, stuffed with hay or straw, down the rows of the plants, slightly propped open (about

$\frac{1}{8}$ in) with a stick or stone on one side. These attract the insects to hide in the daytime and should be examined daily, the insects being shaken out into a container. Or use lengths of hollow cane or bamboo.

Fairy Rings (1900)

Fairy rings, or fungi, on lawns have this season appeared very freely, and have caused much annoyance. Lime water may be applied. Place a stone weight of quick lime in 50 gallons of water, and when it has cooled and settled down, draw off the water as clear as possible and apply it to the area infested. A weak solution of Bordeaux mixture (see below) may be used in the same way, half strength, e.g. 100 gallons of water instead of 50. The grass may be browned for a time, but it will banish the fungi. (Bordeaux mixture is the best fungicide known. Dilute or dissolve 6 lb sulphate of copper in 2 or 3 gallons of water. In another vessel add water gradually to 5 lb unslaked lime, until a thick, smooth paste is formed; then, when cool, mix the 2 solutions together, and dilute up to 50 gallons with water.)

Fusarium in the Lawn

To identify fusarium on your lawn, cut a small piece of the suspected brown turf, take it indoors and, after moistening thoroughly, place it under a jam jar on a saucer in a warm window for a day or two. If you see a white, or faintly pink, cotton-like growth on the leaves of the grasses, you will know that the trouble is fusarium patch disease. The whitish growth is the mycelium of the fungus *Fusarium nivale*.

Greenfly and Soot (1900)

Your apricot shoots are badly infested with greenfly. Use a garden engine and also wash the trees with soot water, made by placing a bag of soot into a tank or tub of water. Quassia chips and soft soap also make an efficient wash. One ounce of quassia chips boiled in a quart of water for 15 minutes, adding 4 oz of soft soap, is a good preparation. Tobacco water is also a deterrent.

Insects in Trees (1865)

A new method of destroying the insects which infest old trees is said to have been employed by M. Robert, who has thus saved the old elms of the Boulevard d'Enfer from decortication. The operation is thus described in *Cosmos*: A little of the old bark is shaved off; then the whole of the trunk of the tree is impregnated with a concentrated solution of camphor in alcohol. This not only destroys all the insects then in them, but prevents others from attempting to penetrate the bark.

Large Whites and Lavender (1948)

In a chapter on butterflies in Mr Eric Parker's *Countryman's Week-end Book*, it is said that a quaint cure for the Large White is to grow lavender next to cabbage beds, when the butterflies will leave the green leaves for the scented flowers, but no proof of the cure was offered. However, Mr Charles Waterhouse of Middleton Hall, Bakewell, reports that it so happens that he has a lavender border right down his vegetable garden and that this summer, when most of the brassica in neighbouring gardens became skeletons, his were scarcely nibbled. No proof, of course, but lavender is lovely anyway, anywhere.

Moss on Gravel

If you spray your gravel paths with a 10% solution of tar oil wash just sufficient to wet the moss thoroughly, you should be able to eradicate it at one application. Use in mild, dryish weather for full effect, and keep the spray away from any lawn grass or plant foliage you wish to preserve.

Moss on Lawns (1898)

Use sulphate of iron in the proportion of 6 lb to a 100 sq yards. The best way to use the sulphate is in solution, in the proportion of 1 lb sulphate to 2 gallons of water. The solution should be made in a wooden vessel, such as an old cask, with soft water, and also just before it is to be used. It may be applied at any season of the year, preference being given to the early months. The sulphate is known to be acting when the moss turns black. If the application has been too weak, the moss only turns grey or reddish, and a second application will be necessary. As moss generally indicates a poor soil, it is advisable after the moss has been destroyed to apply a rich top-dressing.

Red Spider (1892)

The leaves sent are covered with red spider, thrips, and scale. Take the plant outdoors and thoroughly syringe it with Gishurst compound or some other insecticide. The leaves will in all probability all fall off.

The Naturalist

Weather and Calendar

English Summer Weather (1956)

In July the best period, on average, is the 10th–20th. The first Buchan warm spell occurs between 12th–15th and often includes some of the hottest days of the summer. The reason why July comes out as a moderately wet month in the statistics is that the warm summer air holds more moisture than it does early in the year. But most of the rainfall comes in the form of thunderstorms. Mid-July is probably the best time of the year for a holiday, but odd years are of course disappointing. In August the first few days tend to be unsettled, and somewhat wet and thundery. After this one or two heatwaves are probable, though they may not be without thunderstorms. It is worth noting that the 5-day period, 14th–18th inclusive, provides, on average, more warm days than the 5-day periods immediately before or after. August is generally a little wetter than July, but it compensates by giving higher sea temperatures. Although July is the warmest month (on land) for Britain as a whole, August is generally the warmest near the south and west coasts. In September, although a changeable rainy spell is likely at some time during the month, it has recently shown a tendency towards improvement. Shortened evenings are offset by still higher sea temperatures. Early September (1st–10th) is generally the most settled time, but mainly in southern and eastern districts. In the North of England, Northern Ireland and Scotland, the weather is seldom settled for any period of time after mid-August.

Fatal Thunderstorms (1855)

A fatal thunderstorm raged over the district of Dublin, on Saturday last [30 June]. A woman was killed in her bed by the lightning, while a girl sleeping with her was so dreadfully burned that she had to be conveyed at once to the Richmond Hospital, where she now lies, her left side presenting the appearance of a perfect cinder. At the time of the occurrence the atmosphere was charged with electricity, and the sulphurous smell in the air was so oppressive that it was described by the police on duty as almost suffocating, whilst each flash presented the appearance of a sheet of fire. Information has been received of 2 other deaths from the electric fluid, and several head of cattle are believed to have been destroyed by the same agency. The scene along the River Liffey is described as having been grand, but truly awful. The sailors had to leave their ships and take refuge on shore, the vessels, owing to the numerous objects of attraction on board in the shape of anchors, etc., appearing at times to be encircled by sheets and darts of flame.

Lunar Rainbow

A rainbow at night is usually referred to as a 'lunar' rainbow, and beyond that has no special name. It should not, of course, be confused with the rings or halos often seen about the moon particularly when there is cirrostratus cloud about. As far as the colours of the rainbow are concerned, moonlight naturally tends to refract less strongly than sunlight, since it is reflected light anyway. But the definition of the colours depends upon the size of the moisture drops present in the air. The smaller they are, the less vivid the colours, and below 1/500 in diameter they usually refract more or less white light as the component colours are merged.

October (1854)

OCTOBER: The eighth month in the year of Romulus, as its name imports, and the tenth in the year of Numa, who added the months of January and February in 713 B.C. From this time October has still retained its first name, in spite of all the different appellations which the senate and Roman emperors would have given it. The senate ordered it to be called Faustinus, in honour of Faustina, the wife of Antonius the emperor; Commodus would have had it bear the name of Invictus; and Domitian caused it to be denominated Domitianus, after his own name. October was sacred to Mars.

Pulse of a River

Presumably by 'the uneven but rhythmic movement often seen in the flow of rivers' you mean a fresh water flood down the river, and are not alluding to any upstream movement which may be influenced by the making of the tide in the estuary. The phenomenon is, as often as not, individual to a particular river, and will be

governed by a number of factors. For instance, a flow of flood water over a very uneven and fluctuating river bed would induce a rhythm of uneven volume at particular points. Falls, dams, constrictions, and the flow of flood water from a tributary into the main stream may also induce a pulse. Then again, volume alone in water on the move, especially in an uneven, bending river, would induce a rhythm.

Sensitive Weathervane

To make a weathervane sensitive to very light winds you would have to mount the spindle on ball-bearings. The exact method of doing this depends partly on the construction of the mounting of the whole thing; whether on a wooden pole or a building. A simple method is to have the spindle of the vane inserted in a steel or metal sleeve fitted with a cup ballrace, similar to that used on bicycle wheels, and sheathed with a cone against weather; the race being packed with grease. A good improvisation is to use an old bicycle wheel hub, fastening by screw, weld, or nut, to the spindle itself.

Shine Before Seven

There is more than a grain of truth in the saying that a bright morning is usually followed by rain and that a dull morning is a much better sign for a fine day. However, these remarks are generalisations. If the barometer has been rising steadily for some time, or is high and is remaining steady, it is quite likely that a bright morning will be followed by bright, sunny weather for the rest of the day. During changeable weather, when a day of rain is followed by a day of rather heavy showers separated by brighter periods, it quite often happens that the showers do not get under way until about 10 or 11 a.m., and that the morning, particularly the early morning, is bright and sunny. The barometer will again give the indication of showers to come, for it will be moving somewhat jerkily. It will not be steady at the high position in this case.

Visibility and Wind

A probable reason for visibility being good with winds coming from the north west in your area (Ayrshire) is simply that such winds blow from cleaner atmospheres, chiefly over water. Winds from the east, on the other hand, come over extensive continental land areas and only narrow seas, and may be laden with more fine dust and pollution particles. Easterly winds tend to be drier;

westerly and north-westerly winds are more frequently associated with rain, which 'washes' the atmosphere. Visibility is particularly good when wind follows rain or even mist. Unfortunately, comparative figures do not seem to be available.

Warm-water Freezing

The supposition that warm water freezes more quickly than cold is false. The water loses heat and cools rapidly, but its behaviour at freezing temperatures is the same as that of the cold. Water cooled to less than 4°C expands with the formation of ice, and being lighter than the warmer water, forms at the surface; there is no change in the actual freezing point (0°C). Actually, the cold water will freeze 'solid' before the tepid.

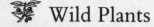 Wild Plants

Amadou

The fungus from which Amadou is most often derived is *Fomes fomentarius* (from Latin *fomes* and *fomentum* for touchwood or tinder). On the Continent it may occur on beech, but in this country on the trunks of birch and apparently confined to the north of Scotland. It is a bracket fungus, growing with a pileus (cap) 4–12 in across; thick, hoof-shaped, attached by a broad base to the bark, roughly triangular in section, covered with a hard, thickish cuticle or skin. It is fawn and black to almost black, concentrically arranged in coloured zones: more fawn and brown at the margins; underneath there are tubes in layers, cinnamon-brown in colour, which increase annually. The flesh is cinnamon-brown or yellow brown, with a felt-like or woolly texture, and the spores are oblong in shape and white. It kills the cambium of its host tree and causes a white rot of the sapwood. Amadou is prepared from the flesh of the fungus, freed from the hard, crusty pileus and tubes. For use in fishing, it is simply dried and beaten. Otherwise it is cut into slivers or slices, soaked overnight in a solution of saltpetre (potassium nitrate) or boiled in lye (for use as a styptic), then air-dried and beaten until it becomes spongy, limp and lax. Saltpetred, it was chiefly used as tinder in former times. Until recently it was also used in dentistry, and for making soft surgical pads. In Bohemian Germany it was used for making picture frames and ornaments, caps, aprons and articles of dress.

Himalayan Balsam

The Himalayan balsam, *Impatiens glandulifera* (syn. *I.Roylei*), was introduced into Britain in 1838. Apparently, the man instrumental in this was Dr John Forbes Royle (1800–1858), a professor of medicine at King's College, London, who became Superintendent of the Botanic Gardens, Saharanpur, India, and wrote on Indian plants. The balsam is an annual and has escaped from gardens to naturalise itself in certain places, chiefly along banks of rivers or streams.

Hogweed Rash

We regret to learn of your unfortunate encounter with Giant Hogweed or Cow Parsley, *Heracleum sphondylium*. This is a native biennial plant; its edible leaves are eaten eagerly by herbivorous animals. There are a few instances in which the plant has been reported as suspect of some toxicity but they are not well authenticated and nothing of a serious or fatal nature. It is of course a relation of the deadly Hemlock, *Conium maculatum*, in the family of *Umbelliferae*, but that seems to be the only connection with any danger, and it is a remote one. From the information you give it seems probable that you are peculiarly sensitive to the plants and your reaction is akin to that of an allergy. The plant is hairy and contact with it causes the skin reactions you describe. There are many plants of this nature, causing allergic symptoms in some individuals but not all.

Houseleeks

These plants are termed xerophytes, because they are able to grow under conditions where the water supply is drastically curtailed. Their ability to do so is due to their leaves being swollen and fleshy, and capable of taking up and storing water freely when available, and having a thick cuticle with relatively few stomata (pores), enabling them to keep moisture loss by transpiration very low in dry weather. They grow easily on old roofs and walls, where their roots find nutrients in the thinnest of soils resulting from the accumulation of dust, atmospheric deposits, lichens, moss and their remains, and the disintegration of the stones or slates themselves in weathering. They do not need any special planting, and will grow if simply fixed in position in a crevice or joint of a roof, in the joints of walls, or clefts of rock in a rock garden, or in the dryest and sandiest of soils.

Toxic Laurels

The common laurel, *Prunus laurocerasus*, is known to contain a toxic principle that can kill sheep and cattle, as well as (apparently) insects, though instances of poisoning in Britain are rare, because it is rarely eaten. In this plant, however, the poison is a glycoside and a source of the deadly hydrocyanic acid (prussic acid) in reaction. The Californian laurel, *Umbellularia Californica*, is a strongly aromatic evergreen, and apparently owes its irritant qualities to a volatile principle, which is different from the poison in the common laurel. Moreover, the 2 species are hardly related, since the common laurel is of the rose family (*Rosaceae*) and the Californian laurel of the laurel family (*Lauraceae*). It appears that the aromatic principle is one of the allergens. Some people are allergic to it; others are immune. In some people it provokes sneezing and (as you report) headaches; in others a skin irritation and running eyes.

Sham Shamrock

Botanically there is no such species as shamrock. It is a common name held to be derived from the Irish name of *seamrog* for trefoil. The name is given to various species, such as *Trefolium repens*, the white clover, but *T.minus* is sometimes called shamrock, and also related species *Medicago lupulina*, also known as the black medick.

Where the Trees Stop

The height at which trees can grow on very high ground is primarily determined by exposure, in which temperature and aspect play important parts. Trees do not cease to grow at any fixed altitude, as local conditions vary greatly, and the tree-line is determined by these. Broadly, the tree-line in Britain lies between 1,000 and 2,000 ft. The more exposed the situation to prevailing winds, the lower the tree-line, since strong winds tend to accentuate the effects of other weather conditions such as cold and dryness. But in a locality where there is higher land to act as a shelter trees will grow much higher on a hill than on a hill fully exposed. Some species stand exposure better than others. Birches and certain pines, for instance, can grow on higher ground than beeches or spruce.

Witches' Broom

The bundles of twigs seen hanging in some birch trees are caused by infection of shoot tissue by the fungus *Taphrina turgidus*. This is a perennial parasite, and excites the abnormal growth seen in the profusion of twiggy growths. Cedar, cherry, larch, spruce, silver fir and pine are all subject to this type of abnormality from species of fungi of the *Taphrina* genus. In some plants, the parasite is believed to be a mite (alder, for instance, and willow); in others a rust fungus is held responsible.

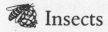 Insects

Ants and String (1887)

The common domestic ant is most difficult to get rid of; string moistened with syrup of sugar is attractive, and can be burnt with ants attached.

Ants Shedding Wings

The flying ants you saw laboriously shedding their wings were maidens after their nuptial flight which they take in late August along with male ants. The males and females mate in the air during flight or immediately afterwards on landing. The males die. The mated queens shed their wings, rubbing and twisting them off, and then seek a place where they can start raising their brood. Many return to the old colony or nest and go on the breeding staff. Others may found new nests. The vast majority of ants in a colony are working ants, sometimes termed neuters, but primarily females in a state of arrested sexual development. They do the work of governing and running a colony.

Butterfly Breeding

For a start you should have sound reference books to give information about the food-plants and seasons of the various species. To obtain the necessary breeding stock, either capture insects with a net, or collect larvae or eggs, or purchase from a commercial breeder. Caterpillars can be bred in specially constructed cages, or by sleeving the growing food-plant in the garden by means of large, loose-fitting muslin bags tied at the plant stems. Should the breeding be successful, you may like to release the specimens in the garden, though it is unlikely that they will stay to add colour to it. It is a subject of absorbing interest, offering great possibilities for methodical research.

Purple Emperor (1953)

The purple emperor butterfly, *A.iris*, certainly still occurs wild in Britain. It is a very local butterfly being found in oak woods where sallow bushes occur, as this latter bush is the food-plant of the caterpillars. The butterflies, however, like to roost and fly around oak trees, the females coming down in the afternoon to seek the sallow bushes on which to lay their eggs. The known localities are in Kent, Sussex and Surrey, and recently we heard of one in Berkshire.

Butterfly Sightings (1900)

(1) A fine specimen of *V.antiopa* (Camberwell beauty) was taken here on the 19 August. [W. F. Beauford, Alconbury House, Huntingdon]

(2) I saw a fine specimen of a swallow-tail butterfly this morning, and should be glad to know if others have been seen in Surrey. The garden I saw it in is situated just in Surrey. I reared some swallow-tails and let them fly last year. [Cuthbert C. Fisher, Apsleytown, East Grinstead]. [As the swallow-tail butterfly (*Papilio machaon*) is now only known to occur in the Fen counties, in all probability the specimen seen was one that had either been turned down or escaped. – Ed., 25 August 1900]

(3) This morning I caught on some lucerne a perfect specimen of *Colias hyale* (female). Have you heard of others being caught in Surrey? [J. Thornhill, C.M.C. Home, Limpsfield, Surrey]

(4) I saw yesterday several specimens here of the clouded yellow butterfly, and I also heard that the clouded sulphur has been seen in this neighbourhood. [F. C. Goodwin, Brook Cottage, Berrington, Tenbury]

(5) On the 18th inst., at Sheerness, 4 nets captured over 60 specimens of *Colias hyale* (mostly males) and about 2 dozen *C.edusa*, including the variety *helice*. From the latter I have obtained about 500 ova, and both *C.hyale* and a normal female *edusa* have deposited freely. If warm weather continues during the next few weeks we may expect *C.edusa* to be still more plentiful towards the end of September. It is 32 years since *C.hyale* was abundant. In 1892 there were a few captured, but *edusa* was then common. [F. W. Frohawk]

(6) Referring to your Devon correspondent's note with regard to the present being a clouded yellow year, that butterfly has certainly been fairly abundant in this neighbourhood, but the pale clouded

yellow (*C.hyale*) is much more plentiful. I took the first *edusa* on the 28th ult. and since have seen many, but since 13th inst. I have seen at least 5 *hyale* to every *edusa*. A very remarkable circumstance in regard to both species is the number of males about to each female. Possibly the latter may appear later. It is worthy of note, too, that the red admiral (*V.atalanta*), which was so common last year, is this season comparatively scarce, while the converse is the case with reference to the peacock (*V.io*), it being very abundant this season about here, while last year there was hardly one to be seen. [H. Huggins, 13 June, Clarence-place, Gravesend]

(7) In a clover field on my farm my sons last week took several specimens of the clouded yellow (*Colias edusa*) and on the walls of this house 4 fine specimens of the scarlet underwing (*Catocala nanta*). [F. J. Coleridge Boles, Baraset, Stratford-on-Avon, 22 August]

[*Editor's note: This collection of letters, all published in the same issue during what was clearly a clouded yellow year, betrays an almost childish competitiveness which tends to run through much of the correspondence in the Naturalist sections of* THE FIELD *in the late 19th and early 20th century. Each writer is eager to cap the last. But it is just that competitive spirit which encouraged the amateur not only to observe but also to publicise the observation, and thus help to build up the mass of knowledge which can be found in* THE FIELD *by those who have the patience to work through its pages and the eyesight to tolerate acres of tiny print. A treasury indeed.*]

Carpet Weevils

From the information you give it seems likely that your carpet is being damaged by Carpet Beetles (*Attagenus pellio*) which may eat nylon and manmade fibres, as well as wool, skins and furs. The larvae, sometimes known as 'woolly bears', are honey-coloured and about $\frac{1}{4}$ in long. The beetles are smaller, dark brown or black with white spots. The term 'weevil' may be loosely applied to them but the two are not closely related. The adult beetles can fly. They are found out of doors in summer, feeding on nectar and pollen of various plants, particularly hogweed and spiraea. They lay their eggs in birds' nests, especially sparrows' nests under the eaves, and can invade the home, where they may breed in textiles and in floor cracks and crevices where wool and organic particles often accumulate. Mice nests and fur can provide food for the beetles as well.

Cockroach Trap

Put down a jam-jar containing a mixture of stale beer and banana with a cardboard lid having a hole big enough to enable the insects to gain access. From the hole a stiff paper cone with an opening at the apex wide enough to enable a cockroach to enter should be suspended. Once in, egress is difficult for the cockroach. Runways should be laid from the floor to the rim of the jar to enable the cockroaches to get up.

And More . . . (1892)

Nothing better than the 'Demon' cockroach trap, from any ironmonger, about 1s. each; but they should be attended to daily.

Cuckoo Spittle (1923)

Several species of *Eupteryx* infest plants, and their larvae suck the juices, from which the froth, known as 'cuckoo spittle', is formed. The most common is *E.spumaria*. Another species infests potato haulms, but it does not cause the formation of froth. It is very unlikely that these insects in any form are poisonous to birds. The froth found in the stomach of your pheasants is probably due to some very different cause.

Flies in the Garden

The summer flies that buzz in clouds round your heads in the garden are probably sweat flies (*Hydrotaca irritanus*), not biting but sipping your perspiration. They breed in animal dung. Stable flies can be a nuisance, breeding in litter. Robber flies (*Asilidae*), breeding in decomposing vegetable matter and rotting wood; horse flies breeding in damp marshy places, rotting vegetation etc.; and black flies, breeding in and near water, are all biters. Then there are the mosquitoes and biting midges which largely breed in or near water or damp places, manure heaps and rotting rubbish. To reduce the nuisance, undertake a vigorous clean-up of all fallen rotting wood, plant vegetation, heaps of rubbish, leaves etc., and, where possible, drain and make good puddles and places where rain readily lodges. Remove ivy and its accumulation of old leaves, dirt etc., from trees; spray the cow sheds or fumigate them with smoke generators (as they are sure to lodge much insect life); spray old sites of manure heaps, bases of compost heaps and damp places with insecticide.

The Speed of Flies

It would be helpful to know the scientific name of the 'deer bot-fly' you ask about but, presuming that it is a tabanid, probably *Tabanus bovinus* (the ox gad-fly), its accompanying hum gives an illusion of speed as the insect approaches. Speeds of flight are given by A. D.

Imms for a number of insects: the 'horse fly', i.e. a tabanid, is given at 8.8 mph while the fastest flier, the Aeshna dragonfly, is only 15.6 mph.

Harvest Bug Bites

The harvest bug (*Leptus autumnalis*) is the immature form of one of the acarina closely allied to the common red spider. In the immature state it is very minute, and of a bright red colour. It generally penetrates the skin at the base of a hair and there dies, setting up the irritation that causes 'harvest bumps'. It is visible to the naked eye, appearing like a small grain of cayenne pepper, and may be extracted with the point of a needle. Apply eucalyptus oil to the parts attacked, which will reduce the irritation, and is a good preventive against their attacks.

Midges (1900)

A new preparation termed Popoff is very highly spoken of for keeping midges at a distance.

Millipedes, Centipedes and Eelworms

Millipedes are segmented animals with longish, slender bodies, usually of 15 segments, with 2 pairs of short jointed legs on each segment. There are 3 common types (black, spotted snake, and flat-backed) and they feed on dead and rotting vegetable matter, and may attack soft tissues of plants. They are found on and in the soil and tend to curl up like a watch-spring when touched. They move relatively slowly and are sometimes confused with *centipedes*, which have only 1 pair of legs per segment, move quickly, and are usually yellowish to reddish brown. Centipedes are carnivorous and are thus held to be helpful to farmers and gardeners in keeping down insect pests. *Eelworms* are quite different: they are tiny, often microscopic, elongated, worm-like, tapering to each end, and light yellowish-white in colour. Most are plant parasites, found on and in plant tissues, in galls on shoots (bulb and stem eelworms), on roots (root-knot eelworms), in buds (currant eelworms) and in leaves (chrysanthemum eelworms). Some are free-living in soils but they are minute and therefore unlikely to be mistaken for millipedes.

Mosquitoes (1892)

Carbolic oil (composed of 1 part carbolic acid and 12 parts oil) is the best protection we know of against mosquitoes and black flies.

Riverside Mosquitoes

There are 3 kinds of mosquito likely to be troublesome in Britain: the Malaria Mosquito or Spotted Gnat (*Anolpheles maculipennis*) of which a sub-species may carry the British type of malaria known as ague (the species is most common in coastal areas); the common Gnat, *Culex pipiens*, which is very abundant but only sucks the blood of birds, not humans; and *Theobaldia annulata*, the largest of the mosquitoes, which attacks humans and animals fiercely. They all lay their eggs in stagnant water, pools, marshes etc., and the latter species is often found in larval form wriggling in water butts, ponds, gutters and even dirty or polluted water. As you are moving to a house by a river, your problems could come from shallows at the margins of the river where there is low marshy ground, perhaps subject to flooding and subsequent draining, and shallow pools form. Such breeding places can be rendered more or less harmless by spraying with oil (paraffin) to form a skin on the water through which the larvae and forming insects cannot rise. Or have suspect ground drained.

Start of a Spider's Web

Very briefly, what happens is that a spider wishing to span a path with a web makes an attachment on a bush or tree, climbs down the tree, then trails the thread behind her just above the ground, climbs a tree on the other side of the path and takes in the slack so that she now has a tightrope on which she can cross when continuing her construction. When bridging small streams, spiders let a sort of blow line of thread fly away till it catches on something across the stream, then they tighten up and so make their first tightrope.

Maternal Instincts in Spiders (1900)

Seeing in the garden one of the common brown spiders which run over the ground below every hedge, and sun themselves there, and that it carried its large bag of eggs in the usual manner, I caught the animal in my fingers and held it for my children to see how the bag was carried. Holding the bag, I liberated the spider, which ran down my finger, but remembering the bag of eggs, deliberately ran back and seized it, and then, as I released the bag, jumped with it to the ground, placed the burden in the usual position between the hind legs, and hurried off.

Tobacco Maggots

It is not only incredible that an insect in egg, larval or any form should be present in a packet of cigarette tobacco and survive the processes of manufacture, but also difficult to believe that it could live, since tobacco contains nicotine, an alkaloid poisonous to all insects. It is possible that the tobacco or container could have become contaminated after processing; or that the 'maggots' may be other than insect larvae. Have them identified.

Scarcity of Wasps (1960)

A scarcity of wasps in Dorset seems to be a local phenomenon rather than a general one, though it is probably true that certain trends are working against the wasp and its survival, such as an increased population, greater vigilance on the part of those with gardens, and the increased use of insecticides, which wasps may pick up from sprayed crops and carry back to the nest to destroy the colony. Natural controls are badgers, which dig out the nests to eat the grubs, and very heavy rain may drown out the many nests built in the ground.

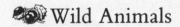 Wild Animals

Adder Young (1900)

The skeletons were those of the unborn young; if the keeper saw an adder swallow its young, why did he not kill it, tie a string round the throat, and claim the £5 reward which has long been offered by *THE FIELD*?

Black Adder

Without seeing the specimen you describe as a black, shiny snake, 18–24 in long, 1¼ in in diameter, and with a 2 in-long forked tongue, it is impossible to be certain, but it was probably a very dark specimen of the so-called 'black' variation of the adder. These vary from extremely dark brown to near-black. If one examines them very closely and the light is shining at the right angle, one can usually see, very faintly, the typical zig-zag pattern of the adder. If a particular specimen is really black, even this may not be visible. Like all adders, this variety is venomous and might well bite, though you say it was lively and swift but did not try to bite.

Badger Deterrent

A harmless deterrent to badgers entering the garden and digging up the lawn might be coarsely chopped gorse, laid in a 2 ft-wide band across places where the badgers enter, or string a nylon-wire electric fence in their paths of approach. This is a smaller version of the electric cattle fencing at about 6 in high which can be set along the edges of the lawn.

Badger Stripes

As badgers have no natural enemies, it is probable that the conspicuous striping on their heads is intended as a warning to other animals that they are well able to defend themselves. It was at one time thought that the striping might be a camouflage in moonlight, but in fact badgers are always conspicuous animals, and they have no need of protection from anything except man. Warning coloration is, of course, known in many other groups of animals able to defend themselves, such as wasps, or that are unpleasant to the taste, such as cinnabar moths and their caterpillars.

Blind Worm

The specimen forwarded is a full-grown blind worm, a perfectly harmless species that feeds chiefly on slugs and small worms; it would be useful and not injurious in your garden. Poisonous adders are only found on dry sandy heaths; they are distinguished by a line of diamond-shaped patches down the back.

Black Shuck

The word 'Shuck' has several meanings. It is dialect for a devil or a fiend. It is a term, sometimes qualified by black or 'owd', applied to a phantom dog or spectre hound or dog fiend, held to be local to East Norfolk. It has been described as a large, black, shaggy dog with a coarse coat and fiery eyes, hardly 'calf-like' or 'one-eyed' as you suggest, but descriptions vary. It was seen in 1893 by one F. A. Paley and reported in the *Daily News* of 22 September of that year, but we cannot confirm any subsequent death associated with this sighting. There are references to an earlier sighting but we cannot trace any very recent authentic and reported sightings of an apparition perhaps too easily conjured up in a bleak, forbidding countryside or situation.

Wild Dog at Niagara (1860)

I can scarce give credence to this story, inasmuch as that on my late visit to the falls, though I learned every legend that was in, on, or by the side of the water, no mention was made to me of this Newfoundland dog. Had I been told of it, and found the tale a true one, I would have devoted another day or two to the rescue of the dog. [Grantley F. Berkeley]

White Elephant (1865)

Elephants, especially white elephants, are all important personages in Siam. In the multitudinous incarnations of Buddha, it is believed that the white elephant is one of his necessary domiciles, and the possession of a white elephant is the possession of the presence and patronage of the Deity. I was escorted by one of the great Ministers of State to the domicile of the white elephant in Bangkok, whose death, not many years ago, filled the court and nation with mourning. He had been discovered in the forests of the interior; a large reward was paid to the fortunate discoverer, and the first king left his capital to meet with becoming ostentatious welcome and reverence the newly acquired treasure. In Siamese history there are many chapters giving an account of invasions and repulses in wars waged solely for the acquisition of some white elephant in the possession of a neighbouring sovereign. When the King escorted his prize to his capital I was conducted to the palace of the honoured dignitary. To say the truth, his colour was not white, but coppery, like that of a red Indian. His stable was painted like a Parisian drawing-room; there was an elevated platform, on whose adjacent walls handsome warlike ornaments were hung, and nobles of high rank were in attendance, who took care that he should be supplied with delicious food, principally the young sugarcane. When the white elephant went to bathe, caparisoned in splendid decorations, he was preceded by musicians, escorted by courtiers, and was received by the people with prostration and reverence. On my departure from Bangkok, after the signature of the treaties, when the Royal letters were delivered engraved on golden slabs for the great Queen of England, and placed in a gold box, locked with a gold key, though many handsome presents accompanied the Royal missives, one offering was placed in my hands with the assurance that it was by far the most precious of the gifts to be conveyed – and the invaluable offering was a bunch of hairs from the white elephant's tail, tied together with a golden thread. [Sir John Bowring]

Ferret, Rabbit and Fox

In large warrens it is not uncommon to find a fox in one part and rabbits in another. Really large earths sometimes contain foxes, badgers and rabbits at the same time. We have never known of a fox killing a ferret, but in a blind hole with its back to the wall it is quite possible that it might. We do not think it would eat it, so the missing ferret was probably lost in another part of the main warren.

Fox-Dog

A fox-dog hybrid is most unlikely. When populations of animals evolve into distinct species they develop physical, instinctive and physiological differences all designed towards the true breeding of that population so that the specific character is preserved. In other words, the members of one species have no inclination to mate with individuals of another species. The fox and the domestic dog are not only different species, but are placed in different genera, so that there are very considerable barriers to be overcome before even mating could take place. It might be possible to induce this under artificial conditions, but there remains the physiological barrier – that the spermatozoa of one could not fertilise the ova of the other.

The Gorilla at the Aquarium (1877)

Pongo, the gorilla at the Westminster Aquarium and the only one living in Europe, is the same specimen as was figured in THE FIELD of 4 November 1876. He is now about $3\frac{1}{2}$ years old and weighs about 45 lb. His general colour may be described as sooty greyish black, the skin being nearly, if not quite, black, and the hair dark grey. The face and expression are remarkably human; it is true the forehead is, as Shakespeare has it, 'villanous low', the bridge of the nose wanting, and that the nostrils are dilated to an unseemly extent; but the expression is human and confiding, and the dark eyes turn towards a friendly countenance with a yearning that is excessively sorrowful. I have seen many human faces infinitely less human. Pongo seemed intuitively to recognise my sympathy with animals; he at once climbed into my lap and, putting one arm round my neck, with the other hand he grasped the collar of my waistcoat, and composed himself into an attitude of serene repose, disturbed only by the rough attentions of those visitors who patted him as they would have patted the hide of a rhinoceros, when the poor,

Young gorilla at the Berlin Aquarium

weary eyes looked up and said, as plainly as eyes could say, with Byron's *Giaour*, 'I want no paradise but rest.' During the half-hour that Pongo was in my arms I had the opportunity of a careful examination of many of his peculiarities. The portrait in *THE FIELD* gives very closely the form of the body and limbs, but does not do justice to the placid expression of the face. I am sorry to say that the animal has a slight cough, and I fear the expression of the face is ominously evil. I cannot regard with much complacency his career as a popular idol, knowing how prone these large quadrumana are to tubercular disease. I should be better pleased if all such human dissipations as beer and cigars, and late hours and crowded receptions were at an end, and that a quiet winter's sojourn in some sheltered haven were employed, to give some chance of life to this, the most anthropoid of the apes. If this interesting specimen were well cared for, fed on fruits and farinaceous substances, with a due proportion of cream, and had those sanitary conditions that are requisite in the case of a child with tuberculous diathesis, I think it might be reared to man's – I beg pardon – to adult gorilla's estate. I have only one more remark to make: the animal is so docile and amenable to kindness that the whip, which is used as a symbol of authority, seems to me painfully out of place. [W. B. Tegetmeier]

Breeding Hedgehogs

It is one thing to rear a juvenile hedgehog in captivity; quite another thing to keep adults in health and induce them to mate and breed. We suggest that the best scheme would be to protect the natural nest under the ivy in your garden run, supplying more leaves and straw during the late autumn. Leave the female to acquire her own male, which is readily done in country districts. Hedgehogs travel far in search of their natural mixed diet – insects, worms, carrion, fallen fruits, seeds, roots. They are fond of milk, with bread or cereal added, and during the rearing season they will come to the door of the house for it. After the season they seem to prefer the natural foods of the garden and the hedgerow. Finally, look carefully before handling hedgehogs to see if they harbour fleas. If fleas are seen, lightly dust the nest occasionally with disinfectant.

[*Editor's note: Thirty years later, it is appreciated that bread and milk diets are totally unnatural for hedgehogs and may even cause them harm. Indeed hedgehog expert Les Stocker claims in his book* The Complete Hedgehog *that bread and milk kill more hedgehogs than motor cars do. Tinned dog food is much more suitable.*]

Hedgehogs and Rats

The idea that hedgehogs keep rats away is an old, widespread country superstition; we do not know that there is any truth in it.

Mice (1860)

What *am* I to do for the mice? Will any kind correspondent of *THE FIELD* help me? My crocus roots are pulled out of the ground, and now they have attacked a pot of choice ixia roots, which stand on the library window seat. They are too sly to allow themselves to be caught in a trap, and we have no cat on account of my birds. I fear, if I steel my heart and poison them, they will die in their holes.

[*Editor's comment: The classic dilemma of the animal lover!*]

Taming Wild Mice

With patience almost all wild animals can be tamed, and mice are no exception. The best method is to get the mice to associate you with the source of their food. If you can make an elastic-wristed sleeve, fit it to the door of the cage, and then put your hand in with cheese scraps – and are prepared to spend lots of time doing it – you should gradually get them to come to your hand. The beautiful long-tailed field mouse (or wood-mouse) is extremely difficult to tame, though it has been kept in captivity quite happily for up to 4 years. If you are ever lucky enough to find a dormouse, it makes a good pet, and so do the tiny, but now very local, harvest mice.

Mice Eat Oak Table (1959)

The mice are apparently attracted by the wax on the newly made oak table in your church and are therefore gnawing the table-top corners and legs. One method of deterring them would be to give the table a coat of clear lacquer varnish or shellac varnish. This would give a hard finish and mask the odour of the wax. Alternatively, you could raise the table on small wooden blocks or inverted small saucers or on wooden leg blocks made for pianos and smear these supports all the way round with fruit-tree banding grease, which is sticky and remains so for a long time. After one experience of getting their feet entangled, the mice will not try to climb the legs again.

Making Molehills

An increase in the number of molehills at this season of the year (February) is more a sign of increased activity on the part of the moles rather than an increase in their numbers. This early activity is no doubt related to the mildness of the weather following the frosts of early winter. Numerous molehills also does not mean that the soil has become increasingly populated with earthworms. It may mean that there is a *decrease*, and the moles are having to move more earth in their quest for them. The very large molehill in your field (about 15 in high and 10 ft 3 in in circumference) is one of those usually referred to as fortresses – a bad name, since they are primarily used to house the nests (often more than one), though they may be occupied throughout the year.

The chief method of tunnelling used by the mole is to probe and loosen the soil ahead by means of its snout, lifting it and thrusting it backwards by the movement of powerful shoulders, and at the same time using its powerful front paws to gain a purchase on the tunnel sides, and also to scrape soil behind it. The precise tactics used depend upon the soil and its texture. In soft soil the mole may make its tunnel as much by compressing the loosened soil into the tunnel walls as by excavating it. When, however, soil has accumulated behind the mole, it will turn around and push it out to the nearest upshaft, and there throw it to the surface by lifting it with its snout and top of the head. The soil is pushed out from the centre of the heap, cascading on all sides, much like a volcano erupting.

Nature and Inbreeding

Conjecture has it that the dogs found by Captain Cook in New Zealand, which fed entirely on fish and were never of mixed colouring but only either white, black or dingy yellow, were a country-bred product and had been in New Zealand for centuries, having by degrees been adopted by the inhabitants. The fact that they do not vary greatly in colour or type is probably due to inbreeding between close relatives. However, nature always takes care of the strong and eliminates the weaklings. Laverack in his book on the setter probably arrives at the solution when he says that inbreeding, with nature's safeguards, has proved itself right. We do not hear of importations of wolves or tigers from one country to another to strengthen the blood. There has been nothing but inbreeding in nature for thousands of years and nature adjusts the balance.

Porpoises in the Solway Frith (1854)

The inhabitants along the shore of Solway, near Annan waterfoot, were lately somewhat alarmed by an extraordinary noise in the frith. On the tide ebbing, the turmoil was explained by a large shoal of porpoises which were stranded on the sands. One of these monsters of the deep measured 20 ft in length. One fisherman secured 8 as his share, from which he expects to receive oil to the value of £30. The tenant of Sea-field had 13, and on attaching 4 horses to one to remove the fish beyond flood mark they were not able to move it. In addition to oil the carcasses will furnish a large quantity of excellent manure.

Law and the Rabbit (1953)

There is, as no doubt you know, no 'code' of law in this country as there is in France, and the law relating to rabbits is very scattered. Rabbits are not game, but neither are they vermin. They have a position all to themselves, rather like pigeons. Although they are not game, the Game Act of 1831 makes it as much of an offence to trespass in search of, say, rabbits as it is to trespass in search of, say, pheasants. By the Poaching Prevention Act, 1862, a police constable may search and arrest anyone whom he suspects has been poaching rabbits just as though they were game. There is no 'close season' for rabbits and they may be killed at any time. The Ground Game Act of 1880 provides that the *occupier* of land has the right to kill rabbits on that land, and this right is inalienable and indefeasible, no matter what the owner of the land may have reserved to himself. Spring traps set to catch rabbits must be set in a rabbit hole and not in the open. They may be gassed but not poisoned. In theory, a game licence is required to kill rabbits, but there are so many exceptions that in practice only a gun licence must be obtained.

Young Rabbits

There is no widely accepted common name for young rabbits. A litter is referred to as a nest of rabbits. At one time the young of the species were known as rabbits and the adult and mature as conies. One authority gives 'bunny' for the young, holding it to be derived from the Gaelic *bun* for rabbit, but this has only too obviously become the pet name for a rabbit of any age.

Rats! (1937)

When I came home from India in 1931 my place was swarming with rats. You could hear rats doing squadron drill in the walls and ceilings, floors etc. We had then an old cook who had been here some years and had about 6 or 8 fat and wheezing and disgusting cats that she grossly overfed. They were always in the house. We tried poison, viruses, traps of all kinds, and everything. After 12 months I sacked the cook and got a man cook, and had all the cats the cook left behind shot. I then got a young tabby cat from a well-known ratting strain from a farm. She was allowed in the house, but only fed once a day and turned out at night. She had several litters a year. Her progeny were never allowed in the house at all. They lived in the stables and cowsheds and got a small bowl of milk night and morning. In 6 months we never heard or saw a rat on the place and have not done so at all until after Christmas this year. A tenant farmer just across the river employed a trapper, and the place swarmed. My cats having no rats and few rabbits here, went over there after his. It is only 300 yards. I now have only one old cat and one other left – all the rest have been trapped. Rats have started to come back for the first time since 1932. [Invincible Tom, Carmarthenshire]

Wild White Rats

The most likely explanation for the 2 white young wild rats in a nest where the rest of the litter were the usual colour, as was their mother, is that over the many years that white rats have been kept as pets, many have escaped and could have mated with wild rats. The white strain would then occur intermittently.

Snakes: Eggs or Live Young?

Some snakes lay eggs, and others bring forth their young alive. In this country the grass snake and smooth snake do the former, and the adder or viper, the latter. 'Viper' is derived from 'viviparous', meaning to give birth to live progeny.

Rearing Red Squirrels (1953)

If you wish to keep a red squirrel as a pet it would have to be taken as a baby from the nest, otherwise it is doubtful whether it would remain tame. Such a baby squirrel would have to be fed by finding a cat to act as foster mother. If the squirrel is young and beyond weaning, it should be given jars of bread and milk on which to feed. When older it can be fed on nuts – Spanish, mixed and monkey – given whole; bananas, apples, lettuce, greens, grapes, cooked potatoes, bread and carrots. These should be chopped before being given to the squirrel. In season, such fruits of the woods as beech mast and haws can be added. Water is essential. In captivity, a fairly large cage is necessary.

A Whale at Pevensey (1865)

The dead body of a full-grown torqual or fin whale (the razor-back fish of the whale-fishers) was washed ashore on Monday last in Pevensey Bay, 8 miles from Hastings. The animal was in an advanced state of decomposition and smelt most horribly. It had evidently been dead for some weeks, and the outer surface was much nibbled and bitten by dog-fish. The Board of Admiralty and the Corporation of Hastings squabbled over the dead body, and it was taken possession of by the former, not, as might possibly be imagined, for presentation to any museum for the purpose of promoting natural history, but on account of its mere monetary value. It was consequently sold by auction for £38, being bought by some speculating fishermen, who have already realised more than its purchase-money by its exhibition. The animal is 67 ft in length, its estimated girth is 25 ft, the width of the flukes 13 ft. Mr Flowers, the curator of the Museum of the College of Surgeons, inspected it on Thursday, and determined the species. The torqual is not an uncommon whale on our coast; it is never pursued by the whale-fishers, as it yields but a comparatively small amount of oil and baleen (whalebone), and is so active as to render its capture alike difficult and dangerous. Several skeletons of this species exist in a more or less perfect condition in England. There is one at Muswell-hill, and a second in the well-known Rosherville Gardens. Of the true Northern or Greenland whale – the 'right whale' of the sailors – there is but one skeleton in England, and that is now being set up in the Museum of the College of Surgeons. [W. B. Tegetmeier]

The Wexford Whale (1953)

The weight of the heaviest whale washed up on British shores was a Blue Whale that beached at Wexford, in 1891. Its length was 59 ft and it weighed 59 tons.

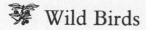 Wild Birds

Removing Birdlime (1861)

To remove birdlime from the plumage of birds, take a camel-hair pencil and spirits of wine. This will do all that is required to clean the feathers and body.

Collard Doves (1967)

The birds you saw which looked like an Indian ring dove and are very similar to the domesticated barbary dove (which is popular as a pet) are collared doves. This species, originally Asiatic, has spread since 1900 from the Balkans across Europe. It first bred in Britain in Norfolk in 1955, and 2 years later there were records of its breeding in Moray, Lincoln and Kent. Since then its range has extended and the birds are increasing and spreading rapidly. They may well become pests where they are numerous. They will eat any kind of grain and seeds, and a certain amount of greenstuff; they often feed on mash, etc., put out for chickens, and would eat crumbs, uncooked rice and bird seed.

Late Cuckoo

Cuckoos in Britain rarely call after 21 June, Midsummer's Day. Although there are several late dates of cuckoos being seen in this country, we can find no reference to the latest date on which they have been heard. To hear a cuckoo after the end of June would be unusual.

Fidelity

The subject of faithfulness to mates among birds is a complicated one. Certain species – swans, for example – are thought to keep their mates throughout life. It would seem unreasonable that, if one of a pair of a monogamous species dies or is killed, the mate should pine and never find another partner. Several authorities have recorded that even among those species which are thought to be monogamous, promiscuity does sometimes occur. Swallows and swifts have shown evidence of this, though swallows are thought to remain faithful to their mates in most cases. As under normal circumstances both sexes feed the nestlings, there is nothing unusual in a cock bird feeding the young of another, as in the case of the male swallow whose mate and young died and who returns to your area each year but merely feeds the young of another pair nesting there.

Gannet Reserve (1900)

Desirous of studying and describing the various phases of plumage in the gannet, the late Mr E. T. Booth of Brighton constructed a large salt water pond with some good big boulders projecting above the surface, the margin strewn with shingle from the sea shore, and the whole surrounded by a high wooden palisade. Into this unique 'reserve' he turned some gannets and guillemots, fed them with a constant supply of cheap fish, and got them into such splendid health and spirits that when the breeding season came round 2 of the gannets paired, made a nest, and in due time reared a single young one. Never was such a thing heard of before as a gannet (of all birds) rearing its young in captivity; for captive it was to a certain extent, one wing being pinioned. The young one grew and went through all the changes of plumage, from the uniform black of the newly hatched chick to the spotted phase of the second year, and the gradually assumed white body with black wings which denotes the livery of an adult bird. The changes being carefully noted, and water-colour drawings from time to time made, the experiment was at length completed. There was no longer any necessity for keeping the birds in confinement and their owner decided to give them their liberty. They were placed in a cart covered with netting, driven down to the shore, where a boat was in readiness to receive them, and were then rowed out to what was considered a safe distance from land. One by one they were then lifted overboard, and flapped exultingly away. But mark what followed! Hardly had the boat returned to shore when the cry was raised, 'Gannets ahoy!' and every cockney gunner who could lay his hands upon a gun was off in pursuit of them. In due course they were overhauled, and the poor half-tamed gannets, which had become accustomed to close inspection when protected by their late owner, unsuspectingly enabled the valiant cockneys to shoot them sitting!

Reintroduction of the Great Bustard (1900)

An experiment is being made to reintroduce the Great Bustard in one of its former haunts in Norfolk. The proposal was to import a number of live birds from the Continent, and, after due warning to shooters, to liberate them here and there in localities suited to their habits, in the expectation that if unmolested in the breeding time broods might be reared, and this noble species might be restored to the British game list. Several live bustards have now been imported at considerable expense and trouble, and by this time have been liberated under conditions as favourable as could be secured. The announcement of the fact has just been made by Lord Walsingham who, in a letter addressed to the editor of the *Norfolk Chronicle*, writes: 'This effort is due to the public spirit of an English gentleman resident abroad, whose love of natural history has induced him to incur considerable expense and trouble in the matter. It is hoped that residents in Norfolk and Suffolk will agree to respect the birds,

The Great Bustard

which will probably be at large before this letter appears, and by preventing their destruction will secure the success of an experiment to which the reintroduction of the capercailzie in Scotland affords a parallel instance and an encouraging precedent.' The bird's only enemies are the selfish individuals who care nothing for the feelings of other people, and, armed with a cheap gun (though not always with a gun licence), think it laudable for the sake of a few shillings from the nearest birdstuffer to slaughter a bird that others are doing their best to preserve.

Lord Walsingham's Record Bag (1888)

1,070 grouse (535 brace) were killed by Lord Walsingham, to his own gun, on Bluberhouse Moor, Yorkshire, on 30 August.

Guillemot Eggs in San Francisco (1854)

San Francisco is supplied with an abundance of eggs of the sea-fowl called 'murres', the thick-billed Guillemot of ornithology. In less than 2 months of last summer more than 500,000 of these eggs were sold in San Francisco, all taken from the rookery of Great Farallon, an island in the bay of San Francisco, where these birds swarm in myriads. The eggs are about $3\frac{1}{2}$ in long, and are said to be delicate eating.

London's Gulls (1937)

It is possible to meet with 3 sorts of gulls on the Thames during the winter months (although stragglers of other specimens do turn up): the black-headed, the common and the herring gull. The names are confusing, the common gull being the least common of the three, while the black-headed is white-headed in winter. Purists maintain that the name of the latter is quite wrong, since the headgear which it dons for the breeding season is chocolate-brown and not black. The vast majority of the gulls which visit London in winter are of the black-headed species.

London Hawk (1957)

If the bird you saw above a church in Kennington was *hovering*, it was undoubtedly a kestrel and not a sparrowhawk. The kestrel is not uncommon in London and has bred in recent years on (a) one of the large public buildings along Cromwell Road, and (b) a ruined building (since rebuilt) outside Waterloo Station. The diet of London kestrels probably includes beetles, cockroaches, mice and small birds.

Looking After Hawks (1952)

When you collect the young fledgling peregrine falcons, get a basket or hamper and fill it with straw and 'nest' the birds in this, in a suitable outhouse or shed. You then want a platform on to which the birds can come out and feed. A hamper with a lid is very useful since the lid can be propped up to serve as the feeding platform; or you can improvise one with a board and supports. Their foods must be the freshest possible; easiest to provide would be young rabbits, rats, freshly killed birds etc. The food should be torn in portions and each portion fastened securely to the feeding board or to separate wood blocks, so that the falcons have to tear it. Feed plentifully, but interfere with the birds as little as possible, placing the food down and leaving them to it. As the birds grow, they will begin to fly, first to supports, rafters, etc., in the shed, but later to nearby trees, and gradually increasing their distances. They will, however, always come back to feed, provided they are fed regularly and, of course, before evening to gather them in for the night. A falcon that stays out overnight, however, may be lost unless prompt action is taken when it returns again.

Hawk Control (1916)

The facts stated in your letter are well known, but the eyries of the peregrine falcon in England are now so few and far between that it is unreasonable as well as unnecessary to kill the parent birds. Undoubtedly they take stray pigeons when they get the chance, but they live principally for half the year on the seafowl which frequent the cliffs, and in winter on wild ducks, teal and plover, of which a few can very well be spared out of the many hundreds which visit us and augment the numbers which are bred in this country.

Hawk Following a Bomb (1916)

The following curious incident occurred in the presence of several bystanders on Tuesday, 28 December, on the 'proofing-ground' of a well-known ordnance firm somewhere in Kent. A bomb had been released from a trench mortar, and whilst on its course through the air was sighted by a hawk, whose track it practically crossed. The bird wheeled round and made a bee-line towards it, from below, then above in its endeavour to attack and arrest the enemy. When the bomb had reached a altitude of about 400 yards and was probably about 450 yards distant, it exploded, but as only the gaine of the bomb was charged nothing serious happened to the bird, except that it probably got the surprise and fright of its life. The hawk was at the rear of the bomb when it broke up, and not very far behind, and the force of the explosion of the gaine was sufficient to crumple the bird somewhat. However, it speedily recovered, and then made for an adjacent wood. The speed of the hawk was considerable, for it only took the bomb 4 seconds to reach the point of explosion. Had there been a full charge inserted in the bomb, there would have been very little left of the bird. It was thought to be a sparrowhawk.

Henpecked Husband (1854)

For some years past a pair of noble eagles have been conspicuously ornamental in the pleasure grounds of Charles Clarke, Esq., at Matlock Bath. The hen was by far the largest and most powerful, as well as pugnacious, and many a castigation has she bestowed on her liege lord, especially at dinner time, when not content with taking the head of the table, she would insist on taking the head and body too, of any defunct rabbit, rat, or other delicacy provided, her mate being only permitted to dine in peace after his lady had bountifully helped herself. Things went on in this unsatisfactory manner until last Saturday, when a sad crisis arrived; as on that day a quarrel arose, followed as usual by assault and battery, but which in this instance ended only with the death of the least powerful combatant.

Dangerous Jackdaw (1948)

With reference to the letter regarding the rook taking matches out of a box one by one, I have seen much the same thing done by a tame jackdaw in Eire. But this jackdaw would, in addition, strike the match if requested to do so, and was most persistent in demands for more. In fact it was so persistent that one had to be very careful in taking as few matches as possible. They were only produced when someone wanted a cigarette which 'Jacky' proceeded to light.

Owl in a Cowl (1916)

[During the last few days of heavy gales of wind, tiles were dislodged from our roof, and as the men were making the damage good, I asked them to grease the cowls on the chimneys, one of them having been groaning badly. Much to the surprise of the men who were handling one of the cowls, a brown owl flew out. I should like to give this bird a more comfortable lodging as it frequents the tall evergreen trees near the house. Could you tell me where I could get a suitable box, and the height it should be from the ground?]

The higher the better to lessen the risk of disturbance, say 15 ft to 20 ft. The nearest carpenter will soon knock up a box that will answer the purpose, and it will be all the better for having the bark left on so as not to attract the attention of passers-by.

Destructive Wood-Pigeons (1854)

There is irrefragable proof of the destructive capabilities of the wood-pigeon. One of these birds was shot and upon examining its crop it was found to contain no less than 937 grains of wheat, besides 94 tares – unmistakeably showing that it had found good quarters, and had availed itself of the advantage afforded. Mr Bedwell, of Breton Court, has sown the grain distinct from his other crops, in order to ascertain the quantity of corn capable of being produced from the consumption of a single wood-pigeon.

The Paris Pigeon Post (1870)

It would be a hazardous assertion to state that more absolute nonsense had been written about the pigeon post and pigeon despatches than about any other subjects whatever, but the accounts that have appeared week after week in the various papers have been characterised by the most profound ignorance of the subject. In a recent number of *All the Year Round*, in an article entitled 'Messengers Aloft', the writer – whose acquaintance with pigeons was evidently derived from his familiarity with them when constituting the contents of a dove tart – confounded together the large-eyed, heavy-wattled carrier of the English fancier, that could not fly 5 miles to save its own life – with the active Belgian *voyageur* and capped his absurdity by comparing both with the migratory dove, *Ectopistes migratoria* of North America. In truth the pigeons employed in carrying messages to Paris are the ordinary *pigeons voyageurs*, such as were shown as working Antwerps at the last Crystal Palace show. The despatches to be sent by the pigeons are first set up in ordinary type; they are then reduced by photography to a size 40 x 30 mm. The first column contains the address to which the despatch sheet is to be sent, in characters legible by the naked eye. The other 3 columns contain each on average 36 messages with their addresses. On arriving at the telegraphic bureau the despatch is read by the aid of a magnifying glass, and each message is transcribed and forwarded to its destination. Instead of adopting the old plan of tying the paper round the leg of the bird, it is rolled up tightly and placed in a quill, which is then tied longitudinally to one of the feathers of the tail. Unfortunately for the Parisians, their supply of *voyageur* pigeons is but limited. Had Antwerp or Brussels been besieged, they might have been sent out by thousands. As it is, each of the ballons leaving Paris brings out its supply of *voyageurs*, and these are liberated with despatches as occasion requires. It may be necessary to inform those readers who are quite ignorant of the subject that the pigeons only journey in one direction – namely, to their homes – and that without previous training the best-bred birds cannot be depended on. Now that the ground is covered with snow, all objects look so much alike that the pigeons are very apt to be lost, and the Belgium national sport of pigeon *concours* or races is in abeyance until the return of the mild weather.

Feeding a Fledgling Rook

Finely minced raw meat should be made into a mash with bread-crumbs and a small pinch of salt. This should be fed to the quantity of a teaspoonful 4 times a day. If the fledgling has not learned to pick up the food voluntarily, you should force-feed him. For this purpose an assistant should hold the rook firmly yet without compressing his chest, while you open his beak and with the other hand insert a pea-sized piece of mash over the root of the tongue, and then allow him freedom of the beak and head in order to swallow. Repeat this feeding until he has eaten a teaspoonful. Mashed cold boiled egg or grated cheese can replace the meat. For drink give water, sips at a time and poured into the side of the partly opened mouth. Do not give worms or insects; let him come at this type of food by learning to hunt for himself.

Rook or Crow? (1892)

A rook may be always known by its bare face; a crow is feathered to the base of the bill.

Skylarks to the Bird Table (1963)

This severe winter has been remarkable for the number of skylarks reported as coming to gardens and bird tables to feed. Also, they have been seen feeding near poultry fields, barns and so on. Undoubtedly their hunger overcame their timidity.

Sparrows and Nesting Boxes

The critical diameter which prevents house sparrows entering a nesting box is supposed to be between $1\frac{1}{4}$ in and $1\frac{1}{8}$ in. If the diameter is reduced to between $1\frac{1}{8}$–1 in, it should be safe enough for blue tits and even great tits.

White Starlings

Not a summer elapses in which we do not hear of white starlings in different parts of the country. White swallows are also reported every summer, but a white swift would be a much greater rarity.

Storks from the Market (1900)

Young storks (*Ciconia alba*) can be purchased from Leadenhall Market in the early part of June. If they are then given their full liberty, they will invariably repay the favour by remaining at home until the due season for their natural southward migration arrives, which generally occurs about 15 or 17 August. It is a rare and interesting treat to see these birds sailing home at a regular hour to take up their positions for the night, perhaps on the roof of the house, circling on widespread wings towards their roosting place every evening at about 7 o'clock and returning to their lake edge every morning at 4 o'clock. Until the migratory season, however far they may fly they will not settle anywhere except on the spot where they regularly spend the day, or upon the roof where they roost: it is evident that they are birds with homing instincts of a very marked kind.

Wild Turkeys (1916)

If turkeys were treated like pheasants, allowed unrestrained liberty, and thus permitted to find their natural food, there can be no doubt that from a gastronomic point of view their quality would be materially improved; and although turkey shooting as compared with pheasant shooting would be tame sport, it is quite conceivable that, after some years of freedom and improved power of flight continued through many generations, turkeys might become as wary and as difficult of approach on large shootings in England and Scotland as they are found to be by sportsmen in America, and it would then require as much skill to bring one to bag as it does to stalk and shoot a capercaillie.

Yew Berries and Birds

Birds are not necessarily resistant to the poisonous alkaloid contained in most parts of the yew tree, nor do they seem to avoid the berries. The fruiting berry, however, consists of a single seed contained in a red pulpy covering known as an aril. In digestion the seed passes through the bird's alimentary system and is ejected, while the red pulp is digested as food. The seed is a concentrated source of the poison, and the red pulp contains little or no poison, so the bird is unharmed. It can be argued that the red colouring actually attracts birds, as a device to ensure the distribution of the seeds.

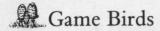 Game Birds

Air Speeds of Game-birds (1887)

In experiments to test the speed of partridges, pheasants and pigeons, the birds flew through a covered gallery and the speeds recorded were, in miles an hour: partridge 28, pheasant 33, pigeon 33. In the open the speeds were: partridge 32, pheasant 38, pigeon 27. In experiments made with 18 homing pigeons it was found that the average speed was 36 mph. In 1886 a covey of partridges kept up, for 400 yards, with an express train travelling at 45 mph.

Air Speeds of Birds (1948)

The speeds are recorded for still air and are average flight speeds. Make some allowance for individual differences. Mallard: 44–59 mph. Wigeon: 50–55 mph. Partridge: 39–45 mph (flight is deceptive since there are quick changes of course and speed). Pheasant: flight is direct and fast but rarely long sustained, estimated at 40–51 mph. Geese: 42–55 mph (occasionally in sudden bursts of speed these rates may be exceeded). Black grouse: flight is strong and rapid but seldom long, estimated at 39–55 mph. Teal: 48–55 mph (flight speed is difficult to gauge owing to the fact that teal fly at comparatively low altitudes). To estimate the flight speed under windy conditions, it is necessary to add or subtract the wind speed according to whether the birds are flying with or against the wind. Thus a strong 15 mph tail wind will enable a mallard to get along about 65 mph. Complete accuracy of flight speeds is impossible for so many factors are variable.

Look Well (1855)

Look well at your birds before you put your gun to your shoulder. You can do so at the commencement of the season.

Black Grouse on Surrey Heaths (1877)

Some broods of black grouse have been flushed and shot in the corn

Red grouse shooting in August

stubbles around Ascot Heath and other parts in Berks, and several head of this game have been bagged on the Merstham hills in Surrey. The supposition made by the daily papers is that they have strayed from the royal preserves at Windsor, but there is no need for any such suggestion. Black game was frequently met with formerly in various parts of the great heath country that runs through the north of Hants, the south of Surrey, and Berks. Bagshot Heath was a favourite resort with the black grouse. In the New Forest 25 years ago they were plentiful, we ourselves on one occasion having killed as many as $7\frac{1}{2}$ brace in a very limited area in the course of 2 days' shooting. No doubt, if they were not knocked down as they are, they would be far more abundant on our great central moorlands.

Moor Water for Grouse

To keep water for grouse on a very dry moor, a variety of artificial containers has been tried but this does not seem to have been very successful. A heavy cast-iron feeding trough about 2 ft long and 4 in wide, set into the ground with a sheet of galvanised iron firmly fixed at an angle, would prove the best type of receptacle, provided it can be sited in the shade. Sheep on the moor would upset most artificial containers. Careful attention to the natural water supply on the lower ground would benefit the birds more.

The Grouse Moor (1854)

Grouse, and indeed game of all kinds, form, to the eye of an experienced sportsman, the chief features of a moor-land landscape. Little does he care for beautiful prospects, rugged hills, or the wild scenery about him. The background of *his* picture is filled up by a covey of birds; whilst a couple of dogs, with himself and gun, may very conveniently form the foreground. The German red-grouse is distinguished from its burly cousin, the moor-cock, by the blackish-blue feathers on its wings, back, and throat. Its tail is of an exceedingly curious form, resembling that of the lyre bird. The taste of its flesh, by feeding on the juniper-berries, with which some parts of Germany abound, makes it dainty eating for epicures. When started they fly slowly, but increase in speed as they proceed; and woe to the unlucky sportsman who gives them time to get well on the wing. He may just see them in the distance, leaving him as quickly as friends leave a man who has his elbows out, and nothing left but a stout heart to support him in his misfortunes.

Albino Woodcock

We have made a number of inquiries and find that several of our experts have never come across an albino woodcock. Neither can any mention about such a form be found in any of the extensive range of bird books to which they have referred. It is certainly a very unusual and most interesting mutation for this bird, and well worth recording. We consider that a true albino woodcock is probably quite a rarity, and not just in Pembrokeshire.

No Scent from a Sitting Woodcock

Man and all animals and birds give off body-odour or scent. It is an excretion of skin glands. Its quality and quantity vary with the activity and state of health of the bodily organs or metabolism. For instance, it is diminished during inactivity or reduced metabolic output, as in birds during the later stages of sitting on eggs or during certain debilitating diseases. The detection of scent by a predator depends upon the amount of scent produced and the acuity of the predator's sense of smell. These conditions are obviously subject to many variables such as direction of the wind, humidity and temperature of the air, the health and purpose of the predator. The probable explanation for the fox passing the sitting woodcock in broad daylight is that, at the particular moment, conditions for carrying scent were unfavourable or the fox had other matters to attend to; not that the woodcock had entirely lost her scent as was suggested to you.

Partridge Chicks in Drinking Trough

You ask for an explanation why partridge chicks should have been found in an empty concrete drinking trough into which they themselves could not have climbed (the hen was flushed at the time of finding them). No doubt the hen had taken the chicks up to the water trough for a drink. In normal weather partridges drink all the moisture they need from early-morning dews and the natural sap of greenstuff, of which they eat much. The recent weather, however, has been so dry that early-morning dews have been non-existent and the herbage very dry. When rearing by hand, partridge chicks must have water – very shallow and always clean. Partridges kept on game farms, running loose in open pens or folds, drink as much as pheasants, but it is surprising how rare it is to see a partridge drinking in the wild.

[*Editor's note: But this answer still does not explain how the chicks*

Partridge shooting

managed to get up into the trough, which is no doubt what was puzzling the correspondent.]

Partridge Clutch in the Garden

You need have no worry about the partridges damaging your garden. They will leave the area almost as soon as they are born; even if they stayed in the garden and grounds for a day or so, you would not find any damage to crops. The eggs will hatch approximately 23 days from the commencement of incubation. Eighteen eggs is a very nice clutch. It will be most interesting and a very kind gesture on your part if you do what you can to protect this much harassed sporting bird during her patient sojourn in your Yorkshire garden. Protect the nest while the parent is sitting, with large mesh 4-in wire netting, a surround of sheep hurdles or spiky boughs. If you leave her sitting in the open the dog or some other animal will almost certainly find her and the nest will be destroyed. The parent birds will move off on the day following the hatch, and seek the safety and seclusion of the arable fields, where, thanks to your assistance, let us hope they grow into a fine covey.

Melanistic Partridges

Colour mutation does not frequently occur in partridges, except perhaps the rufous variety known as Montana. Albino and melanistic (which your almost entirely grey birds were) are quite rare. These colour varieties are usually perfectly healthy birds, and produce offspring of the normal colour.

Nothing Scares . . . (1855)

What a fool a man having a shooting-ground will be who takes out men to shoot with him, particularly on small preserves, who make a practice of firing at game at 70 and 80 yards, either wounding it or frightening it off the beat. Nothing scares a covey of birds so much as shooting into them; and nothing is worse than the habit of wounding game.

Broodies for Pheasant Eggs

Select good quiet broody hens, preferably 2-year-olds; avoid Leghorn breeds. Rhode Island reds are best. Put broodies first on china dummy eggs; keep them on these for 4 or 5 days. Make nests for broodies in draughtproof boxes on damp sand or soil, or scoop saucer-shaped hollows in the ground and line with soft hay. Give the eggs plenty of room, they must not pile up, so the nest must be big enough to keep eggs spread singly all over. Put 18 pheasants' eggs to each broody; take broodies off for feeding and watering once every day at mid-morning. Leave off for only 15 minutes the first week, cover pheasants' eggs while broody is off. Increase to half-an-hour after 10 days. Feed the broody on hard corn and wheat. Damp down the nest and eggs if the weather is very hot and dry; do this once or twice during the last 10 days. Eggs take 24 days to hatch. Leave the hen alone after eggs show chip marks on 23rd day; wait until all chicks are dry and running about before removal.

Coccidiosis (1923)

The young pheasant was suffering from a form of enteritis known as coccidiosis caused by the presence in the intestines of a micro-organism known as *Coccidium avium*, or *Eimeria avium*. The caeca of the birds contained large numbers of the spores of this organism. The disease is very infectious, and fatal to young game and poultry. The best treatment is to give all the birds a solution of catechu, 15 grains to the gallon, to drink instead of their ordinary drinking water. After a few days' treatment the healthy birds may be moved to fresh ground. It is most essential that all the birds that die should be *burnt*, and not buried.

Cocks to Hens

It is not absolutely necessary to do as you suggest (i.e. turn in 2 cocks with your dozen hen pheasants in early June); most of the eggs laid by the birds after release will have been fertilised by previous matings. It is a very good plan, however, to put down some cock birds with these hens as they will take the hens off in various directions, which is better than having a number of hens together probably laying in each other's nests. You could perhaps have 3 cock birds put down with your dozen hens, and if you could arrange to release 4 hens and 1 cock on 3 successive days you will have done all possible to ensure success.

Egg Colours

Pheasants' eggs vary considerably in colour, especially when the birds are penned to produce eggs for setting. Blue-shelled eggs are probably the commonest variation from the normal greeny-brown. Soil has a big influence on the colour; clays produce pale shells, gravel and sand, brown or even chocolate-coloured shells.

Footless Pheasant

Your discovery of a hen pheasant with the loss of both feet, apparently for some time, is very uncommon. Either it is an acquired mutilation due to accident or disease, or a congenital deformity. Cases of the loss of a single foot are encountered rarely, but the birds rapidly adapt themselves to perching on one foot. In the present case, the bird could roost only on a flat surface, and although deprived of claws would be able to scratch about to some extent with the hard, horn-like 'stumps'. It illustrates the ability of birds to survive serious injuries provided these do not impair their ability to fly.

The Harem

No, it is not true that cock and hen pheasants pair for life and never mate again if separated. Pheasants do not pair up like partridges. The cock bird may have up to 10 hens during the breeding season and after they have laid and hatched his interest in them is then nil. He will probably find quite a different harem the following year.

Luring Pheasants

A person who rears no pheasants himself, and puts down food to allure those reared by his neighbour, is guilty of a very unsportsmanlike and dishonest act. Unfortunately, as the law stands, there is no redress so long as the wrong doer abstains from 'trespassing in pursuit', there being no property in game until reduced into possession by the occupier of the land on which it is shot by him or his friends. The only plan is to have the bounds beaten so as to keep the birds from straying as much as possible, and to see that there are no thick hedgerows on the boundary which would be likely to harbour them.

Mouse Catcher (1930)

[I was shooting with a party on a small farm a week back, when we walked through an old pit. A pheasant had been winged, and while it was being gathered, a cock started to crow. I went to the 3 guns and found that the cock was in the middle of them – within 3 ft – and while we were talking of the curious incident he crowed again. I put my dog in the nettles where he was and he got up quite all right and was dropped in some water. When he was opened a week later, a full grown field mouse was found in his craw.]

Pheasants often crow in response to noises inaudible to human beings, such as distant gunfire or thunder. They occasionally swallow field mice, and even adders.

Nest in a Fir Tree

Pheasants' nests on ricks, tops of walls and in old nests or squirrels' dreys are exceptional, as is your discovery of a nest with 3 eggs and 3 chicks about 25 ft up a fir tree, but they have been found up to 30 ft from the ground.

Pheasant Plantation

For quick-growing, permanent, natural cover for pheasants, try something both profitable and attractive to the birds. Larch would be most suitable. Leave wide drifts through the larch at intervals and plant them, and odd corners and difficult headlands, with Dunn's Game Mixture. It stands up well through the winter and attracts game. Maize makes an excellent temporary cover for game. Artichoke will make a dense patch of cover in the right soil, but maize of Game Strip is preferable. Establishing permanent natural cover is a long, uncertain business; it would be safer to concentrate on temporary crops, anything which will stand up through the winter and, most important, feed the birds.

Sex Change

It would appear that your 2-year-old hen pheasant, who has donned cock's plumage, has changed her sex – an occurence which is by no means uncommon amongst poultry. It is extremely unlikely that she will lay any eggs although she is now in a movable pen with a cock. If she should do so, the possibility of their being fertile will, of course, depend upon her domestic relations with the normal cock bird which also occupies the pen. If the birds are mating and eggs are produced, then there is no reason why they should not be fertile.

Turps for Pheasants (1923)

The pheasants were suffering from a complaint known as Cutaneous Psorospermosis, an infectious disease affecting the head and neck of birds, and which causes great emaciation; the treatment is to bathe the heads of the birds with soft soap and warm water and paint them with turpentine. The coops should be disinfected with Lysol.

Yew and Pheasants (1923)

The seeds found in the crop of the pheasants were those of the yew. These seeds contain taxin, the poisonous property of the yew, and are often the cause of death in pheasants.

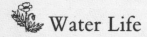 Water Life

FISH
Overland Eels and Lampreys

Lampreys, like eels, can live for 2 days out of water – longer if the ground is moist. If the ground is really wet, they will make some attempt to reach a stream or puddle, but neither eels nor lampreys can move along on dry ground. It is possible that the lamprey you found stranded some distance from the river had been left by a bird or an animal, perhaps a gull or heron, otter or fox. Various predatory creatures prey on lampreys when they are spawning in shallow waters and it would be difficult to pinpoint the culprit. One thing is certain – the lamprey did not climb out of the river over the high bank and it was not migrating over dry land, as is so often wrongly assumed. Both eels and lampreys have a slime on their skins which aids them in their movements. Should this slime become dry, they quickly die.

Fish and Engine Smoke (1900)

We are inclined to attribute the death of the fish to the action of the intense heat of such shallow water, and not to the smoke from the railway engines. Trout require shade to be maintained in health.

Fish and Thunder (1923)

[About 7 months ago I put some yearling rainbow trout into a small stream in my garden. Until the storms a few weeks ago the fish appeared to have done very well and were constantly seen feeding just below the surface. After the first storm, which was very violent, I did not see the fish. Other storms followed, and I then found 3 fish dead, subsequently more, and I have not seen a living fish since then. The water is about 2–3 ft deep and 8–10 ft wide, and, as far as I know, pollution is out of the question. Can the thunder have been responsible for the mortality?]

The death of fish after severe thunderstorms has often been recorded and it was for a long time a complete mystery. Just before the War, however, a little light was thrown on the matter by correspondents of *THE FIELD* and an article in our issue of 18 July 1914, gave their experiences and conclusions. Briefly, in one case fish were killed in a big ballast hole after a severe thunderstorm and cold heavy rain. Analysis showed a slight excess of albuminous ammonia in the water and a lack of oxygen due to 'the effect from some cause or other of a very powerful deoxydising agent'. In the other case there was also evidence of high oxygen absorption and a marked increase in ammonia. The only conclusion was that the thunderstorm was responsible for both conditions, but it remained doubtful how the effect was produced and whether electrical disturbances in the air would do it or whether actual contact of lightning with the water was indicated. In 1920 similar cases were described and suggested the probability of direct lightning shock being the chief destructive agent: in the opinion of a scientific authority, 'fish would certainly be affected by the shock in the neighbourhood of a flash of lightning, and if the discharge took place directly on to the surface of the water the concussion might well prove fatal to the fish in the immediate neighbourhood'. Another possibility lay in 'the effect of sudden alterations in barometric pressure, such as are common in violent storms, upon the state in which air exists in solution in the water'.

Finnock Trout

Finnock is a well-known name for young sea-trout which have descended to salt water as smolts in the spring and return to the rivers in the summer or autumn after 2–5 months of feeding and growth. This name is used chiefly on the east coast of Scotland, and in other parts of the country these fish are known as herling, whitling or Lammas trout. These names are used for the fish until the spring of the following year. Finnock have been called the grilse of the sea-trout, but this is not strictly correct for they have not spent a year in salt water, and their return is not always, or even usually, for spawning.

Omnivorous Goldfish

Goldfish are not vegetarian: they are omnivorous and are very partial to live food. They will readily eat the larvae and pupae of gnats and mosquitoes, water-fleas, blood-worms, white-worms, caterpillars and wood-lice. A garden pond rarely contains enough natural food to satisfy the goldfish, and additional feeding is necessary. The warmer the weather, the more food the fish need: feed them once a day in summer, but in cold weather they hibernate and do not eat. A satisfactory diet would include garden worms chopped up, scraped raw meat, chopped fish, crab, lobster, scallop, shrimp, and the like. Scrambled egg and oatmeal (dry, or as porridge) are also welcome. Avoid an excess of starchy and fatty foods. If you come across any wood-lice in your garden, throw them into the pond. They are an excellent food for fish due to their calcium content.

Black-spotted Goldfish

The pigments, and also the guanine of which the iridocytes are composed, are by-products of the digestive processes, which are secreted in the skin. This does not mean that the coloration of an individual fish can be altered materially by a change of diet, but that, if it differs from its relative, the differences are associated with some deeper physiological change. At the same time, certain black pigments can be utilised as food by re-absorption, and the black cells (melanophores) serve as storage for these materials when food is plentiful, and secretion is therefore high. This accounts for the black patches which are sometimes seen to come and go in goldfish, much to the surprise of inexperienced pond-keepers. There is, however, a disease (melanosis) which manifests itself as dark-grey fuzzy patches on the body, which later turn black, peel and leave raw spots.

Dead Goldfish in a Carp Pond

Regarding the half-eaten goldfish in your pond, normally goldfish and carp will associate together more or less peacefully as they are closely related and of the same family. All fish, however, are cannibalistic by nature and tend to be aggressive bullies, particularly if not well matched in size. If your carp were larger than the goldfish, it is possible that they caused the injuries. The other possibilities – fish-eating birds, such as the heron – would be unlikely to cause the injuries described or to leave fish in the pond, and this is true of fish-eating animals such as the otter or cat.

Goldfish Sizes

There are no records of the weight of goldfish; and the size of a fish, and in consequence its weight, depends largely on the way in which it is kept. We have heard of a goldfish that lived in a 6-gallon aquarium for 25 years and was only 4 in long at its death. In good conditions, however, a goldfish should reach a length of 12 or more inches. Goldfish have been naturalised in many lakes and rivers in Portugal and South Africa, and specimens taken from them have been more than 15 in in length. Because goldfish carry on growing throughout their lives – although the older they are the less they grow – you may expect your 2 lb 10 oz fish in South Africa to reach a length of from 10–12 in, provided it is well fed. The length of a fish is measured from the tip of the snout to the base of the caudal peduncle, and excludes the caudal fin.

Goldfish in Winter

As long as there is green weed in the pond and the bottom is not very foul, there is very little danger of suffocation for fish while the pond is frozen. Under the action of light, the green weed fixes the carbon dioxide and releases oxygen and so keeps the supply renewed. If snow falls after the ice has formed, keep the pond swept.

Wermland Pike (1865)

'An Old Bushman's' pike makes my mouth water – a 40-pounder (for we can throw him in the extra pound) – I never saw such a pike alive, though I have seen some severe ones, and my largest capture would not scale above half that weight. Well might he have felt astonished and puzzled how to deal with him. It is possible that the monks might have put him in. I wonder whether they ever kept a monster of that kind as an appendage to their sanctums, and as a terror to refractory novices, who might be tempted to take the water? – as Port Royal Jack (that celebrated monstrous shark who kept guard over the ships off Port Royal) was said to be kept as a deterrent to deserters, who might otherwise be tempted to swim ashore. I wonder the ducks of Wermland did not present our friend with a testimonial, for surely many a callow brood must have fallen victims to his rapacious maw. [Francis Francis]

Hungry Salmon (1953)

There is a great deal of evidence of salmon feeding on worms and flies while in fresh water, and it is now generally accepted that they often take food in this way. They do not, however, feed to anything like the same extent as they do in the sea, and during their sojourn in fresh water they subsist mainly on their accumulated store of fat.

Salmon in Fresh Water (1953)

May I put forward a theory to the endless question as to whether a salmon does or does not feed in fresh water? Could it not be that the change from salt to fresh water so disastrously affects the digestive organs of the fish that it cannot 'keep anything down' as it were and is immediately sick? This would account for the following: (a) That a salmon will take a fly or a bait (particularly a worm or a prawn) with the intention of eating it. (b) That if cut open there is nothing to be found in its stomach. (c) The pathetic condition of a kelt. (d) The 'well mended' kelt which one sometimes finds in tidal pools where the re-introduction of salt is beginning to have its effect. [G. I. Thwaites (Major), London S.W.1]

Trout and Birds

Moorhens do not eat fish ova, and will only attack small fry when other food is not available. Herons will attack adult trout, kingfishers are a danger to small yearlings and fry, and there may be trouble with gulls.

Feeding Brown Trout

Natural food is better than artificial mixtures for fish, but if your lake is small you will probably need to supplement with meat and sea-fish mixtures. Beef liver and heart, not too finely ground, are considered about the most successful food. Fish feed most from May to October; in winter they eat less, and in June and July the maximum natural food is available in most waters, so the spring and autumn months are the most important for artificial feeding.

Garden Trout

The very fact that goldfish and carp have multiplied in your large garden ponds, each connected by a waterfall, rules out any possibility of the ponds being suitable for trout, as it would seem certain that the water temperature reaches too high a point for safety. If anxious to have variety, roach and dace could live in harmony with the carp and goldfish.

Muddy Trout

You ask why pink-flesh trout from a lake should taste good in April but muddy in July. The trout may have changed their food between those months and the muddy flavour may have been caused by the fish feeding mainly on leeches. The flesh of fish is governed by the kind and condition of their food. It is, of course, impossible to say what is necessary, but we imagine the bed of the lake to be of soft mud with a meagre water supply to keep it fresh. If the lake is to be enlarged by excavation or the flooding of other land, both the condition and the taste of the trout will be much improved. It would appear that the present acre is unsuited for trout and badly in need of cleaning. Small lakes will produce wholesome food for trout only if periodic cleaning is done. Probably this water holds many molluscs which give the fish their pink flesh, but if these molluscs are feeding on a muddy bed continuously, though the trout may keep in fair condition they will taste muddy.

Restocking Trout

Stocking a small trout stream in autumn is quite often successful but the main dangers are twofold. (1) If the fish have been artificially fed they may find the larder too bare and drop downstream. (2) If they are pond-bred fish they may find the current too strong. The best precautions to take are: (1) See that you get fairly slow-growing fish which will thrive on a small food supply. (2) Get stream-bred fish if you can; if not, make 'hides' of large stones or low weirs standing a few inches proud of the bottom to make lay-bys for the fish in case of strong water.

Spawn-bound Trout

Trout can become spawn-bound, but they rarely die whilst still in good condition. With fish unable to express the ova, the cause can usually be found if the fish is opened. All eggs nearest to the vent will be white and in a state of coalescence. Some fungus would show round an enlarged vent. Fish dying from this trouble are usually rather thin along the back.

Twigs in a Trout

Occasionally such occurrences are reported, but the finding of small twigs in trout is not very common. It is probable that the fish take them in mistake for something else, and apparently this does not happen only in waters where the fish are largely bottom feeders, as fish have been taken from the river Test with twigs present. Occasionally filamentous algae finds its way into fish even when they are non-vegetable feeders. It is usually in times of flood, say following rain, when the waters are cloudy, that fish seem to mistake twigs for other things.

OTHER POND CREATURES
Frogspawn?

We are having some difficulty in identifying the objects found near a pond from your description. It most closely accords with frogspawn, which is a conglomerate mass of individual cells or spheres, 2–3 mm in diameter, swelling to 10 mm in water and floating to the surface. But frog's eggs are black in the centre. Your phrase 'with black caviar attached' suggests that the eggs may have hatched and there were tadpoles present in the early stages of development. The clumps may have been landed by 'fishing' animals such as a cat. They do not seem to be toadspawn, as toads lay their eggs in strings or chains. There are some algae of a gelatinous nature but usually coloured, and the deposits are hardly likely to be of fungi. An outside chance is that they might be fish roe but very unlikely.

Catching Leeches

Immerse pieces of fresh meat, preferably with as much skin on as possible, such as a bird's drumstick or a rabbit's leg, into the pond where the unwanted leeches are. Have the meat on a cord which can be withdrawn, and weight the meat to make it stay where required. The idea is to attract the leeches; when they adhere to the meat, pull it out and scrape the leeches off. You may be able to catch a few by thrusting stiff plant stalks into the pond such as sweet-corn stalks, cabbage stems, etc., but leeches are usually blood-suckers and meat is the best bait.

Lugworms and Razor Fish

Locating lugworms and razor fish calls for some experience. The lugworm burrows in a U-shaped channel under sand. The top of the two openings of the U-shaped burrow are about the size of a halfpenny; but the entry hole to one is slightly smaller than that of the other. Worm casts at low tide give evidence of their presence. Razor fish are not nearly so common. They live in the sand in a vertical position and burrow down if uneasy or scared by extending a thin feeler into which they can pump their blood and drag the rest of the body down against the anchorage of the expanded end. They show their presence by squirting up water if they hear footsteps in the vicinity.

Captive Newts

Newts naturally prefer land, resorting to water during the breeding season, and leaving it in July–August, usually to hibernate for the winter. On land, they are largely nocturnal, but lie up in damp, cool places, in moss, crannies or moist ground. They do not need an airtight container, but should have something that reproduces conditions such as exist on the sides of ponds. A carboy may be suitable with an artificial 'shore'. Keep it in winter in a cool, shady, moist place out of doors. Newts will seek water in spring.

Shrimps and Watercress

The only safe method of reducing the freshwater shrimp population in your watercress beds, without injuring the cress or spoiling it for consumption, is to introduce a natural control of the shrimps, and the best is fish. Your only other alternative is to drain the beds, as convenient, allowing to dry out before restocking and filling again.

Snail Nuisance

The great difficulty in destroying water snails (*Limnaea* sp.) by chemical means is that the introduction of a chemical strong enough to kill the snails generally has bad effects upon plant life and other animal life in the pond. Copper sulphate is effective, but not more than 20 g per 1,000 gallons of water should be used. The copper sulphate should be placed in a small muslin bag, and drawn through the water on the end of a stick so as to get even distribution. Baiting overnight with cabbage stumps, leaves, or gone-to-seed lettuces is effective, and should give good control if persisted in for several nights.

Subtropical Snails

Marisa cornuarietis is a snail of subtropical origin, and is apparently being investigated in the control of such rampaging weed as the Water Hyacinth and others that grow with abundance in waterways of warmer countries. As far as can be ascertained, it has not been tested for the control of outdoor weeds in waters in this country. Indeed, in view of its omnivorous appetite, it might do more harm than good except in waters that need to be kept entirely plant-free.

Carnivorous Tortoise

It would be unwise to introduce European pond tortoises (*Emys orbicularis*) into a pond containing fish as they are wholly carnivorous, eating aquatic insects, tadpoles, frogs and fish.

Water Tortoise in Winter

Frosts will almost certainly kill your water tortoise if left out of doors in winter and allowed in a pond. Even in summer it should not remain permanently in water. Give it the means to get out. In winter, bring it indoors when it goes off its food and the weather is colder. Put it in a large box filled with moist leaves and a good sprinkling of soil, or a mixture of damp moss and straw. It will bury itself for hibernation. Store the box in a cool, frost-proof place and leave it there at least until the weather is warm and there is sunshine. Alternatively, leave in a greenhouse (above 60°F) with a water tank, supplied with easy exit and entrance.

POND MANAGEMENT

Copper Water-lily Tub in a Goldfish Pond

It is unlikely that the amount of copper that would dissolve in the pond water would be harmful to the fish. If anything, it should help to keep the water clear of algal growth. The inside of the copper, however, may, in time, build up a toxic amount of copper salts, and a sensible precaution would be to paint it with a bitumen paint before planting with the water-lilies. Let the paint dry well before adding soil, etc. The bottom of the copper should be pierced so that water and a little air can percolate through or exchange with the water of the pond. The containing ring of copper should not be too deep; it should enclose only the water-lily roots – the crown of the plant should be more or less level with the rim of the container. It would be useful to make a few holes in the sides.

Lime for a Loch

Continuous dressings with lime powder, either limestone or chalk, will do much towards increasing the food supply for trout in a small loch diagnosed as hyper-acid. It would be wise, before going to the expense of stocking with trout, to make attempts to increase the general food potential, then to wait a year before introducing stock. Try applications of lime in the feeder streams which enter the loch. The object in liming is to get a good deposit over the entire bed of the loch where it can be used by both animal and vegetable. Applications at the rate of 10 cwt per acre twice a year, in spring and late summer, should be enough to begin an improvement. If this procedure is carried out for 3–4 years it should help considerably. Introduction of lime while trout are in the loch will do them no harm. If access to the feeder streams is difficult, your idea of scattering chalk powder on the loch by helicopter is an excellent one.

Pisciculture (1898)

We are not able to give you any advice regarding 'pisciculture as a livelihood', nor can we say whether a fair profit can be made on a fish-culture farm. The fact that there are so many establishments of the kind in existence, and that they are increasing, would lead one to suppose that it is a promising business; but the fish culturists themselves would be able best to tell you about the amount of capital required, and the income which might be expected.

Pond Stocking (1860)

The best time to stock a fish-pond is early in the spring, say March, as the fish have not then spawned; and if transferred then you get the year's spawning without the year's risk of losses. The best fish are carp, tench, perch, and bream. Do not put in roach or eels, nor allow the pond to become overstocked.

Railway Sleepers Around Ponds

Railway sleepers are impregnated with creosote, which, when fresh, is harmful to plants and fish. Much would depend on how weathered the old sleepers are. (The same would apply to telegraph poles.) There is danger of some seepage of creosote oil and this would contaminate, if not greatly injure, the growth of watercress. It would also coat the water, impair oxygenation and possibly interfere with insects in the water. A sleeper could be placed on a flat surface (such as concrete) and hosed down until a shallow puddle formed. If any tract of glistening oil was seen on the water, there should be some doubt about using the sleepers where they are likely to contaminate the water. Sealing the wood with a coat of bitumen paint would not only enable the sleepers to be used, but also give them longer life.

Red Pond Water

The russet red colouring of the water in your ornamental garden goldfish pond is caused by organic dyes (Xanthophyll, etc.) released in the decomposition of some plant remains washed into the pond or from plants growing in the water. The foliage of the ice plant is rich in the colouring matter noted and could have something to do with the pond water becoming red.

Duckweed and Blanketweed

In a small pond, blanketweed can be kept at bay by creating some movement in the water – perhaps making a waterfall or fountain – to improve the lack of oxygen. In a farm pond, it is true that an excessive amount of nitrogen fertiliser residues filtering through the soil and carried in drainage waters to the pond have been noted to result in the eruption of coarse weed and algae, especially at or near the surface. The idea of placing straw bales in the feed stream may filter out some of the soluble fertiliser, but as they themselves decompose they would contribute organic matter to the pond and unbalance the water chemistry for fish. The Chinese grass carp (*Ctenopharyngodon idella*) has acclimatised and bred in Europe and has a good reputation as a feeder on soft water weeds such as Hydrilla and Chara algae, and if these are your weeds then stocking with a few grass carp would help, nor would they harm the trout. Duckweed can be difficult to eliminate but, on the positive side, it excludes light and gives very clear water underneath for fish to enjoy. Ducks and geese are helpful in keeping down weed: the mallard is a great weed eater. It is not likely to have much effect on the water-lilies, however, though their growth might be discouraged if a number of the flowers and leaves are destroyed by the ducks. It is suggested that a few pairs of pinioned birds are brought to act as the parent stock and the ducklings from them could be wing-clipped.

The Country Estate

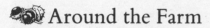 Around the Farm

Agricultural Institutions (1892)

There are 4 such agricultural institutions – the Royal Cirencester College and the Downton College, Salisbury; less expensive are the College, Aspatria, Carlisle, and the Colonial College, Hollesley Bay, Suffolk.

Black Malm

The word malm comes from the Old English 'mealm', meaning manure. In the sense used by Gilbert White and others, it is applied to soft friable rock, primarily consisting of chalky material to a great extent. It also came to be applied to the whitish loamy soil formed by the disintegration of this friable rock. Thus light or whitish malms are more common than dark ones. It seems certain that what White had in mind was that the 'warm, crumbling mould, called black malm' had the disintegrated rock of the upper greensand formation for the mineral fraction, plus, of course, the blackening influence of heavy additions of humus-forming organic matter over many years.

Casual Employment (1937)

A man whose employment is of a casual nature, and who is employed otherwise than for the purpose of the employer's trade or business (and not for the purpose of any game or recreation and engaged or paid through a club) is not a 'workman' and has no protection under the Workmen's Compensation Acts. Employment of a casual nature is incapable of exact definition. Each case depends on its own facts. Employment of a charwoman Friday of every week is *regular*, but employment of a man to clean windows at irregular intervals, say, about once a month without fixing the days, and so on, is casual.

Cost of Horse Labour (1937)

Investigations made by economists show that the cost of horse labour varies generally between 5½d. and 7½d. per hour, the lower figure where the horses are regularly employed through the year, and the higher where there is considerable idle time. An average of 6d. per hour may be taken as fairly representative. This figure includes part of the horseman's wages.

Distilling Daffodils (1854)

The French Decree on distillation from corn will cause a great quantity of corn and farinaceous substances, hitherto used for distillation, to be again given to consumption. That result, joined to the abundance of provisions, will contribute much, it is to be hoped, to speedily reduce prices in the market to their normal state. It is to be hoped that the expectation will be realised. A decree which, however temporary, must be ruinous to a considerable number of persons who have embarked their capital in distilleries, and throws out of employ a very large number of workmen, can only have been resolved upon from a strong conviction that it is for the necessary welfare of the masses. The Minister of Agriculture, in the report on which this decree is founded, states, as one of the motives of it, that alcohol is now made or can be made from substances which do not form part of the food of the people. The Minister does not mention any of these substances, but probably one of them is the asphodel or daffodil, which the *Moniteur* has stated to be distilled for alcohol in Algeria, and which, according to the account in that journal, gives a spirit of very fine quality. This may be a remunerative process in Algeria, where the plant grows in abundance in a wild state, or where there are large tracts of land on which it would be cheaply cultivated; but it does not follow that there would be the same result in Europe, where this plant would occupy land which is not cultivated for food or other remunerative products. We do not imagine that the Minister can allude to the distillation of wood for spirit, for it is a new industry and as yet there are no results which warrant a conclusion that a pure and cheap spirit can be obtained from this process.

Drainage Mills

When draining of the Fens began in the 16th century, wind power was used to help in the land reclamation. This is how the drainage mills first evolved. They were used as water pumps. Drainage mills had a Dutch look about them with their dumpy towers, common sails and tail poles. Marshmen lived in them with their families and they were often so remote that the only way of getting to them was by water. Some fine examples still remain – notably the preserved 'High Mill', Berney Arms, Norfolk, which is one of the few drainage mills that also performed a milling operation.

The Duke of Marlborough's Ploughing Matches (1854)

It has long been a well-known fact in agricultural circles that his Grace the Duke of Marlborough is one of the most able promoters of the useful science of agriculture in all its branches. In furtherance of his object, his Grace has announced a variety of ploughing matches to take place on 22 September next in a large piece of land (oat-stubble) situated at Campsfield, a short distance from Blenheim-palace. The best ploughman with a pair of horses will receive from his Grace a prize of £1.10s.0d., and the owner of the team that performs the best work, a silver cup, value £5.0s.0d. The noble Duke has set an example which we hope to see more generally followed, not only in the liberal manner shown in the announcement of the prizes, but in the treatment of the labourer, who is ever ready to work on his estate, where he can obtain constant employment and better wages than are given in the neighbourhood of Oxford. His Grace has of late years bestowed considerable attention upon the culture of flax, of which he grows a very large quantity, and occasions employment for a great number of hands.

Farmers and Middlemen (1887)

The theory of supersession of the middlemen by the agricultural producer is by no means a novel theme in the political economy of farming. The middleman grows visibly fat from year to year, while the producer finds it harder each season to make ends meet. If he could only obtain for his produce one-third more than the existing difference between the prices at which the middleman buys from him, as compared with those at which the latter sells to the public, the farmer would find his circumstances comparatively easy, even in these days of depression. One of the latest schemes is that agriculturists should combine among themselves to form a 'Farmers' Union or Agricultural Alliance'. This theory is propounded by Mr W. Vernon, dating from the Travellers' Club. The policy of the proposed 'Alliance' would be that of combination to resist monopoly and unfair prices as against farmers, and to dictate to the middlemen the basis of terms of bargain and sale between the parties. The middlemen would be treated as agents for the sale of agricultural produce rather than as unfettered principals. Those who might decline to recognise the autocracy of the Alliance would be boycotted.

Farming Abroad (1887)

(1) Lake, Yolo, and Napa are all suited for fruit growing and general farming; but you had better call on the British Consul on your arrival at San Francisco, who would doubtless put you in communication with the Immigration Society, whose advice you would do well to follow. (2) Plenty of strong working clothes and boots. (3) Cheap in the country, expensive in the towns.

Farming in Virginia (1887)

(1) In some parts of the State, farming is carried on profitably. The price of improved land, with farm buildings, varies in different districts from £3 to £20 per acre. (2) The lands that are unoccupied are either worn out or worthless. (3) Owing to the differences in elevation and situation, the climate of Virginia varies greatly in several sections. In the mountain country the summers are cool and pleasant; but the winters are severe, and you would have to feed stock at that season. In the east and south-east the climate is much warmer. The Tidewater country is unhealthy.

Fencing a Ditch

The best way of preventing lambs and young animals from getting under a wire fence spanning a ditch would probably be to install a barrier of 2–3 in mesh netting. This could be of metal wire (such as square-meshed welded formation Weld-mesh); or a heavy gauge of wire netting; or you could use a plastic mesh panelling; or a metal mesh and chainlink fencing. You would probably find it best to fix on metal tubular posts, driven into the banks and base of the ditch. The netting should extend up the banks as well as in the water. The alternative would be to 'hedge' the sides of the ditch to keep the animals away from it.

Fencing Staples (1930)

Mr Robert Wigram asks in your issue of 29 November for the name of a firm who used to make a staple from which the wire of a fence can be removed without drawing the staple. Instead of buying a special staple at, possibly, a high price, I would recommend your correspondent to fix the wire to the post by means of two ordinary fencing staples driven horizontally, the one immediately above the other and far enough apart to allow the wire to pass between them. To keep the wire in position, drop an ordinary galvanised slate nail (which has a large flat head) through both staples, on the side of the wire farthest away from the post. The nail will hang by its head on the top staple and so keep the wire in position. To remove the wire, simply draw out the nails with the fingers. [J. Stormonth Darling, Kelso]

Grains Per Ear (1958)

The maximum number of grains per ear in a barley crop is controlled genetically, and not by manuring, cultivations or any farming operation. But good farming is necessary; the barley will not produce the maximum number of grains if it is starved. If the farmer wants barley with a longer ear, therefore, he has to select one from the varieties available. This by no means ensures that such a barley will give him a heavier yield for a variety chosen for this reason alone may not be suited to his soil or climate. The weight of grains in the ear also varies. An outstanding cereal example is Atle wheat, which has a short ear and which, when growing, looks far less impressive than many other varieties. Yet, on certain soils, it outstrips its competitors in yield because of the heaviness of the individual grains.

Hay Stack Combustion (1923)

The 'critical point' in the temperature of a hay stack, according to McConnell, is 194°F. When that temperature is reached the stack should be cut open; 230°F is the 'explosive point'. No danger or harm is considered probable up to 140°F, but from that level the stack should be carefully watched for signs of over-heating and even firing.

Hedge and Ditch Ownership

Imagine someone wishing to have a hedge and ditch between him and his neighbour. He will dig the ditch as near his boundary line as he can. He cannot throw the spoil on his neighbour's land as that would be a trespass. So he puts it on his own side and on the spoil he plants a hedge. This is how things usually happen, and the presumption is that they did happen in this way. There may, however, be evidence in the deeds or documents of title that this was not so. If the evidence is strong enough it will displace the presumption.

Hedges and High Farming (1855)

Seeing in the articles which appear weekly in your excellent paper, that you are an advocate for what is called scientific or high farming – as a sportsman neither possessing nor knowing anything either about the practical or theoretical part of farming – I am induced to ask you the following questions; and I must request you to have the courtesy to inform me whether, in your opinion, I am right or wrong in my conclusions. I am told that where scientific farming is pushed to its fullest extreme, as, for example, at Mr Mechi's farm, there is not a tree or hedge to be seen; and that on such farms as this the boundaries which separate the fields are formed either of iron railings or water dykes. First, does not this entire want of cover, as well as spoiling and defacing what was probably before a beautiful and luxuriant landscape, deteriorate from, and vastly interfere with, the health-giving and manly sports of the field, by tending to the entire destruction of the game, especially of hares and rabbits? Secondly, is it not the desire and avowed intention of some farmers, who advocate this extreme system, to destroy every hare and rabbit on the place, instead of being content with thinning them down to a consistent number? Thirdly, do you not think that it would be better for the farmers of the present day, while adopting all the necessary improvements, to remember and act up to the maxim: 'There is a medium in all things'; and can they not, for the sake of preserving the beauty of our landscapes, be persuaded to be content with cropping their hedges tolerably low, and thinning the trees where absolutely necessary, instead of entirely destroying them? Many, if not most of our farmers, I rejoice to say, are ardent lovers of the beauties of the country and the sports of the field. God forbid that they should ever be otherwise. [Reader's letter]

Hop Growing in Kenya

Yes, hop growing in Kenya is possible, provided soil conditions and water supply are satisfactory. The hop (*Humulus lupulus*) is native to Asia as well as to temperate Europe and southern counties of Britain. Propagation is by seed, or by division or by cuttings, the last two where special strains or varieties are concerned. You need 1 male plant to 200 female plants as flowers are unisexual. Brewers maintaining their own hop fields may let you have special strains. Cultivation is specialised, and requires a good deal of initial capital expenditure.

Horse-sick Grass

Take the ponies out of the horse-sick paddock in mid-March, harrow and roll the field. Apply a top dressing of lime in March and in early April another dressing which your local agricultural adviser recommends for grass reproduction. Graze it heavily with strong cattle in May and June and in July run over the field with a mowing machine set high. Let the cattle eat up the toppings and then take them out of the field at the end of July. Let the field remain unoccupied during August. In September the ponies can come back again. If you cannot obtain strong cattle, cut early for silage or hay, and put young cattle on in August and September.

The Milk Question (1887)

The milk question, it can scarcely be denied, has recently been brought to the fore in a most remarkable manner, and has commanded attention which, years ago, would scarcely have been credited. This question, however, has arisen more particularly with reference to its manufacture and sale, between the farmer and the retailer. The public in general have, so far as it is possible to see, not manifested any particular inclination to recognise one milk as being better than another. It is, however, for the producer and salesman not only to point out that milk is a food of the greatest value, and one which is excessively cheap at the price at which it is ordinarily sold, but to show them how to detect and appreciate a superior, as contrasted with an inferior milk. On 1 May the summer contracts between farmer and salesman commenced, and it must have been very disheartening to numbers of those producers who supply milk to London and other large towns, to hear that their prices had been suddenly knocked down to 13d. a barn gallon, which is equivalent to 2 imperial gallons and a pint. It is unfortunately true that dairy farmers themselves have, by their action in over-producing a particular article – believed to be lucrative in its sale – brought this rod about their own backs. There are far too many farmers who will insist upon producing milk in large quantities, in the hope that others may prove mortal and give up, and that they may hold the field.

Old Wheat (1916)

A few months ago Lincolnshire wheat was threshed and sold in good condition that had been kept in stack for 34 years. We know of no specific test of the limit of time for which this grain can be kept in a fit state for human consumption. The vitality of the cereal certainly continues for more than a restricted period. After the first year the germinating power diminishes rapidly, and wheat more than 3 years old should never be sown. The longest known period of viability is 10 years, though some of the early Greek and Italian writers gave the period as 40 or 50 years.

Ploughing Societies

Most of the ploughing and hedging societies are comparatively recent. For instance, the Cruckton and District Ploughing and Hedging Society, which is one of the most flourishing today, dates from 1927. It was formed simply as the result of a wager between local farmers as to who could plough the best and straightest furrow. Such societies probably sprang up spontaneously in many places at various times, flourishing for a while and then dying when a handful of enthusiasts retired or died. An agricultural society which claims to be the oldest of its kind in the country is the South Avon and Stour Agricultural Society, based in Christchurch, Hampshire, and founded in 1794. It organises many competitions, including a ploughing match, but it is not known whether such a match was part of the original programme.

Extraordinary Potato Crop (1854)

Mr Robert Charlton, nurseryman, of Wall, near Hexham, has just reaped a portion of his potato crop, of the lapstone kidney variety, producing at the enormous rate of 130 loads of 20 stone each, per English acre, of large clean potatoes, perfectly free from disease. It is stated that the above satisfactory result was effected principally by allowing a sufficiency of space in planting, viz., 3 ft between each row, and 1½ ft between each potato or set – the sets being whole potatoes, and tolerably large ones. It is believed that the adoption of this measure is the best preventative of disease, the plant being thus kept in a healthy condition by a free admission of air.

Ragwort

Ragwort (*Senecio jacobaea*) is definitely poisonous to ponies if they eat it, fresh or dry. Normally, animals do not eat it when other more palatable herbage is available, but this is not invariable. The poisons are alkaloids (jaconine, jacodine) and are cumulative. They persist in the dried plant present in hay, which probably constitutes a greater danger to animals than the growing weed. The trouble is that symptoms, though sometimes shown fairly soon, may be delayed.

Because the poisons do slow but permanent damage to the liver, it is wise to exclude the weed entirely from any feeding. The weed is susceptible to selective weedkillers, but the younger it is the more easily it is destroyed. It is best to remove by hand, if you have only a slight infestation, because spraying means keeping the animals out of the field for a day or two.

Rape for Sheep and Game (1967)

The crop you have in mind is forage rape. This is a good crop for sheep feed, is hardy and provides useful cover for game birds. It is not yet in general use, but various promising strains are being developed. Another crop with similar advantages is fodder radish. A new crop, oilseed rape, is being widely grown this year. This provides excellent cover for game birds in summer, but is harvested for its seed in autumn.

Russian Comfrey (1953)

It is too early to say whether all the claims being made for Russian comfrey can be substantiated over long periods, but there is no doubt that many smallholders and farmers are finding it a most useful and very astounding crop. Such reports as have come to hand indicate that given suitable soil and proper cultivation, it well repays a trial, despite the healthy scepticism with which most people approach it. It seems a better proposition than lucerne at any rate, though whether you would in fact get 100 tons of silage off an acre of Russian comfrey, compared to 70 tons of silage off 10 acres of grass, is not known.

Russian Comfrey as Silage (1959)

Russian comfrey can be made into good silage with a protein content ranging around 17–22%. Being rich in protein, it benefits from the addition of judicious though not over-generous applications of molasses when being made into silage, and it is as well to let the crop wilt for 24 hours after cutting. The crop is established by transplanting either in autumn or in early spring. It grows with extreme rapidity, thrives on frequent cutting and should produce yields from 20 or 30 tons in the first year to 100 tons or more in the third and fourth years. It should not be grazed, but can be made into hay, silage or even compost, and can be fed as a ration of greenstuff to all farm livestock from cows to poultry. However, little experimental work has been done on a field scale, and in practice the cultivation of comfrey is at present confined chiefly to smallholders.

It needs a fairly deep, fertile soil, does well on clay, but is not suited to chalk.

Saloon Tractor (1930)

Driving a tractor during the cold and wet weather of the winter months is a severe physical strain upon a man, often resulting in illness, with its consequent loss of time and work, as, unlike the horse-drawn implement, the driver is not walking to keep warm, and has to make frequent stops to restore his circulation. The saloon tractor overcomes this difficulty, and is very easy and cheap to make. Two pieces of bar iron are bent, drilled and bolted to the chassis fore and aft. Strong sticks are lashed lengthways to these, and a few pieces of hoop iron from barrels serve as curves for the roof. Old stack-cloths or implement covers can be cut up to give a waterproof top, and old corn sacks form the remainder of the sides, being sewn into place with binder twine. During a biting north-east wind the drivers of several of these vehicles were carrying merrily on whilst a man with a horse-drawn plough even had to stop at the end of each furrow to warm himself up. In wet weather it prevents the men getting covered in sludge, and in dry weather serves as considerable protection from the clouds of dust, whilst even in very hot weather the roof is left on to save them from sunstroke and eyestrain. [John Fenman, Cambridge]

Sootigine (1887)

(1) Manures that are derived from mineral sources. In this sense both sulphate of ammonia and nitrate of soda are mineral manures. Coprolites, potash, salts, gypsum, etc., are all mineral manures.
(2) We do not know the composition of sootigine.

The Value of Straw (1865)

Mr Mechi, 'irrepressible' as the negro, has reappeared in new grandeur, after being, as people thought, lost in the depths of the Unity Bank. He is greater than ever at Tiptree-hall; still ready to show his farm, and 'develop his plans' to all comers, still giving in the newspapers his views as 'a practical man' on long fallows, deep ploughing, and the whole *res rustica*. We do not plough half deep enough; if we did, we should be less troubled with weeds, and so should save a good many millions a year. We still, despite all the drilling, sow our corn too thickly. Mr Mechi only allows ½ peck to the acre, and gets 52 bushels to the acre – about 416 fold; but then he selects his seed. His latest bit of advice is about straw; don't sell it off your farm, not even if you live near a town and can buy manure instead. Feed your stock on what you don't want for litter. 'Ah, master, you couldn't keep half the beasts you do, if you don't give 'em straw,' says Mr Mechi's man to him. In wheat straw, he says there is 32% starch – no inconsiderable element in forming fat – besides the more or less useful mineral ingredients which we know help 'to build up the halm'. The French have long made a good deal of use of straw. The little Norman and Percheron stallions which, with a great deal of amusing whinnying and biting, whirl those big 'buses from one end of Paris to the other, eat very little else till they get their heavy evening meal; and no one would wish to see horses in better condition. One sometimes fancies a little starving might do them good.

Wheat in North America (1854)

Wheat was first sown in the North American colonies in 1692, on the Elizabeth Islands, in Massachusetts, by Cosnold, at the time he explored that coast. That has been just 162 years ago, and since that time so great has been the increase of this cereal, that in the year 1849, according to the census of 1850, the product amounted to 100,503,899 bushels. Up to 1610, and perhaps later, England supplied the colonies with the greater part of their breadstuffs. How changed is it now. All Europe is looking to America for bread. The bread sent to the colonies in 1610 was not cast upon the waters never more to return. Two hundred and forty years afterwards it rolls back in a continuous stream to gladden the hearts of half-famished millions in England, France and Belgium. The descendants of men originally lashed and scourged from their shores, and forced to make their future habitations beneath the uninviting sky – more humane than the task-masters of their fathers – are now striving to return food for what was considered an evil, by supplying them with bread. [Reproduced from *American Paper*]

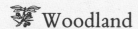 Woodland

Age of a Tree

It is not possible to determine the exact age of a tree without cutting it down, so that all the annual rings can be counted on the stump. A reasonably accurate estimate can be made by assuming an average rate of growth in girth for the kind of tree and the district concerned.

Such growth rates are usually expressed as 'annual rings per inch of radius' and a usual figure for an old oak in Buckinghamshire is 10. Your tree, which is 14 ft round, has a radius of about 27 in and can, therefore, be said to have an estimated age of 270 years.

Axe or Saw?

The superiority of the axe, slasher or billhook in coppicing hazel and ash, over the saw, lies largely in the cleaner cut. With the axe or other single-edged cleaving tools properly wielded, there is one sharp, clean cut, and the surface left is smooth and surgically clean. As such it is resistant to the entry of weather, fungi and parasitic organisms, and the root and base soon recover by thrusting new buds from the barked butts left. A saw, however, no matter how sharp, makes several cuts, and the cut surface is really one of torn fibres. Fungus spores, bacteria and disease organisms are apt to lodge more easily, and rain and weather produce a surface favourable to infection. In either case, the cut must be oblique and not right at ground level.

Chestnuts and Cedars (1860)

I can bear testimony to chestnuts being a most valuable wood if cut when young or comparatively young. Chestnuts grow as quick as larches, and for most purposes are quite as durable as oak. Chestnut makes better gate-posts than oaks; and for lock-gates, or anything connected with water, is A.1. It is a most valuable wood, and on a dry, sunny site would do excellently in Yorkshire. Old Monteith, now dead and gone, urged chestnuts on the 'guid folk of bonny Scotland' I don't know how many years ago. Now, I will tell you the reason it is not propagated in the north. It arises from the exorbitant prices asked by nurserymen for the plants. I can get first-class larch at 15s. per 1,000, ditto oak at 4s. per 100, but chestnuts are 8s. per 100! If C.P.C. wants to propagate that most useful of trees, his own bantling – he must get nurserymen to reduce their too high charges for plants. There is another tree C.P.C. ought to agitate for with nurserymen to propagate generally, namely, the cedar deod. That wood grows quicker than larch, and is better for roofs and house purposes than oak or any foreign timber. I believe it to be quite impervious to dry rot, as in India the white ant will attack every sort of wood except teak-wood and the cedar deodaru. [Eboracum]

Cork Acorns (1860)

I have a quantity of remarkably fine acorns from the *Quercus suber*, which are just beginning to sprout. I intend raising 1,000 in pots for my own use, and the rest I propose giving away to any of your readers who may desire them, and who are not nursery and seedsmen – who, in fact, may be desirous of raising them for planting in their own grounds. These acorns were the produce of a remarkably fine cork-tree, one of the finest, I am told, in Great Britain. There is no more picturesque tree than the cork, as every one who has ever seen a fine one is aware; it is, however, rarely to be met with in this country, and the reason assigned by nurserymen for this is the fact of so very few soils being suitable to its growth. The soil upon which the tree, the parent of these acorns, stands, is a good loam, of the colour of a mixture of brown umber and yellow ochre, in which the latter predominates. Twelve acorns can be conveyed by post, in a small box, for 6d., and the box would cost another 6d. [C.P.C.]

Measuring Tree Heights

Accurate measurement of tree heights requires the skilled use of an expensive theodolite or hypsometer. Approximate results can be obtained by setting up a long pole of known length beside the tree, and then comparing the two heights visually. For example, if a 15 ft pole is placed against a 60 ft tree, an observer standing well back from both will see that the tree is 4 times the height of the pole. Or fix a pole of measured height at some distance from the tree. Move the eye at ground level until the top of the pole lines up with the top of the tree. Then, by trigonometry, the height of the tree equals the height of the pole multiplied by the distance from the eye to the base of the tree, and divided by the distance from the eye to the base of the pole. For trees near buildings, compare their height with that of the nearest building, which can be accurately sized up from standard features such as number of storeys or dimensions of windows.

Monkey Puzzle Timber (1948)

Despite its appearance the monkey puzzle tree yields a satisfactory softwood timber which is used in South America for building, box-making and paper pulp. But the specimen trees grown in Great Britain are of little commercial value, as they are usually open-grown, and so their persistent side branches cause dark brown knots which spoil the appearance and working qualities of the light yellowish-brown wood. As a rule, only a few trees are available for felling at a time, and timber merchants are seldom ready to experiment with such small parcels of a little-known species. The wood is resinous and burns well, provided that it is allowed to dry for a few months after felling, preferably after being first sawn up. The cultivation of the monkey puzzle as a timber-producing tree in Britain has been considered, but its wood has no special advantage over the common conifers such as Scots pine.

English Oak (1854)

English oak, when it is used for church or other external doors, should be felled in winter, when the sap is concentrated. When the sap is flowing through the tree, it injures the timber, and leaves a vacuum in the pores, which, being exposed to the atmosphere, imbibes the wet, and mixes with the acid and stringent quality of the sap, causing the discoloration of the wood.

Seasoning Oak

Oak planks need seasoning for 1 year for every inch of thickness. Half-inch planks can, therefore, be used after 6 months' seasoning, but 2-in planks will require 2 years. Stack planks flat, separated by small pieces of wood called stickers, so that air can circulate. Successive layers of stickers must come vertically under those above, or the planks will warp. To season a small quantity of oak, store in an open-sided shed or barn, fully exposed to air but not to sun or rain. If seasoning must be done out of doors, paint the ends of each plank to lessen the risk of splitting.

Slow Seasoning and Bark

Because bark is virtually waterproof, its presence or absence on a round log has a marked effect on the rate of seasoning of timber. Where rapid seasoning is desired, as for example when pine fence stakes are to be preserved by treatment with creosote, all the bark is removed after felling. For the gradual seasoning suitable for turnery poles of birch or alder, the bark is taken off in small patches only. Hardwood logs such as oak, intended for good joinery work, must be seasoned very slowly, and therefore it is usual to leave the bark until the trunk is sawn into planks.

Livestock
CATTLE AND DEER

Brittany Cows (1860)

Pray allow me to add my humble testimony to that of Mr Buckland in favour of this 'smallest specimen of cows' and 'well-made little creatures'. But it so happened the other day, when walking near Isleworth ferry, that I met a youth driving 3 of them, and felt certain the moment I set eyes on them that they could be no other than the Liliputians in question. This I found to be the case, and that they were the property of Judge Haliburton, who resides close to the ferry; nor do I believe that any man, either 'down east' or in 'the far west' can produce so nice a little cow as one of them is, either for a judge or for a lady's pet, or I'm no judge of cows. [Birdcatcher]

Birch Bark

The chief reason why cattle sometimes eat bark from sapling birch trees is probably a hunger for nutrients that is not being provided in the grass or food resources otherwise available to them. Normally, birch bark is somewhat bitter and astringent: it contains a 'tar' and a volatile oil, *Oleum betulinum*, which has some medicinal properties. When the sap is rising, this would tend to flood the tissues under the bark with nutrients. The sap has a sugar content of about 2%; and there will be several mineral nutrients present, which the cattle may be seeking. Wine has been made of the sap, and the bark is sometimes used in herbal medicine.

Chicory and Bloat

It would be doubtful wisdom to rely on the introduction of strips of chicory in leys as a complete preventative of bloat. Bloat, as you probably know, is generally associated with turning cattle into pastures where there is a lush, young flush of growth, particularly of legumes – clovers, etc. As far as herbs like chicory are concerned, there is no doubt they are valuable and probably play a part on old pastures where bloat seldom occurs. But chicory itself is diuretic and laxative rather than carminitive, and it is difficult to see what direct action it can have in prevention of gas formation. Probably it would be better to introduce other herbs, too, such as yarrow, cat's ear, ribgrass, burnet and possibly caraway.

Lucerne for a Cow

Lucerne is an excellent fodder crop and soil improver, and is well worth growing for cows. It is, however, best grown for hay, and a 5–6 year ley can be put down consisting of a mixture of, say, 12 lb lucerne (Province or Canadian Grimm), 4 lb each of Timothy and Cocksfoot grass, 2 lb late red clover, 1 lb Alsike and ½ lb white clover, per acre. Lucerne needs special care, however. The ground must be clean, well drained, and in good heart, with plenty of organic manure from a previous crop; it also needs lime and phosphates, but not dung. The seed is best inoculated with suitable bacteria to ensure good germination and results. Drill in April. It should not be cut until after 8–10 weeks, and then remaining growth can stand for the winter. Other things being equal, the crop succeeds best on well drained, light loams, and in south, east and north-east England.

Tree Protection

There is only one way of stopping cattle and horses barking trees. Put a collar of chestnut paling round each tree. No posts are required: one just measures the circumference of each tree requiring protection (allowing a few inches in excess of each measurement for growth); place it round the tree and wire the two ends of the paling together. The pales should be 2 in apart, so that horses cannot get their lower jaw between them. Five feet is sufficient height against cattle, higher for horses. Dressing trees with various mixtures is unsatisfactory as the dressing has to be constantly renewed, but chestnut paling will last very many years.

Weight Assessment (1892)

You appear to misunderstand the problem. Those actually in the showyard all had the same particulars given them before they made their guess. They did not accept the help of the weighbridge, nor was the block test conducted to prove the efficiency of the weighbridge. It was carried out to prove the inability of even men of experience really to determine weight by the hand and eye. And this inability has now been proved repeatedly, i.e., at Stirling, on the Duke of Portland's estate near Ayr, in Notts, and at Welshpool. In all 4 cases a very large percentage of men occupied as graziers have failed to guess, even approximately the carcase weight.

Deer for a Three-acre Paddock (1960)

Although you have been inspired by having seen domesticated deer on small lawns in Holland, you should bear in mind that all male deer become dangerous at certain times of the year and pet deer become more dangerous still because they have lost their fear of man. The following are the suitable species in order of size, starting with the smallest: Chinese water deer (both sexes are without antlers); Reeve's muntjac or barking deer; roe-deer (males very dangerous); and fallow deer (probably most easily obtainable). All require shelter and feeding during the winter, as well as iodised salt licks or common rock salt. Their food should consist of cattle cake, good hay and abundant branches which they peel. The ground should be limed every few years or in rotation by fencing off 1 acre for a few months. Your best plan would be to obtain fawns and hand-rear them. Though this is tedious, the result is well worthwhile. Roe and fallow are more frequently and easily obtainable in Germany and Holland.

GOATS AND SHEEP

The Nubian Goat (1955)

The first known importation of Nubian goats to England was in 1883, but this breed did not become popular, and the purity of breeding of the various early importations was open to doubt, as there was much mixing of the various types of Asiatic and African goats. They were bred fairly extensively in France, where fantastically high milk yields have been claimed from them. From the various specimens imported into England, and crossed with our English goats, has evolved the Anglo-Nubian goat, which is now a recognised breed of considerable popularity. Its milk yield is not usually as high as that of the Saanen, British Saanen and British Alpine breeds, but contains a higher butter-fat content, and the Anglo-Nubian is frequently termed the 'Jersey cow' of the goat breeds. It is not generally considered to be as hardy as the other usual breeds.

Australian Sheep-rearing (1870)

There are several methods. The whole secret of success of one method, described in detail elsewhere in this issue, 'is in doing everything for ourselves, and by good faith keeping on good terms with the blacks. Except a bit of tobacco, flour, and meat, we never pay away any wages. At lambing time we get the whole of our work done for a bit of ration and 2 or 3 pairs of blankets given away in the winter.' This family admits that somehow beginners always do get a good lambing; they give it their undivided attention, and, if they cannot get black labour, most white men whom they happen to hire will do more justice and strive more for new beginners than they will for a big squatter. Wool, they say, grows night and day and interest of money accumulates in the same ratio. Other plans open to those who have a good knowledge of sheep, and who are of well-known honour and integrity, for obtaining stock without capital, include the following. Many of the large graziers in New South Wales and Queensland are ready to let to such persons sheep at a rental of £30 or £40 per annum per 1,000. The lease is generally for 7 years, the lessee returning the same number, the same ages, and the same quality of sheep at the expiration of his lease. Or they rent them on halves, half the wool and half the increase, the former delivered at the shed, returning them at the end of a period of years in the same way as before mentioned. Sheep are often leased in this way when a practical man has been out and discovered the country, but is without the means to stock it. Settlers going home to England or Scotland for a few years' spell have been known to let their station, with stock, at a rental or on halves, with the use of the run, drays, bullocks, horses, milking cows, cattle, and rams, and the whole establishment. The lessee in this latter case is generally a person whose abilities and character are well known to the proprietor – a brother, old friend, manager, superintendent, or overseer of the station. Several men have laid the original foundation of very large fortunes in this way, commencing life on nothing but the industry of their characters and the abilities of their brains.

Sheep and Geese

The old saying that 'geese poison pasture' is not strictly correct; or perhaps it would be more accurate to say that its meaning is not always understood. Goose dung is as good for the soil as is any other poultry dung. It certainly does not 'poison' grass. The trouble is that geese are rather dirty creatures and will quickly get a pasture so foul that sheep or cattle cannot graze without putting their noses in goose droppings. This they naturally dislike. Take your geese off the pasture for a time and allow time for the dung to be absorbed into the soil before turning cattle or sheep there to graze. It is difficult to say how long will be required. The muck will disappear more quickly in wet weather, naturally. You may possibly find it helpful to assist the process by harrowing the pasture. Once the surface fouling has disappeared, you should have no difficulty in getting your animals to graze behind geese.

Sheep and Horses (1870)

Keep an area of sweet, rich grass free from sheep; for horses, like cattle, in Australia will not feed after sheep, their excrement being extremely offensive to the former.

Old Sheep (1958)

Sixteen years is the longest recorded life of the domestic sheep in this country.

A Sporting Ewe (1854)

While some shepherds in the Highlands of Banffshire were lately gathering their sheep from the more retired parts of their pastures, for the purpose of clipping them, they were surprised by observing a ewe descending the hill with great speed, and apparently in pursuit of some beasts. They were not kept long in suspense, when the sheep with some difficulty captured the object of her pursuit, a well-grown grouse; but, not being so well accustomed in securing her victim as the canine species, it escaped from her. However, not satisfied at losing her anticipated repast, she set off again in pursuit, and, after coursing for some time, again seized the poor creature, devoured it greedily, feathers and all, and was seemingly much satisfied with her illicit prize. It is very probable, says our correspondent, that she had been in the habit of killing such game previous to this, but how she should disgrace the innocent character for which her kind get credited is left for naturalists to determine.

Thorn in a Lamb

The 'thorn', just 3 in long, which you carved out of a leg of lamb, is almost certainly one of those short lateral branchlets, terminating in a spine, which commonly occur on the thicker branches of the white thorn. On inquiry we learn that smaller thorns are occasionally found in similar circumstances; but, fortunately for the animals, one of the dimensions you sent is probably of very rare occurrence.

PIGS
Castor Oil for Pigs (1916)

Castor oil is one of the commonest drugs given to pigs, and no ill effects have been noted.

Gloucester Old Spots (1920)

The spotted pig of Gloucestershire is fortunate in its supporters. It would be unfair to it, and to them, to suggest that its growing popularity is mainly the result of the pushful policy they pursue, for the root cause of the progress recorded at the annual meeting in Bristol the other day, when Lord Bledisloe and others were sounding its praises, is its own merit as a utility animal of the farm. If the Old Spot pig were a new breed it could be predicted that it had come to stay, but, being an old variety newly raised to the dignity of a registered breed, the more correct prophecy is that it will extend its territory and deepen its hold upon popular favour.

RABBITS
Silver-grey Rabbits (1861)

In answer to your correspondent 'Tip's' question respecting the silver-grey rabbits, I am pleased to inform him that a few years since I bred large quantities of these rabbits on a piece of ground of 3 acres, walled in. They soon opened burrows and multiplied amazingly, and returned a good percentage for the trouble taken with them. My rabbits were imported from a warren in Normandy, and therefore fit to turn out; but rabbits bred in hutches are not fit, therefore your correspondent should know how his stock have been bred before purchasing. Since I have given up possession of the above ground, I have been breeding in courts – that is a paved space inclosed with wire netting and a large mound of earth thrown up for the rabbits to burrow in. The mound is roofed over with a slight span roof of felt to throw off the rain and to keep them dry. Rabbits bred like this are always fit to turn down, and I have been selling large quantities for that purpose. The Himalayan, or, more properly speaking, the China rabbit, I keep in the same way, and they are also being turned down. The Chinchilla silver-greys are much sought after in consequence of the Chinchilla fur coming into fashion, and for which the Chinchilla rabbit skin is used in imitation and called 'mock Chinchilla'. In reply to your correspondent 'Grey Buck's' query for the large Patagonian rabbits, I beg to inform him I have 6 does and 1 buck of the largest and purest strain, bred from imported animals; and if he will give me his direction I shall be pleased to give him any further particulars. [Alpha, Brompton, S.W.]

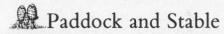Paddock and Stable

Arab Horses (1900)

The bone of the Arab horse is admitted to be of very close texture, superior, in fact, to that of our English thoroughbred, which, in its turn, is far more dense and substantial than that of the Shire or Clydesdale, and it is on this superior quality of bone that the advocates of the Eastern horse base their claims to its being considered as powerful over a country as the English hunter of greater stature. The Arab horse has its literature, and Capt. Upton, the author of *Arabia and Newmarket*, gives it as his opinion that 'God, by a special interposition, directed to the ark the two most perfect animals then in existence, whence they found their way to Central Arabia, and their offspring, preserving their pure blood to this day, have sufficed to ennoble and improve the studs of the world.' Nevertheless, there is no doubting the fact that the Arab does not, as a rule, 'go' in England in the same sense as does the thoroughbred, the hackney, or the Shire. He has his admirers, as everybody knows, but he is not much sought after. One point to be considered is how far the real nature of the Arab is altered by English surroundings. Years ago the Exmoor pony was in great request, and, because it was so good at its small stature, sundry people came to the conclusion that if you could raise its height by a cubit or thereabouts an animal would be produced without price. Efforts were consequently made to breed the Exmoor on a larger scale, but it was found that with increased stature came diminution of power, and there are those to be found who assert the same in the case of Arabs. We may remember, too, the saying of Abbas Pasha to Herr Von Hügel (once Chief of the Staff of the King of Würtemberg): 'Even if you succeed in getting hold of genuine Arabs, you will never have real ones from them, for an Arab horse is no longer an Arab when he ceases to breathe the air of the desert.' In this connection it may be mentioned that the Shetland Pony Society have fixed a limit for height, and that many breeders experience a difficulty in keeping their stock within that standard as soon as they are removed from their native wilds to the stables and the richer pastures of the south.

Before Foaling

Your mare may be ridden as usual up to half time, after which only very gentle riding exercise should be given and this stopped when the abdomen becomes greatly increased in size. Exercise, however, should be given right up to the time of foaling. There is no need to separate her from the gelding at all, if they are good friends. To be on the safe side, the mare should not be ridden until after the foal is weaned. The foal may be separated from the mare at 6 months. An excellent booklet on the subject entitled *Hints to Mare Owners* can be obtained from the Hunters Improvement Society.

Bleed the Toes (1860)

Bleed at each toe, after which blister the fetlock and turn out to grass for 2 months.

Blind Pony (1919)

A blind Iceland pony became so familiar with the meadows in which it passed most of its time that it used to venture to amuse itself by occasional gallops, and instead of crashing into a hedge, always pulled up short, just in time. This may be accounted for by the supposed sense of feeling when any obstruction is approached; but I suggest that it is far more likely that a hedge has a smell very distinct from that of the grass, and that a blind pony would very soon learn that that smell meant almost instant collision, unless the warning was attended to very promptly. [Alfred Heneage Cocks, Skirmett, near Henley-on-Thames]

Boiled Carpet (1900)

It will be news to practical veterinarians to learn from Colonel Nunn's letter that a foot packed with cotton waste will derive equal advantage to one enveloped in a poultice. If the seat of a prick (previously enlarged by the drawing knife or searcher) had been specified some comparison might have been drawn, but in the case of a foot suffering from concussion and some degree of bruising of the sole (from the horse having been ridden a distance without a shoe) it is desired to afford general expansion of the whole foot by absorption of moisture from a poultice completely enveloping it. It is also commonly known that the oil present in crushed linseed makes a poultice partly composed of that substance very much more emollient in its effects than one entirely made up of bran, which practical grooms do not favour. That a scale of bran should enter and convey the pathogenic organism is an attractive theory, but there is no reason why the bran, like the poultice boot, should not be rendered aseptic before application. The country practitioner, accustomed to all sorts of improvisations, will scarcely be assisted by the suggestion of boiled carpets. In my experience, a horse suffering irritation enough to make him scrape with a poulticed foot will take no longer in clearing a space covered with sawdust than he will one bedded with any material that will not stick to the poultice. [Harold Leeney, MRCVS, Burgess Hill]

Broken-winded Brood Mare (1887)

It is certainly not true that 'broken wind' prevents a mare from breeding. It is much to be wished that it were the case.

Diuretics (1860)

(1) Stewart, in his *Stable Management*, says that diuretics should never be given to a horse within 24 hours following or preceding severe exertion. Horses require some time to recover from the exhaustion consequent upon a severe run, and cannot at first bear any depressing secretion, which diuretics produce. (2) We should recommend giving a hunter nearly half a bucket of water early in the morning. It is absorbed long before the time at which hounds meet, and does not then interfere with the wind.

Flat Feet (1860)

(1) A proper attention to shoeing for the space of a year will do much to curtail the expansion of horn noticed in flat feet. It is impossible to give a description of treatment, as it will vary at each shoeing. (2) Apply swabs around the feet, and stop them with cowdung and salt.

'Forging' (1898)

Unless it is the case that the animal is suffering from extreme weakness, there must be some error in conformation to account for the excessive 'forging'. A clever shoeing smith might be able, by shortening the toes of the hind feet, to alter the angle which the pastern bones form with the fetlock joints, so as to throw the hoofs backwards. The fact of the blow being inflicted on the front of the hoof seems to indicate the necessity for some adjustment. The toes of the shoes should of course be kept with the hoof; but this is all that can be done so far as the shoes are concerned.

Grooming at Grass (1898)

We do not see that you can easily combine all 3 requirements. If your mare runs at grass and you drive her sometimes 10 miles a day, she must have corn – about 2 feeds a day. She will then keep herself in exercise for slow and short work; but she would be the better for a little walking. Grooming a horse out of grass is but labour in vain, though with her summer coat on she might not look amiss.

Hayracks (1860)

The best way of preventing horses from pulling their hay down upon the bedding is to place the rack near the ground, which saves 30% of the hay, and the expense of the alteration is soon paid for.

Horse Eats Sheldrake (1900)

[I had 2 tame sheldrakes and a horse out at grass. One morning I found the horse chewing placidly at the head of a sheldrake, which he must have caught, for it was still struggling. I took it from him, and a few hours afterwards gave it to him again in order to photograph him, and he took it and began chewing it again with apparent enjoyment.]

The carnivorous propensity which is occasionally manifested by herbivorous animals, notably in the case of cows by the riverside devouring fish left on the bank by anglers, has been the subject of comment in these columns.

Itching Tail (1930)

Some horses have the habit of rubbing their tails on every opportunity. This is caused, in some cases, by eczema at the root of the tail, or some other form of irritation. Your case may be caused by small worms about the anus or the rectum. If you inject common salt, or an infusion of quassia chips, the trouble should cease.

Long-backed Horse

For a horse with a long back which, you suggest, might over rough country give riders extra comfort, the Australian Waler would be similar to the English-bred Arabian, which grows to 16 hands, and sometimes a trifle over. English-bred Arabians make excellent hacks and, though not played much here, would (we think) play polo. They should also be ideally suited to pig-sticking. They have a little more length in the back than the very close-coupled Arabian horses. In this country, the Cleveland Bay is the breed of horse with the longest back. They are bred as carriage horses, though often crossed with thoroughbreds to produce good hunters. They are big horses, with great bone and substance.

Mud Fever (1887)

Mud fever is associated with irritation of the skin on which the mud has lodged, with loss of hair. A little vaseline will allay the irritation.

Mud Fever (1954)

Mud fever, cracked heels, grease and eczema are names given to an inflammation of the skin at, above or below the fetlock in horses. The cause of the inflammation is a germ known as the haemolytic streptococcus which usually settles primarily in the throat and lungs. From there the infection may spread to any part of the body. If it settles in the skin of the lower part of one or more legs it is usually because the legs have been abraded or otherwise injured, clogged with water and mud, and neglected in grooming. For treatment it is advisable to consult a veterinary surgeon since internal medication with vaccination or antibiotic drugs may be necessary in addition to local dressings applied to the affected parts of the skin. The infection is contagious, so the horse should be isolated.

New Forest Grazing

We cannot trace any weed found only in the New Forest that is poisonous to horses that are not native. Poisonous plants that may be found in the New Forest can also be found elsewhere. But it is possible that St John's wort (*Hypericum perforatum*) may be convicted. It contains a pigment which excites sensitivity to light, if eaten in any quantity, particularly in light-coloured animals, and losses have been recorded from this effect (more in sunlit countries, New Zealand and sub-tropics than in our own).

Non-sweating Racehorse

The cause of non-sweating is not definitely known, but it is associated with the action of strong sunlight on the nerves supplying the sweat glands, and the humidity of the atmosphere. The skin plays a great part in the regulation of the body temperature, and in conjunction with the kidneys in getting rid of waste products via the sweat glands. When these are inactive, therefore, some of these waste products are retained and exert a detrimental effect on the general health of the subject. In order to increase thirst to promote increased kidney action, at least 3 oz common salt may be given with the food daily, and water to drink allowed ad lib, of course. It might be well also to try the effect of including dry brewer's yeast in the ration, as this acts as a tonic, and on the nervous mechanism of the skin.

Old Mare's Teeth

It is probable that your 20–year-old mare's loss of condition in winter is due to the fact that she is unable to masticate properly when put on to hard food owing to dental wear or irregularities, both of which are quite common in aged animals. She needs exercise every day, not only hacking once a week. Her diet many consist of crushed oats and bran and fine soft hay, chaffed, in 4 feeds daily, with a bran linseed mash once or twice a week. Sliced carrots may be given as an extra, as well as any available green food. For the work she is doing, 12–15 lb of food per day would be a basic ration.

Pony for a Four-year-old (1953)

An Exmoor pony of 18 months to 2 years would be quite unsuitable for a child of only 4 and, in any case, you will not find a pony of that age already broken in. What you need is an older pony which has been ridden and handled by children for years. A young pony would be much too quick and also inexperienced for such a young child. We realise that you will not want too old a pony; if you get one of about 8–10 years he will last the child, if carefully looked after, for very nearly another 10, by which time the child will have grown out of him. An Exmoor pony is a very good choice and we suggest you get in touch with the Secretary of the Exmoor Pony Society at Taunton, Somerset. Explain to him what type of pony you are looking for and give the child's age and he will know exactly what you need, and the most likely place for you to find one.

Population of Horses and Mules (1892)

In the United States there are 15,000,000 horses and mules. The approximate number of horses and ponies in British India is 500,000.

Rain Phobia (1892)

We can suggest no other remedy than that your horse should be led about in the rain. Well-bred horses frequently dislike the feeling of falling rain. Of this there were several instances at Peterborough show.

Sawdust Bedding (1861)

'Springbok' says that he has tried bedding with sawdust, and that it does not answer; that his horses have lost condition; that his stables are foul; and that using it as manure he has killed his grass. Now I beg to say that I also have tried bedding with sawdust and, after a winter's trial, have come to a directly opposite conclusion. In November last I laid it down in a 4-stall stable occupied by 3 horses, and which was not removed until yesterday (4 March). My horses have done well, and my stables have been perfectly sweet, and what is more, the stalls, which are brick-floored, were quite dry when the sawdust was removed yesterday. With regard to the manure part of the question, it was the strength not being sufficiently tempered, not the turpentine, that must have killed 'Springbok's' grass. A sawdust bed is excellent for a horse given to eat his litter. It is not so well for a horse who paws with his fore-feet, as he stirs it up; nor does it answer so well for a white horse, or one with white legs as the stains from it are somewhat difficult to get out. I may add that 5s. has bedded my 3 horses for 4 months.

Silage for Horses

Silage is a cattle food and is made scientifically from the long cut of May grass with various sugar products and chemicals. Lawn mowings make excellent compost, but not silage. Starving horses have been known to eat cattle silage, but it is not a ration to be recommended. As a recommended alternative, cold water, good hay and a bucketful of oats has stood the test of many centuries of horse management for young horses at liberty.

Slicing Carrots (1860)

Why cut them at all? I have fed with carrots extensively in my stables for the last 12 years, saddle and carriage-horses, and, after being well washed, I have always given them whole. It is just as well as cutting them longitudinally, and certainly much better and safer than cutting them diagonally. I grow my own carrots, and have a couple of large barrowfuls washed at a time, and deposited in a receptacle in the hay-chamber appropriated for the purpose. I give a gallon basket for a feed, which I substitute for a feed of corn, on Saturday nights, or when a horse may be short of work, or otherwise requiring the same. To a horse used exclusively for carrying a lady I feed 3 times a day on carrots, and give no corn. [One who feeds his own horses, and occasionally dresses one before breakfast]

Sweet Itch (1954)

There is no cure for 'sweet itch' which is a seasonal, allergic condition. The best that can be done is to palliate the discomfort by swabbing the affected parts, several times a day, with a solution of washing soda in water – 1 oz to the gallon – and smearing any abrasions with oily calamine liniment.

 Poultry
CHICKENS

Battery System (1953)

There is almost no limit to the number of head of poultry that one man can cope with under the battery system. Certainly 1,000. Much depends upon the sort of battery you use, but if you instal one of the modern types there is very little for one man to do. The work is simply to fill the hoppers with pellets, collect the eggs and scrape off the dropping boards now and again. Modern batteries are often equipped with an automatically controlled water supply, so that if the man wants to get away for a couple of days he can easily manage it. If, however, you are going to rear your own chickens for replacements, that is a very different matter. That could easily become a full-time job.

Croad Langshan

The Croad Langshan breed of poultry was introduced into this country from China by a Major Croad in 1872. It is the ancestor of most of the modern breeds which lay brown eggs, and it does indeed lay eggs of various shades of brown, some being almost purple. It is a dual-purpose breed and rather heavy, and as such cannot hope to compete in egg laying with the specialists such as the leghorns. It is, however, quite good and well worth keeping.

Crowing Hen

Sex changes, such as you describe with your hen of jungle fowl strain who recently stretched out her neck and crowed several times like a cock, are not uncommon and are usually due to acquired disease leading to degeneration of the ovary. In case it should be one of the contagious diseases, the hen should be isolated in order to protect the health of the other fowls.

Custard for Hens (1900)

The bird appeared to suffer more from a weakly constitution than any definite disease. When young they should have egg and milk set into a crumbly custard, bread or meal and milk in addition to the vegetables and insects they find in their free range. Give them custard made with about equal parts of egg and milk, heated so as to set into a crumbly mass, bread dipped in milk and squeezed dry and crumbled, and canary seed and dari. If the hen is placed in a movable wire inclosure, or tethered so that she can scratch for them, they will do much better than if she is confined in a boarded coop.

Egg Supplies (1854)

The largest supplies to the English markets are obtained from Ireland, from which country the annual export of eggs, according to official returns, amounted in 1835 to 72 million; but now it is estimated that we yearly receive 150 million. Of this number London and Liverpool respectively consume 25 million each.

Endless Eggs

The excessive egg-laying by your spangled bantam (27 eggs laid without any sign of wanting to sit) is certainly unusual, but one meets with it occasionally. It is not confined to bantams, but perhaps more often encountered in the case of cage birds, even parrots, where eggs will be laid over a period and the bird will make no attempt to sit on them.

Feather-pecking Bantams

Feather-pecking is caused by boredom brought on usually by too close confinement, stale ground and lack of greenstuff to scratch about in. It is difficult to check. Try moving the fold on to deep grass, feeding a high-protein ration or adding house scraps to the usual food. A plain corn diet may tend to make the birds bored. Use some good pellets mixed with corn. A certain cure would be to have the birds debeaked. This does not hurt the birds or hinder their feeding, but prevents their seizing feathers. Keep the cock bird separate for some time and he will grow his feathers again in about a month. Probably only one of the hens is doing the feather-pecking, but it may start on the others. Watch them carefully and remove the culprit.

They Eat Feathers (1892)

They eat feathers in the absence of worms and natural animal diet. Give them as many house bones to pick at as you can spare, or smash the softer with a large hammer.

Feeding Poultry (1948)

It is difficult to lay down any hard and fast rules regarding the feeding of poultry in these days, since the diet provided must to a large extent depend upon what is available. Generally speaking, the foundation will be house scraps, including potato peelings, etc., which should be thoroughly boiled, and broken down as far as possible into a 'pudding'. Stale bread scraps, which are likely to be of most value, should be soaked until soft, and then squeezed out and mixed with the other. To this will be added whatever meal is available. Balancer meal may be augmented by unrationed foods of various kinds, including up to 20% of grass meal. It may also be possible to obtain some unrationed meat or bone-meal, and various other meals. It is not wise to attempt to feed the birds on a quantity basis, since the composition of the food will vary to a large extent, and it is better to allow the birds to judge for themselves how much they need. The best plan is to feed twice a day, and allow the food to remain in front of the birds for about 1 hour when any remaining should be removed. You will soon be able to judge how much is required. Better results may be obtained if the birds are fed 3 times daily, but it is doubtful whether this is worth the extra trouble; once started, it is inadvisable to discontinue it.

Foul Fowl (1854)

As to the change in the appearance of the Cochin cock, it occurs to us that is attributable to the presence of foul blood. It is not always that a cross can be observed, in a bird which at other periods will not conceal its degenerate origin. We know of a case in which a black hen moulted white, and also one in which another had moulted speckled.

Free-range Hens (1900)

There is no special food or medicine equal to a free range, sound grain, and outdoor roost for getting your fowls speedily through their moult.

Free-range Poultry Breeds (1964)

The breeds of fowl not prone to broodiness are the light breeds, which are also the best layers. Try the Leghorns, Minorcas and Anconas. Anconas and perhaps Minorcas are now rather rare, but there should be no difficulty in buying Leghorns. The Black Leghorn is possibly the best breed. They may be rather nervous and inclined to take alarm, but they will not go broody and they will lay well on free range.

Game Bantams (1860)

(1) In reply to 'Bantam', my father, about the year 1822 or 1823, bred between a Bantam cock and a small black Game hen, and after a few years produced very small fowls the exact miniature of black-breasted red Game. I believe they were the first bred. [B.P.B.]

(2) Your correspondent 'Bantam' asks for an opinion on the origin of the Game Bantam. I venture to offer a solution of the question – that it is the common Game fowl bred small, and I think this may be effected in no great number of years by the following process: crossing with small birds, breeding in and in, rearing chickens late in the year, and keeping them when young in towns, which will prevent them from attaining so great a size as they would in the country. [A Poultry- fancier]

Hay-box Brooders

Ideally, one has an interior surround of wire-netting to the box, with hay rather loosely packed around it. The size of the compartment within the wire can then be adjusted to the size and number of birds occupying it. There should be just room for them to fit in snugly. The surround should be circular, to avoid the possibility of chicks crowding in corners. The hay should be dry and sweet-smelling. Sprinkle a little hay on the wire floor. The idea of the hay-box brooder is to conserve the natural warmth generated by the chicks. This warmth rises. Therefore, once the hay is packed around and above the brooder, the whole quickly become warm. Some poultry-keepers, however, warm the floor before putting the brooder on it.

Lime for Ship's Hens (1860)

In winter, when fowls have less access to the ground, or when they are confined in small inclosures, they have less opportunity to select the mineral substances which they require; hence an artificial supply becomes necessary. Place the articles within their reach, so that they may take just the quantity which they are prompted to by nature. By slaking lime in a vessel, in water so that it will form a paste, and letting it dry, it can readily be broken into the desired form in which it appears to suit fowls best. Old mortar and broken shells, where they can be had, will answer the same purpose. Eggs are a luxury in winter, and whatever promotes their production is of interest. The wants of poultry for lime are very clearly shown by a correspondent of the *Boston Medical Journal*: 'A most pleasing illustration of the want of lime, and the effects of its presence, came under my notice on my voyage from South America to 'Sunny' France. We had omitted to procure gravel for our poultry, and in a few days after we were at sea they began to droop, and wound up their afflictions with the pip, or, as the sailors term it, the scurvy. Their feathers fell from their bodies, and it was perfectly ludicrous to see the numerous *un*feathered tribe in the most profound misery moping away their time in a state of nudity. Amusing myself one day by fishing up gulf weed, which floated in immense fields upon the surface of the ocean, I shook from it numerous small crabs, about the size of a pea. The poultry with one accord aroused themselves from their torpor, and seemingly, as if by instinct, aware of the therapeutic qualities of these interesting animals, partook of them with greater avidity than any invalid ever swallowed the 'waters' of the 'springs'. After a few hours the excellence of the remedy was apparent; the roosters began to crow, the hens began to strut and look saucy, and in a few days all appeared, in quite a holiday suit of feathers, derived from the lime, the constituent part of the crab shells.' [C. N. Bement, Springside]

Orchard Hens

It would not be harmful to the hens to let them have free range in an apple orchard, provided they are excluded at spraying times, and lead arsenate is not used. But after the first year, the presence of the hens may unbalance the nutrition of the trees. Poultry droppings are rich in nitrogen, and the tendency would be to encourage wood growth and shoot extension in the trees. Much depends upon how intensively the hens range the ground.

Prepotent Impregnation (1887)

If a new bird of a different variety is put into a run, and the old bird removed, the eggs laid the following day will be impregnated by the new introduction. The last impregnation is prepotent.

Profit from Hens (1953)

If a hen lays 200 eggs a year (which is good) and the average price is reckoned at 4s. a dozen, the gross income per hen would be about £3.5s.0d. per year. How much of this is actual profit would depend on a variety of circumstances (food, labour and incidence of disease), but it might well be the odd 5s. per hen. That would amount to £125 profit per year on 500 hens, plus the selling price of the hens when they had finished laying. In fact, the calculations come approximately near the generally accepted proposition that 1,000 laying hens will, if efficiently managed, bring in a net income of about £6 a week.

Record Hen's Egg (1959)

There are several records of hen's eggs of 8 oz. The most recent of these, as far as we know, is the one laid by a hen belonging to Mrs G. Bosman, of Windlesham, Surrey, in March 1950.

Roup (1860)

We know of no specific for roup, but believe care, warmth, bathing the head with a solution of sugar and lead, and a stimulant – such as ale – will often effect a cure. As in human ailments, good nursing stands first.

Sebright Bantams

Sebright bantams were originated in England about 1810 by Sir John Sebright as a result of some 30 years of selective breeding. He organised the Sebright Bantam Club about 1815, and it is the first specialist breed club on record. Ever since then Sebrights have been one of the most popular breeds of bantam, bred to a consistently high degree of perfection, in silver and golden varieties. Another early name in connection with Sebrights is a Mr Hewett, who wrote on them in 1835 in *The Poultry Book*.

Shell-less Eggs (1923)

Shell-less eggs may result from a lack of shell-forming material, such as crushed oyster or cockle shell, the excessive use of stimulating foods, or over-feeding. The mash should be scalded, but thoroughly cooled before feeding, and with birds on a good range little, if any, meat or fish meal should be needed at this season (July).

Sunflowers for Chickens

The most useful crops for poultry are cereals (wheat, rye, oats and maize), semi–dwarf sunflowers and sweet lupins. Of these, a semi–dwarf sunflower would seem to answer your conditions and situation best, i.e. crops for growing in a garden with a view to feeding about 18 hens in Northumberland. You need an early-ripening variety, such as Pole Star or Jupiter. Cultivation is not difficult. The crop likes sun, but is not particular as to soil, provided it is supplied with lime. A reasonable yield is 30 cwt per acre, but you should get more. Feeding rate is $1\frac{1}{2}$ oz per head, per day in winter. Maize or sweet corn is more chancy where you are, but if you do try it get an early-maturing variety. Sweet lupins are easily grown, but seed is scarce. There is no reason why you should not sow oats or rye if you have the room for it. It is getting too late for wheat. As a green crop, a few drumhead cabbages would be useful. For the rest, potato chats and peelings, and kitchen waste such as outer vegetable leaves would be forthcoming from crops grown for domestic use.

Turkey Profits (1953)

Profits from the fattening and sale of turkeys can vary according to a number of factors, so that your question is not an easy one to answer. We can, however, give the costs based on a group of turkeys on the farm of the Nottingham University School of Agriculture in 1949. They were hatched on 21 May and killed on 16 December and the net profit per bird was £1.0s.10$\frac{1}{2}$d. It seems that all possible expenditure was taken into account, including such items as paraffin oil, blackhead treatment and depreciation of equipment. It would be fair to reckon, therefore, about £1 per head profit.

DUCKS, GEESE AND SWANS

Aylesbury and Muscovy Ducks

Muscovy and Aylesbury crosses make very good table birds. The progeny of such a cross would probably not breed. It would not matter which way the cross was effected. Although your Muscovies are practically pure white it is not unusual for such birds to produce pied ducklings, since the wild Muscovy – which comes from South America – is pure black, and domestic white ones must have been bred from 'sports'. A throwback or so must therefore be expected.

Fish for Ducks (1892)

Your wild ducks cannot do well without animal food; they are not exclusively vegetable feeders. Try some fish refuse. The one sent was in full moult, and died from inanition.

Mechanical Duck (1865)

The celebrated mechanical duck of Vaucanson is being exhibited in the Rue de Paris, at Havre, in a small museum which takes its name from that illustrious mechanician. The bird, standing on a sort of box, shakes its wings, eats, drinks, and imitates nature so accurately, that the other day a dog flew at it, without, however, doing any mischief.

No Duck Farms (1900)

Your friends are perfectly right; there is no duck farm in existence; scores have been started, but none ever survived 2 years. You may read with advantage the details given of many in Tegetmeier's *Poultry for the Table and Market*, published by Horace Cox, Windsor House, Bream's Buildings, E.C., price 2s.6d.

Orchard Ducks (1954)

While it is quite beneficial to run ducks in an orchard and garden, and any of the hardy breeds (Aylesbury, White Pennine, etc.) would be suitable, Chinese geese are a better proposition, being hardier, living largely on grass and herbage, and requiring little supplementary feeding and then only in the severest weather; and only open-fronted shelter against the most inclement weather.

[*Editor's comment: I have a strong suspicion that during the 1950s one of* THE FIELD's *experts bred and sold Chinese geese: they tend to be recommended for all sorts of problems and situations, from the control of ground elder to companion grazing. This questioner, living in Tralee, was specifically interested in ducks and had not asked about the possibility of geese at all, let alone Chinese geese!*]

Broodies for Goose Eggs

Getting broody hens to sit on early goose eggs is one of the major problems confronting goose breeders. Rhode Island Reds are as prone to broodiness as any, and older hens, moving towards the end of their egg-laying period, are the best. If you can arrange to start some Rhode Island Red hens laying fairly early this autumn you should have a proportion of them liable to go broody next February or March. The warmth and snugness of a deep-litter house helps too.

Clipping Geese

In the case of practically all geese normally kept under conditions of captivity in this country, the power of flight has largely fallen into disuse, and the suggested 4 ft 6 in wire netting will be more than sufficient to keep them within bounds. If you wish to make doubly sure, you could clip the flight feathers of one wing only.

Geese and Trees

Geese might debark apple trees in a hard winter if other food sources were scarce; while the foliage of rhododendrons can be poisonous to livestock if eaten. Willows and pines are unlikely to be attacked by the geese. *Berberis x darwinii* would give further cover, but hedge off plantings at least for the first few years. This can be done inexpensively and unobtrusively with plastic netlon fencing, 4 in mesh on posts.

Two Mothers

The 2 broody geese sitting together on the same nest hatching out a dozen eggs should be separated: give them half the eggs each. However, as you have allowed them to sit together, your best plan now will be to remove the goslings as they hatch out, and keep them in a warm place until the hatch is completed. You can then separate the geese and give some of the youngsters to each or, if they do not all hatch, allow one goose to do the rearing. The geese should not require any special assistance in hatching out the goslings, but you should certainly supplement feeding during the period when they are sitting, otherwise they will probably get badly out of condition.

Watchdog Swan (1860)

But for a terror to passers by, we have known few creatures to surpass an old swan. We had one who reigned for many years the undisputed sovereign of a pond, along the borders of which there was a road sometimes traversed by persons passing from one village to another. It happened one day that two tailors walked that way, and being proverbially better acquainted with the goose than the swan had probably stopped to admire these beautiful creatures on the water. However that might be, it is certain that shrieks were heard, and that when some of our people rushed to the rescue, one of the tailors was down on his back, and the swan flapping him with his terrible wings. Our people said one of the tailors ran east, the other west, and were never heard of again; but we doubt the authenticity of this statement.

Sexing Water Birds (1900)

In selecting any water birds whose plumage is alike in both sexes, and which cannot, therefore, be distinguished with certainty, the best rule is to see them in the water and take that which swims deepest for the female and that which floats with greater buoyancy for the male, all males having the largest lungs for their size. The neck of the male swan, or 'cob' as it is technically termed, is usually thicker than that of the female, or 'pen'.

OTHER FOWL
Guinea Fowl Problems

[What would you advise for 4 guinea fowl cocks which will not eat mixed corn or pellets, nor leave the garden except to fly on to the roof, and 3 of which bully the fourth?]

There is almost certain to be some bullying amongst 4 cock birds. They are obviously having plenty of natural food in your garden, hence the lack of interest in corn. Try them with pellets slightly damp or mixed with house scraps, potatoes, bits of meat, bacon or cake. Try making them an artificial perch from long larch poles and shoo them off the house a few times. This may work. Buy a couple of hens and dispose of 2 cock birds. The new arrivals may stay on the ground and so keep the cocks off the house. Further, hens will probably wander off to nest in some overgrown spot.

Spiteful Peacocks

Peacocks can become very spiteful, especially in spring, when they will peck at children's legs and also attack dogs. To stop the 'brutal warfare' between your dogs and peacocks, probably your dogs could be trained to ignore the birds rather than vice versa.

Gold and Silver Pheasants (1861)

Gold pheasants are very hardy against cold, if well protected from wet and wind, and placed in a situation where they can enjoy the morning or mid-day sun. They must, however, have a house of considerable height – say, 12 or 14 ft – so as to be able to perch at night out of reach of stoats and strong voracious rats. Instinctively they seek the loftiest perch they can find. Silver pheasants, being very strong and martial birds, have little to fear from vermin, yet height of perch will conduce to their health. Except during the moult after breeding, or in autumn, they cannot be trusted not to injure or kill a species so much smaller as the golden; but they will consort amicably with domestic hens, as the golden will with bantams.

Sexing Golden Pheasants

Young golden pheasant cocks do not attain their full plumage until after the moult of the second summer. Thus they are not at all easy to distinguish from the hen poults. At 10 weeks the plumage of the males will definitely be a bit brighter and the neck feathers will be coarser. The eye of the male birds will be lighter in colour and the bone structure of the head more substantial. With these aids you should be able to separate them at 10 weeks; if not, there should be no difficulty at 12–14 weeks.

Mixing Ornamental Pheasants

It seems best to keep the various ornamental pheasants in separate pens. Sometimes they mix happily if they are kept together when very young. Putting older birds together may result in severe damage through fighting. In a large aviary, 30 ft long by 10 ft wide, with low shrubs growing inside, you could safely mix many of the birds. Complications will arise when laying starts. Golden pheasants seem to agree and a large, tall aviary with 6 or 7 cock birds makes a fine display. Quail will be better on their own. A pen 4 ft x 6 ft x 12 ft is adequate for 1 pair or a trio of pheasants. More birds than this would necessitate moving the pen more often.

Chinese Quail

Chinese quail are very much like our partridge except that they cannot stand our winters and must be kept inside from about November to April. Quite a small pen will serve when inside and the birds can be kept together. The floor should be kept very clean, using peat or sand. Some greenstuff should be given, preferably lettuce or brussel sprouts. The roof of the pen should be soft covered. Give the usual bird seeds and millet sprays, ample fine grit and clean water. Put them outside in a small run on short grass during the breeding season. They will lay a great many eggs, sometimes 25 or 30. If the eggs are left, the hen will eventually sit on them, but they are unreliable in captivity. Separate the birds into pairs for the breeding season. The birds must have shelter from rain,

Fantail

and their pen be rat-proof. Supply a box with an inch or two of very dry soil for dusting.

Fantails (1865)

The Fantail is a generally distributed and well-known favourite and it appears tolerable certain that this breed originated in the peninsula of Hindostan. The principal property in the Fantail is the extra-ordinary development of the quill feathers of the tail, and the mode in which the tail itself is carried. The normal number of feathers in the tail of all the varieties of pigeons is 14; in the Fantail the number often approaches 40. The specimen from which the engraving was taken possesses 36 feathers, when in full plumage. In order to constitute a good Fantail, however, the tail must be carried over the back, being brought well forward, in the manner shown in the engraving. The neck of the Fantail should be long, slender near the head, and curved in a graceful, swan-like manner. A thickly feathered neck – such as is found in all the Indian birds – is a great drawback to their elegance. The neck is constantly moved in a peculiarly tremulous manner, which gave rise to the old name of 'broad-tailed shakers', formerly bestowed on the breed.

Nuns (1887)

Nuns are not different from other pigeons in their influences on doves.

CAGE BIRDS
Silent Canary

It is often difficult to account for the loss of song apart from the fact that this may happen if the bird is ill. In a healthy bird it may be due to sudden change of environment, or it can occur temporarily as a result of a heavy moult. We know of no specific treatment but you might add a little glucose to the drinking water. This is a very useful source of readily available energy.

Nyasa Lovebirds

The Nyasa lovebird should be fed similarly to the budgerigar, on good quality millet 2 parts, and canary seed 1 part. The bird rarely shows much interest in green food, but may develop a liking for bread and milk, sweet biscuit, cake or cold potatoes.

Breeding Australian Parakeets (1861)

In the year 1859 I purchased in Leadenhall-market a pair of these birds, having observed signs of pairing. The hen laid in December, which is the time in this country for their nesting, it being summer in the country from which they came. I have some that have reared from 1 pair 32. I have also proved that those bred in England will breed again, but not till over 2 years old. With care they make excellent nurses, and the young are very hardy and tame. I have written this to encourage those who have them to try and rear young from them, being in my opinion the handsomest pets kept in cages; and to observe the actions of them is most amusing. [T. Moore, Fareham]

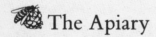 # The Apiary

Bee Bink

A bee bink is the handiwork of a swarm of honey bees, the queen of which must have settled in the open, when the remaining bees of the swarm settle around her, and in the failure of the scout bees to find better quarters (such as a hole in a tree trunk), the worker bees build the ranks of honeycombs and the colony establishes itself naturally. Unhappily, in colder weather, the colony will not be able to conserve its energies and natural heat to survive without protection. An expert beekeeper might be able to save them, but it is rather unlikely that the bees have enough reserves of honey stored for their nourishment.

Pollen on Thighs (1900)

If the examiner's words were correctly reported he must be profoundly ignorant of the subject. The honey is carried internally and cannot be seen. It is the pollen that is carried on the thighs.

Stealing Sealocrete

It would certainly be wise to prevent bees from collecting the Sealocrete recently applied, either by temporarily covering the painted surface with a screening material such as sheet polythene, sacking or tarpaulin, or by providing slightly sweetened water in shallow dishes near the hives. It is just possible that the bees may be finding water on the treated surface, and once it is dry it is not likely to be harmful. The occurrence is surprising, since it does not appear to have been recorded before, but perhaps the black colour attracts them.

Three-week Swarm

Bee swarms have been known to make combs in trees and remain there for up to 18 weeks until after leaf fall. It is uncommon for bees to hang in the swarm for more than a few days. This swarm, which hung on a branch for 3 weeks but there was no comb afterwards, was probably a prime swarm, and the little swarm which came to the next tree 2 days after the main swarm arrived was a cast swarm. It seems to have been a case of abandonment swarming, and fairly complete. The prime swarm would have been headed by an old queen, and her condition, possibly absence, may have dictated the length of time the swarm hung. It is an old saying and a true one that bees do nothing invariably. It is possible that the swarm was what is known as a 'starvation swarm' (absence of comb suggests absence of much food), and the swarm may have built up its sustenance while hanging, and while scout bees found a place for colonising.

Ventilation (1860)

We are not partial to ventilation, and have never found it requisite in winter. In spring we regard it as decidedly injurious, as lowering the temperature of the hive, and so preventing breeding. The account of the plan followed in America was quoted as an interesting circumstance, not as an example to be followed in this country.

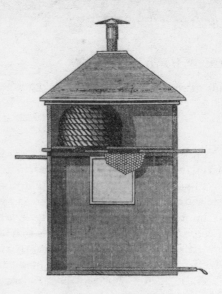

American box hive

Wild Honey

Because the colony of wild bees have been under the slates of your low dairy roof for some time, it does not mean that there will be huge stores of honey awaiting you. There is not a great deal of honey carried over from year to year, and a wild colony will not make very clear distinctions between the combs in which they store honey and the combs in which they rear their brood. Any honey worth harvesting will tend to be in the top of the combs. The bees are most likely to have accumulated a good surplus after the honey flow, either from white clover (in late June–July) which could be taken in early August; or from heather in late July–August, which could be taken from September to October. To get the honey from naturally built combs you would probably have to destroy the colony, by smoking them out with burning sulphur. This would have to be done with great care in a roof where timbers would be dry and inflammable. An alternative is to use a non-poisonous insecticide (derris, pyrethrum) to kill the bees. But you would be well advised to call in an experienced beekeeper to handle the matter, as wild bees are more vicious than hive bees when disturbed.

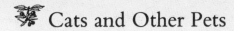 # Cats and Other Pets

Foster Mother

Your report of a cat which had brought up 2 rats and 2 kittens is interesting but there is nothing unusual in cats with a superabundance of milk fostering the young of other animals.

Mother Cat

As far as can be traced, there is no record age of any authenticity at which a cat may have kittens. The average life span of a domestic cat appears to be 14–16 years, though there are plenty of instances where a longer life has been recorded. Nevertheless, it would appear unusual for a cat to have kittens at 18 years 4 months, though perhaps not exceptional, since life spans of up to 24 years have been recorded. Apparently, fecundity does not entirely disappear with age. The difficulty in records is establishing their authenticity.

Persian Cat's Fits (1900)

The Persian cat is an artificial breed much subject to disease; its eyes are destitute of the natural colour, its ear organs are often rudimentary and useless; its brain is irritable, and consequently fits not unfrequently occur in the animals. You may try the effect of feeding rather sparely, chiefly on milk and fish, keeping it quiescent, and if the fits continue giving a grain of bromide of potassium in milk daily.

Rubbing

Cats are attracted by smells and rub their heads or roll on the attractive agent. This has nothing to do with deficiency of minerals in the water supply. In addition to rubbing themselves against the particular agent, they will sometimes eat it, as with catmint.

Tortoiseshell Toms (1916)

[Is there such a thing as a tortoiseshell tom cat? I am told that there is not, and certainly I cannot remember ever having seen one; but I have also heard that 1 out of every 40,000 tortoiseshell cats born is a male. What is the truth of the matter, please?]

In the second volume of his *Variations of Animals and Plants Under Domestication*, Darwin remarks: 'The peculiar colour called tortoiseshell is very rarely seen in a male cat, the males of this variety being of a rusty tint.' The late Mr Lydekker, in his volume on cats, thus refers to the tortoiseshell variety: 'Another well marked breed is characterised by the male being usually *sandy*, and the female of the so-called *tortoiseshell* colour; although at least one instance of a true tortoiseshell tom has been recorded. . . . The true tortoiseshell should be a mixture of fawn colour and black; but there are numerous parti-coloured cats, such as white fawn and black, and grey white and sandy, which are frequently termed tortoiseshell, and it is probable that the majority of so-called "tortoiseshell toms" belong to this class.'

Ferret Death (1900)

The ferret died of disease of the brain. A very large proportion of the ferrets die from the unnatural conditions under which they are kept, closely confined in foul hutches, where no exercise is possible, and fed on unnatural foods.

Guinea-pigs on Grass

Guinea-pigs can be kept outside all the year round if the runs and hutches are really well made and draught-proof. They should be situated in a place sheltered from winds in winter and from too much sun in summer. Hay is best for bedding. We suggest a smooth-coated variety for a start; the rough-coated varieties are likely to need grooming. Their food consists of hay, crushed oats, a little bran (dry), and, to a lesser extent, apple peelings, groundsel, dandelion, clover and lettuce.

Green Lizard

The lizard you describe is a European species commonly known as the green lizard, plentiful in pet shops in summer. During the warm weather lizards will eat any kind of insect, including, of course, mealworms. They will sometimes eat a piece of tomato, orange or half a grape. Water must be supplied. They are not easy to keep during the winter; if they are allowed to hibernate they usually die, and unless supplies of mealworms are available they are very hard to feed. They must be kept warm in a temperature of 60°F.

Python Care

The Royal python from Ghana is normally a very gentle species. They require heat (65–70°F), and benefit if some of this comes from a light-source such as a 60 watt bulb hung about 18 in above the floor of the cage. The cage must be reasonably large, though the creature is not terribly active. The front should be of glass and the top well ventilated. Put soft sand on the floor and a few large stones to give a retreat. Supply a fair-sized bath of water. These pythons sometimes are slow to feed in captivity. They eat rats, mice and will take a freshly dead bird such as one may find as a road casualty. Offer food weekly, but it may be 2–3 weeks or so before another meal is required. Reduce heat a little at night and switch off the light.

Pet Squirrels (1861)

(1) I am happy to be able to inform M.L. that I had a pet squirrel for upwards of 2 years, and always kept it in a small cage with a sleeping box attached. A small collar with a light steel chain is useful to take the little animal out of doors. It should be constantly provided with bread soaked in warm milk, and squeezed dry when cold. This should be changed every morning. It may have as many nuts as it can eat, and occasionally a few acorns. Mine would sleep in my pocket, and run over my shoulders with the greatest familiarity. [Clwyd, R.M. College]

(2) A few years ago I purchased 3 nestling squirrels, and believe they had been captured about 10 days. Considering the ordinary squirrel-cage as cruel, I obtained a large double breeding-cage, in which I had bred canaries. From this I removed all the lower perches, leaving only the 2 upper ones. Removing the lid of a cigar-box, I fastened the box with wires at one end of the cage, near the top; this, partly filled with soft hay, formed the bed. The bottom of the cage I strewed with fine dry sand, and then turned the squirrels into their new home. Their food consisted of bread soaked in milk, and squeezed nearly dry. Occasionally I gave them a few nuts, almonds, and similar fruits. They were constantly supplied with water, but drank sparingly. They consisted of 2 females and a male; the 2 former became extremely tame, but the male was always a little shy. Their antics were most amusing, and I frequently opened the cage door, and let them scamper about the room. The male never left the cage many inches, but the females gambolled over every corner of the room – would get on the dessert-table, and assist themselves to nuts. There was no difficulty in getting them into the cage again, and all three would readily take nuts from the hands of those they knew – but were shy with strangers, and were very irritable if handled. They all knew their names, and would come out of their bed when called. They seemed quite happy and contented.

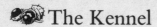 The Kennel

Beagles as House Dogs

Beagles are usually considered to be very charming characters and very even tempered, both with other dogs and with human beings. They should be reliable enough with children. They are not, however, very easy to train, as they have the independent nature, and strong desire to roam and hunt, that is common to all the hound breeds. They are robust little dogs, and eat a good deal for their size without becoming fat.

Beware of the Dog

The notice 'BEWARE OF THE DOG' has this disadvantage, namely that if your dog does bite any one, it can hardly be denied that the dog was known to be dangerous. In court this may be important. 'GUARD DOG' is probably better.

Biscuits: Why?

While dogs are basically carnivorous, they are also omnivorous. In their wild state they will eat viscera from the abdominal cavity, including the guts and its contents, along with flesh and skin, the latter in many ways acting as roughage and so assisting movement of the bowels. Dog biscuits, apart from producing energy, also act as roughage. In the main, carnivorous animals feed on herbivorous ones.

Buckthorn Cure (1892)

Reduce the diet, and with bread and house scraps mix green vegetables, which give him, and plenty of exercise. Rub the places well daily with the following mixture: Sulphur and whale oil each 4 oz; oil of tar and mercurial ointment each ¼ oz; of course mix well. When cured, do not feed him so freely, and give every month or so a tablespoonful of buckthorn and castor oil.

Cold Soup (1900)

At the age of 10 years a dog may be expected to suffer from digestion troubles. Keep the animal on liquid food, chiefly milk and cold soup without salt, for some time. Leave off the cod liver oil, which is likely to make any animal sick.

What is a Colley? (1887)

In the Dictionary of Husbandary, published 1793, the word 'colley' is defined as follows: 'Colley (sheep) such sheep as have black faces and legs. The wool of these sheep is very harsh, with hairs, and not so white as that of other sheep.' Modern lexicographers have not followed the compilers of this agricultural work, and now a colley is known as a certain variety of sheep dog – a Scotch colley, to wit. The latter, according to modern ruling, may be of any colour, and as a fact their coats are not particularly harsh. The name colley is understood to spring from a Gaelic one, signifying rough or shaggy, but some dictionaries have 'colley' as a variety of dog much esteemed by Scotch shepherds, and also 'to render black or dark, as if with coal smut'.

Crackling Joints (1916)

A crackling noise in the joints is often indicative of the rheumatoid diathesis.

Crossbred Gundogs (1865)

We have thought of the Colley as a good cross, and of the black or black-tan setter, but we should decidedly select the Newfoundland as the mother. A great authority has declared to us that the most useful general dog for the gun will be found in the foxhound and greyhound combined; Colquhoun prefers the mixture of the beagle and pointer, and puts the weight at 10 lb. We cannot say we agree with either. And the extraordinary feats of 'Craven's' bull-terrier retriever would not induce us to break a dog of *that* breed for such a purpose. We believe, however, the size of the Newfoundland must be reduced by the selection of the smallest specimens in litters, and that it will be a work of time to obtain these desiderata – economy in keep or food, portability, and yet strength and activity, combined with *sense*. The other essential faculties we have little doubt will be heightened and improved by an admixture of fresh blood, for the cross-bred dog is frequently more 'cute' than either of his high-born parents.

Evolution of the Dachshund (1948)

The dachshund may have originated in Egypt as your friend says, but it is solely conjectural; and the bas-reliefs of a dog something resembling the dachshund are possibly only coincidental. There is no evidence of it having come from Cornwall. Reasoning from evolution, the dachshund is a dwarfed, short and crooked-legged, sharp-nosed edition of the bloodhound, the most familiar missing link between the two being the Basset Hound. But even a greater resemblance is seen in the Dachsbrach, of Germany, and the Basset Braque of France (the same dog – both black and tan). Thus, through the bloodhound, the dachshund is directly descended from the St Hubert Hound – whence come all the hounds of scent. Therefore the dachshund is truly a hound, and so classified. The German 'Hund' of course means dog, not hound – *Dachs* (badger) *Hund* (dog) – a dog used for going to ground to the badger. They were used in Germany for this purpose, although terriers are preferred in this country. The breed first arrived in England about 1850, and attained a fair share of popularity especially a few years later when it was taken up by Queen Victoria and Queen Alexandra, the Princess of Wales.

Distemper (1900)

Your description is so graphic that it is quite easy to tell the story of your dog's illness. The dullness, swelling, and discharge from the eyes meant distemper, from which the animal recovered except the 'jumping', which indicates a not uncommon sequel, viz. chorea (St Vitus's dance). The itchy skin is another common result. Chorea is rarely cured, but if the dog is a favourite or valuable, consult a veterinary surgeon; otherwise have the animal destroyed.

The Dropper

The first cross pointer-setter, known as a 'dropper', was at one time quite popular with bird-dog enthusiasts in this country and Scotland. Providing the parents come of good working stock there is no reason why your puppies, the result of an accidental mating of an English setter bitch with a pointer, should not make very efficient pointing dogs. We have heard of 3 droppers which the owners consider far superior to either pure pointers or setters.

Feeding a Mastiff

[Would the addition to a household of an English mastiff cause a noticeable increase in the household budget?]

An Old English mastiff would indeed cause a considerable increase in the household budget inasmuch as his requirements of raw meat alone would be 3 lb a day. He would also need a suitable quantity of biscuit and rusks mixed with his meat.

Homemade Dog Biscuits (1953)

It is doubtful much economy can be effected, but quite a good formula for the making of dog cake or biscuits is as follows: Wholemeal flour 65 parts, oat meal 25 parts, white fish meal or meat and bone-meal (feeding quality) 10 parts. The dough may be mixed with water, or milk and water.

Labradors and Children

The question of colour has no bearing at all on the temperament of the dog. Both black and yellow occur in the same litter and the majority of strains carry both colours for generations. Blacks are frequently preferred by shooting people, as the yellows are often very difficult to see in light-coloured undergrowth, and in consequence many of the best field trial strains are mostly black. Certain strains in all breeds produce faults of temperament, such as nervousness or bad temper, and though the Labrador is less liable to this than most breeds, care should be taken to inquire about the parents. Usually the best temperaments are to be found among dogs which are not only trained to their natural work but are themselves used to everyday human companionship and affection. Labradors are very clean as house dogs, and their short coats bring in the minimum of dirt, and require the minimum of grooming. They do not need an enormous amount of exercise, and the family dog will keep very healthy on a short daily walk, particularly if it has freedom about the house and garden and a child to play with.

Labrador Club (1900)

'Labrador retrievers' are attracting some special attention just now, and classes have been provided for them at two recent shows. There is little difference between them and the ordinary flat-coated retriever. There are so few of the breed in the country that the success of a club would be unlikely. Moreover, dog clubs are not altogether an unmixed blessing, partaking too much of the family party character.

Mottled Labrador Puppies

[Before mating my black Labrador dog with my yellow Labrador bitch I was assured that the puppies would be black, yellow, or, perhaps, both. However, 6 of the puppies have grey, mottled coats. Why?]

The explanation is that the yellow bitch has a black dog somewhere among her ancestors and that, in breeding parlance, she is not a true yellow. In genetical language, black is dominant to red or yellow, which accounts for the mixture of colours in the puppies.

Light Iris (1923)

The light colour of the iris is not attractive, but a very good one for sight and endurance. Climatic influence must be kept in mind, with always in hot countries a tendency to reversion to the type of the region. No, a second or super-fetation is always possible, but the primary one stands good. In the case of dogs we cannot wholly exclude mental influences, as they are on a wholly different intellectual plane from that of animals of the farm. Such close in-breeding is not desirable but the experiment would be a very interesting one to observe.

Lurcher Breeding

These dogs have been evolved mostly by gypsies for catching rabbits and hares. The basic breed in their ancestry is a running dog, usually greyhound, and less often whippet. These are crossed with a working breed such as (and usually) collie, flatcoat or golden retriever, saluki, and even Bedlington terrier, and then perhaps back to greyhound, the aim being to produce something fast, silent and enduring. The collie cross endows the lurcher with sagacity. There is a strain called a Norfolk lurcher – a particularly shaggy beast. Most lurchers, incidentally, are broken-coated, but there are a few smooth ones because of a heavy infusion of greyhound or whippet blood in their ancestries. The most successful cross is greyhound and Scotch Border Collie, i.e. the working sheepdog. To cross Labrador and greyhound, which is your suggestion, would be working completely at cross-purposes: the heavily built Labrador would detract from the greyhound, and the greyhound, which hunts by sight, would detract from the Labrador's 'nose'. The same arguments apply against a cocker and whippet cross.

Mexican Hairless Dog (1948)

I lived in Tucuman, a province of the Argentine Republic, for 10 years before the first world war. There, one frequently saw hairless dogs in the homes of the natives, generally of the poorer class, who often used them as a cure for rheumatism, making them take the place of a hotwater bottle in their beds. The most usual colour was a dark grey, others were pink and yet others spotted pink and grey. The pink ones usually had a tuft of white hair on the forehead. Quite a few had a considerable number of warts. I do not remember if they were mute. Size and shape were very variable but none were bigger than a fox terrier and in general they were smaller. The natives called the dogs *Peludo*, meaning bald. [C. M. Dammers, late Commander R.N., Riverside, California]

Milk Eyewash

We think the running from the eye will disappear in due course. In the meantime foment them night and morning with lukewarm milk and water; ordinary eye lotions are likely to do more harm than good under the circumstances.

Nose Colour Change

[The nose of my lemon and white cocker bitch is constantly changing colour from black to light brown. How can I make it stay black?]

It is possible that the addition of a complete mineral mixture specially compounded for dogs, and containing the trace elements cobalt, copper and manganese, would have the effect of stabilising the metabolism of the iron in the food, which at present appears to be erratic.

An Old Man's Gundog

The clumber spaniel has long been looked on as an old man's shooting dog. They are slow but painstaking, and are quite outstanding in retrieving runners if you give them time. The breed declined in popularity because clumbers were not fast enough when compared with the English springer. Clumbers were used at Sandringham by King Edward VII and King George V, but the kennel was sold between the wars.

Dog in a Rabbit Trap (1955)

The law may be stated as follows: (1) Spring traps set for catching rabbits must be placed under cover – for example, down the hole and not in the entrance. (2) One is not liable for damage which is done by one's trespassing dog provided that the damage is that which it is natural for a dog to do. This is a general rule; but there is the Dogs (Protection of Livestock) Act, 1953, which makes the owner of a dog guilty of an offence if it worries livestock or poultry on agricultural land. (3) If a dog does trespass on one's land and is injured, for example in a rabbit trap, one is not liable to the owner of the dog although, if the trap was set in the open, one would have committed an offence.

Relative Speeds (1860)

[In regard to your leader of last Saturday, and in reference to what you call 'the trail hound' and a cross between the 'greyhound and foxhound', I can assure you that one of the best trials of the relative speed and stoutness of a bloodhound, and a dog between the Scotch deer 'gaze hound' or 'greyhound', once removed from the first cross with foxhound, took place with me while hunting deer on the prairies of the Far West. In the first twenty minutes the greyhound cross in silence and speed had all his own way, but after that he stood still and the bloodhound left him out of sight.]

This supports our statement, as the greyhound cross was first for 20 minutes, and our remarks were only intended to apply to the distance run over in half that time. We all know that the foxhound is stouter than the greyhound, and outlasts any other dog, as well as the horse, when the trial is extended beyond 5 or 6 miles. But the present question is in relation to the speed for 4 miles only.

Retriever or Labrador?

There are 4 varieties in the retriever group recognised by the English Kennel Club: curly-coated, flat-coated, golden and Labrador. Colloquially they are referred to as curlies, flats, goldens and Labs. A retriever is not necessarily a Labrador, but a Labrador is a retriever; thus for clarity in definition it is advisable to use the full name Labrador retriever, golden retriever, and so on. There are a few retrievers in England named Chesapeake Bay retrievers, having been imported from America and Canada, but they do not figure in the Kennel Club breeds.

Rheumatism in the Kennels (1916)

It should be treated as rheumatism by, first, an aperient, and then by doses of salicylate of sodium. Hounds may be given 10 g nightly, for 5 days at a time. It is well to make an interval, and give for a few days a dram of sulphate of sodium dissolved in water as a drench every morning before having any food. A gelatine capsule containing a dram of aloes and 10 g ground ginger should be given before another course of the salicylate. As an embrocation, the addition of 1 part oil of turpentine to 3 parts ammonia liniment of the pharmacopaeia. 'Very well-built kennels' does not inform us as to the most objectionable feature in a kennel or a pigsty, namely, the tendency to condensation of the breath and of moisture from other causes. We have seen most rheumatism and cramp in 'model' buildings, so called, and for the foregoing reason.

Seal Oil and Epsom Salts (1892)

Rub the sore places daily with powdered sulphur and seal oil each 4 oz, oil of tar and mercurial ointment each ¼ oz. There is no occasion to muzzle the dog. On alternate mornings give as much Epsom salts as will lie on a shilling. Wash thoroughly with any of the dog soaps before commencing the applications. In case the treatment is not successful, in place of the salts sprinkle on his food daily 5 drops Fowler's solution of arsenic, increasing it gradually to 12 drops. Then discontinue for a week, and recommence with the 5 drops. A dog that has been in the state of yours for 12 months cannot easily be cured.

Spaniel and Horse

Spaniels are often independent, preferring to use their own initiative. If your 3-year-old cocker spaniel bitch enjoyed following when you are on horseback, she would do so. As she apparently no longer does so, there would seem little pleasure in forcing her. Maybe she has received a kick at some time, which naturally would make her wary of continuing the practice. Perhaps she had a break in the opportunity to accompany the horses and fell out of the habit. Or possibly she was following you, if you were leading the horses in on foot when she was a puppy, rather than following the horses. If you now ride through woodland or other inviting country, the spaniel probably has interests of her own to investigate, more exciting than jogging along behind a horse's heels.

The Talbot

The Talbot dog appears often in our literature. It seems Chaucer first made mention of it and apparently he implied that Talbot was the individual name for a 'very goode dogge' he knew. There is a tradition that soon after the Norman Conquest a member of the Talbot family brought a dog from abroad that took its name from the family. However, in due course, the Talbot dog was well known as an animal of the chase. It seems to have been a modified form of the early bloodhound. It was heavily jawed, had great power and endurance, delighted in the pursuit of blood and was particularly good at staghunting. It was good at tracking as well. It is extinct now and is mainly remembered as the ancestor of sporting dogs.

Tannin and Whisky (1900)

Try a lotion composed of 10 grains of tannin in a wineglass of whisky. To be applied with a small soft brush 2 or 3 times a day.

A Terrier's Friends

I have a rough fox terrier dog just 2 years old. He frequently goes off by himself, and comes home after a time accompanied by other dogs. A few days ago he brought home a large retriever, which followed him upstairs, and I had some trouble in getting rid of him. This afternoon he left me when out for a walk, and came home an hour or two later with 7 other dogs, among which was a large St Bernard which belongs to a house in the same road. It is getting rather a nuisance. Can anyone explain this for me, or tell me how to stop it? There can be no possible doubt as to the sex of my dog. [Teufel]
[*Editor's note: This slightly desperate letter failed to evoke any helpful response, either from* THE FIELD *or its readers.*]

Tomato Cure (1897)

They may be cured by the application of the juice from the stems of the tomato plant. Bicarbonate of soda applied slightly damped is usually effectual, but it is dangerous to use nitric acid or nitrate of silver. There is nothing to account for their appearance.

Trespassing Dog

It is well established in law that a dog owner is not liable for his dog's trespass. Try shutting your neighbour's dog up (if you can catch it) and decline to release it until the damage it has done has been compensated. The difficulty would be to quantify the damage. The most effective remedy is to teach the dog not to trespass on your property. The methods used need not be too gentle.

Trimming (1923)

The best instrument for trimming is a pair of barber's clippers; the face may be lathered and close-shaved with a safety razor. Do not attempt to shave the loose lips or under the jaw. The throat is optional. The front legs are clipped or shaved all round in a ring about 3 in wide above the knee, leaving a 'bangle' of long hair on the pasterns. The same with the hind legs above and below the hocks. The docked tail is clipped like a drumstick, leaving a rounded knob, or a long tuft of hair at the extremity. The waist is also clipped all round from the middle of the body aft to the loin, and it is fashionable to leave islands of hair on either side of this girdle, shaped according to fancy. The ear feathering, the top knot and mane should be kept full length, but abaft the shoulders and about the hips the coat may be shortened by judicious trimming. Keep the hair fluffy by frequent use of brush and comb.

Warts and Blood (1900)

A correspondent some time ago described the curative effect of fresh blood in a case of warts in a dog's mouth. The dog was taken to a slaughter house and the mouth was pushed into a tin of warm blood. The operation was repeated on 3 occasions at intervals of a week or two. The warts gradually dropped off.

[The questioner wrote again 8 months later: 'Before trying your suggestion I allowed my old gardener to try his hand, and he got rid of all the warts (there were dozens on jaws, tongue, and roof of mouth) by rubbing them with the inside of the pod of a broad bean. Another excellent remedy is the application of the juice from the tomato plant.]

The Sporting Life

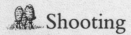 Shooting

Boiled Pistol

The best way to treat the corrosion in the barrels of your 6-chambered pinfire pistol is to detach the barrels, boil them in water for a short time and then take them out and dry them. While they are still hot, immerse them in a good oil. In this way the oil gets right into the pores of the metal and seals up the corrosion.

Bolting Rabbits (1892)

If you have only a small number of rabbits to turn out, there is no method so certain of success as running ferrets through the burrows. If you, however, expect to kill a good many rabbits, the management of ferrets will occupy too much time, for by burning fuse, and using paper saturated in a liquid as described, *one* man can work as many burrows in an hour as it would take a man with ferrets an entire day to attend to, for ferrets will often perversely remain underground, and require frequent digging to free them, or else perhaps fasten to a rabbit, and refuse to leave it. The first time in the current season you bolt your rabbits, utilise fuse and paper saturated with spirits of tar. The second time you will probably have to resort to ferrets, as rabbits *never* bolt on the second occasion nearly so freely as they do on the first. The third time you may be forced to dig most of your rabbits out – in fact, catch them and turn them loose, as, from their previous experiences, they will often prefer to die in their burrows rather than quit them for a third time. If you wish to kill, let us say, about 300 rabbits in the day, you will have to show above ground from 350 to 400, though this is a question that will in great measure depend on the weather, on the amount of shelter available, and also whether the rabbits have a chance of avoiding the guns. The details of using fuses and paper are set out elsewhere in this issue at considerable length.

The Gun-maker Knows Best (1855)

Sir – It being a well-known fact that gun-makers know a vast deal more about sporting matters than anybody else; and, although they may never have seen hill or moor, may have passed the whole of their time behind a counter in London, may have acted as light porter 'and made themselves generally useful', yet I repeat, no sooner do they muster the means, open a shop and sell guns, than they know more about sporting matters than sportsmen can possibly know; for, if this were not the case, how could I, along with some others of my shopkeeping compatriots, presume to publish *Instructions to Sportsmen*, telling them how to behave in the field, and cautioning them against shooting themselves? I do not know exactly how this immense amount of information gets into us, but I think it must be by a kind of inspiration. . . . Let it be granted, then, that I have this knowledge – and you may be sure I take it for granted. . . . Let us proceed. The first thing to be avoided is shooting yourself; and in order to avoid this you should hold your gun as far off as possible, and upright. . . . This position may not be either elegant or convenient, but with that I have nothing to do; it is safe. . . . It may also be rather fatiguing, unless you use one of my light guns (here the printer is politely requested to add my name and address, for you cannot suppose I am taking all this trouble and giving all this important information for nothing). There is only one other objection that I can see to the arm's length and upright principle; you may, in going through heather, which I am told is tough stuff, stumble against hidden obstructions, and so fall down headlong, with the muzzle of the gun pointing forwards; but you have this consolation, it cannot shoot you, though it may your dog or your companion. Secondly, you must not let your companion shoot you and the way to avoid this is to make him go first, for he is not likely under any circumstances to shoot behind him. Thirdly, you must not shoot your companion, should you have one; but, as this is more his look-out than yours, I need not enlarge on this head. Fourthly, you must avoid as much as possible shooting your dogs; the best way is to let your birds get a good way off – say 60 or 70 yards. This will not be too far, provided you use one of my long-range guns. . . . Perhaps after all it would be as well to clothe your dog with a good thick blanket, which would serve the double purpose of keeping out the shot and keeping your dog warm on the cold and bleak hills of Scotland, where there is snow all the year round; and in order to protect the sportsman from the incessant snow and rain of that dreary region, I would advise the use of my 'patent dorsal umbrella', which, being inserted into a socket between the shoulders, protects the shooter and leaves both his arms at liberty. By attending to the above instructions, particularly those about holding the gun upright and at arm's length, and the umbrella contrivance, you cannot fail of cutting a good figure and of being tolerably safe at the same time. . . . P.S. I intend shortly to publish a book. . . . It will be richly illustrated by a gentleman who knows nearly as much about shooting as I do.

[*Editor's note: The above extracts are from a letter from a London gun-maker, written with tongue in cheek, in the context of considerable correspondence in which gun-makers and gun-users did their best to outwit each other. The anonymous writer's full letter, and its sequence the following week, are worthy of publication in their entirety but unfortunately we only have space for a few lines here to whet the appetite. The second letter described important matters such as deep thought, blow-pipes, long-bows, crooked guns for one-eyed men. . . .*]

Jubilee Long Shot (1892)

A shot was fired at Shoeburyness in 1887 (and called the Jubilee shot) from a 9 ft 2 in wire gun at an angle of 40 degrees elevation, by which it was thought an extreme range would be obtained. The actual range was 20,236 yards (or about $11\frac{1}{2}$ miles).

Needle Rifles (1854)

In a few weeks I shall perhaps be able to speak to your correspondent 'Caledonia' with authority respecting 'Needle Rifles'; but I know little about revolving fire-arms, and I am rather prejudiced against them, because I am certain that if they are got up cheaply, and not most carefully made, they are very dangerous. It strikes me that, except with an air-gun, it would be impossible to shoot rabbits with the small bullets with such success, because the report of the gun would drive them away so as to afford you time to load over and over again; and, for that reason, a revolver would be of no use. As to very young – almost unfledged – rooks, it might be different; because they would sit, without moving, for several successive shots to be made at them. But bullets are nasty things to play with, and are useless and dangerous for running and flying shots; you never know where they go, or what damage they may do. I shot at a small bird with an air-gun last year out of a parlour window. The bird was sitting on an iron fence; the bullet struck the hurdle and glanced back, and hit the window-sill close to myself and a friend who was sitting by me. We immediately put down the air-gun and resumed our bottle of port; a much more safe and agreeable pastime than playing with bullets. [Umbra]

Pepperbox Revolver

Your muzzle-loading pistol with 6 revolving barrels, inscribed J. R. Cooper, Patent, is known as a Pepperbox revolver. It was made by Joseph Rock Cooper, who took out a patent for this on 20 September 1849. It is, of course, English made. It was loaded from the muzzle with a charge of black powder and a round lead bullet, and primed with a copper cap.

Pinfire Gun (1955)

Your old double-barrel, breech-loading gun, the hammers of which when it is fired strike pins which are in the rims of each shell and protrude through a hole drilled in the barrels where they close flush with the breech stock, and engraved 'William Moore, London', is known as a pinfire and its date will be between 1862 and 1865. The maker, William Moore, was one of the finest gun-makers of London. He made only the best-quality weapons and his guns are collectors' items today. The firm went out of business about 40 years ago. The pinfire fired the first type of gastight cartridge used in breech-loaders. These guns are quite obsolete in England and cartridges are no longer made for them. However, some are still used in Europe, and you might be able to obtain cartridges from Paris. You must first ascertain the actual gauge, as pinfire guns were commonly made in 14 and 16 gauge as well as 12. If your gun happens to be the 14 gauge we are afraid it is very doubtful whether you will get 'shells' as this size became obsolete long ago. We would add that the gun should be used only with ammunition loaded with black powder.

Record Bag in Hungary (1909)

On 10 December 1909, 8 guns shooting on Count Louis Karolyi's estate at Totmegyer killed 6,125 pheasants (all wild reared), 150 hares and 50 partridges.

Ring Bulge (1930)

The 'narrow circular expansion' which you describe as having occurred in one of the barrels of your gun about 8 in from the breech is undoubtedly what is known as a 'ring bulge' – that is, a bulge in the barrel which extends all round the circumference and gives the appearance of a ring on a finger. A ring bulge can be produced in one way, and one way only – namely, by the presence of some obstruction in the bore, and the existence of such a bulge is conclusive proof that some sort of obstruction must have been present in the bore on one occasion when you fired. It is quite possible for a light obstruction to be present and to result in a slight ring bulge being formed without the shooter being aware of anything unusual occurring at the time. It is impossible now to say definitely what the obstruction in your gun could have been, as the ring bulge may have been produced a comparatively long time back. But we agree with your gunmaker that the most probable cause is a card wad being left in the bore. Such an occurrence is rare, but is by no means unknown, and can only be regarded as a bit of extraordinary bad luck.

Shooting Boots (1861)

It is well known that the happiness of life is made up of trifles – so of walking and shooting. The man who neglects, in sporting matters, what may appear to be trifles, will generally meet with disappointment. Well-fitting boots are of the first importance; for more men, while shooting, fail in their feet than from bodily fatigue. Even bad boot-laces are an annoyance. We can confirm that the only good laces are those which are cut out of circular pieces of leather. The strongest lace is from the collar-maker's whit-leather.

Sniperscope (1916)

We are not quite sure what a 'sniperscope' is like. This is evidently the trade name of some kind of cousinly relation to a periscope. You had better ask Messrs Thos. Walker and Son Ltd., of 58, Oxford-street, Birmingham, to send you printed particulars of their periscope rifle stock, and ask your son whether this is what he wants.

Sunday and Christmas Day (1887)

Under the 1 & 2 Will.4, c.32, s.3, any person whatsoever who shall kill or take any game, or use any dog, gun, net, or other engine or instrument for the purpose of killing or taking any game on a Sunday or Christmas Day, is liable to a penalty of £5.

Sunday Shooting (1969)

We assume that your questions relate only to land on which you have the shooting rights. Hares are game and it is illegal to kill them

Duck-shooting in July

on Sundays either by shooting or coursing. A game licence is not required to course hares, but it is required to shoot them. You may both course and shoot rabbits on Sundays. So far as birds are concerned, in most areas it is permissible for you to kill pigeons on Sundays, and also wildfowl, but in certain areas the killing of birds on Sundays has been prohibited. You must make inquiries from the police in the area where your land is.

Teamwork with a Loader

There is no hard-and-fast etiquette for shooting with a pair of guns, though certain basic principles must be observed. When the gun is shooting from the right shoulder the loader should stand to his right and slightly behind. When no. 1 gun is empty the shooter passes it to his loader with his right hand, the gun being held at the small of the butt; the loader takes it with his right hand, grasping it at the fore-end and at the same time presenting the second gun so that the shooter can grasp it by the fore-end with his left hand. This is the usual drill, but when a gun and loader shoot regularly together they may adopt a slightly different drill, the point being that the loader gets to know the shooter's movements and can anticipate them. Shooting with a strange loader is always inclined to be a little slow at first, as the essence of success with 2 guns is team work, leading to quick changing of weapons. It is not usual for the shooter to break his gun before passing to his loader; it is the loader's job to eject and re-load and have the second weapon in readiness as quickly as possible. One essential to be observed is safety. When changing guns the barrels must be pointing to the sky, while the loader usually turns slightly to the right, away from the shooter, when putting in fresh cartridges. The gun is handed over at 'safe'.

Winged Duck (1860)

A duck, if pursued after being winged, usually makes the attempt to dive, and unless the wing is broken close to the body he is able to get under water, but cannot dive far. If the wing is broken close to the body he cannot dive at all.

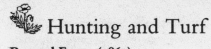 Hunting and Turf

Bagged Foxes (1860)

We cannot encourage the purchase of bagged foxes.

Bloody Shouldered Arabian

The Bloody Shouldered Arabian painted by John Wooton was sent from Aleppo *circa* 1719 by Nathaniel Harley to his brother Edward Harley who gave him to his nephew, Edward Lord Harley, afterwards second Earl of Oxford. Among the progeny of the Bloody Shouldered Arabian, so named from red hairs on his shoulder, was the Duke of Bolton's Sweepstakes, who got the dam of Lord Rockingham's Whistlejacket. He was also the sire of Sir N. Curzon's Brisk, winner of several Royal Plates and also great-dam of the famous Old Tartar mare, from whom descended Queen Mab and many of the winners bred by Lord Strathmore and whose blood is found in some of the best pedigree today. The Bloody Shouldered Arabian was eventually bought for £115 from Lord Oxford by the 6th Duke of Somerset for his stud at Petworth.

Gingering (1898)

Thomas Sizeland, groom, in the employ of Capt. Scot, Worcester Park, Surrey, was summoned by the Royal Society for the Prevention of Cruelty to Animals for having cruelly treated two thorough-bred horses, named respectively Telegram and Leopold, by a practice commonly called 'gingering', on the occasion of the competition between the two English thoroughbreds and the American mustang, ridden by Leon on the 10 November at the Agricultural Hall. Christopher Nicholls stated that during the race Leopold was taken to the stables in a distressed condition. In the stables he saw the defendant take something from his mouth and apply it to the horse. The horse was then run from 5.25 p.m. on the Friday until 7.40 p.m., when it was stopped, owing to a protest from Mr Colam, the secretary of the Society for Prevention of Cruelty to Animals. Telegram was then brought out and ridden for an hour, and covered 6 miles. The witness saw the horse in the stable, and he saw the defendant take some ginger from his mouth and treat the animal in the same way as Leopold. Telegram then appeared very uneasy and lashed out. The race was stopped after that on the protest of nearly everyone present. Telegram was taken to the stable because he could not be induced to go round the hall further, not because of distress. Cross-examined, Professor Wm

Pritchard, Royal Veterinary College, bore testimony as to the cruel nature of the practice of 'gingering': he would swear that the application of ginger in the manner described would not give a distressed animal a feeling of comfort and warmth. The conclusion was that it was a case of cruelty, and that the whole affair was very discreditable to all parties concerned. The penalty would be £5, and £5 costs.

Guaranteed Sport (1900)

There is no county in the United Kingdom in which a good day's sport can be guaranteed. Provided that you subscribe the requisite amount, the Whaddon Chase can easily be reached, and so can the Essex, Essex Union, and Hertfordshire. Within reach of London are the Queen's, Lord Rothschild's, Mr Rawle's, the Essex, Surrey, and West Surrey Staghounds. Bletchley, for Whaddon Chase; Chelmsford, for Essex; Slough, for The Queen's; Aylesbury, for Lord Rothschild's; Redhill, for Surrey, are convenient centres.

High Jump (1898)

The best-authenticated high jump we know of is that achieved by a horse called Rosebery at the Chicago Horse Show in 1893. He is reported to have cleared 6 ft 11¾ in.

High Jump (1953)

The world record high jump was achieved in 1949 by Captain A. P. Morales. Riding Huaso, he cleared 8 ft ¼ in, at Santiago, Chile. The record in this country was set up in 1937 at Olympia when Mr Fred Foster's Swank, ridden by Donald Beard (brother to 'Curly' Beard) cleared 7 ft 6½ in.

Jumping Down Perpendiculars (1919)

At the riding school at Torres Novas there is a vertical descent of 15 ft, which has to be negotiated several times by each of the cadets, and it is, as may be seen from the photographs, an obstacle which requires exceptional qualities both in the horse and his rider. At Charneca de Atalaya, about 8 km from the riding school, there is another vertical drop of 15 ft, measured from the ground level to the water level of the river which flows at its foot, and this has been taken hundreds of times by cavalry cadets who have passed through the school during the past 10 years. It may be said in passing that these jumps are not altogether exempt from danger, but this we consider adds to their value not only from the sporting but from the military point of view, as they give confidence and boldness to our young cavalry officers. As regards the position of the rider in taking the jump, this may be clearly seen from the photographs, wherein the rider has his body inclined forward. Cadets are taught in the riding school to assume this position, which is surely the one which should be taught at all schools of military equitation. The rider should gallop and jump with his horse; it is only so that he obtains the necessary solidity and flexibility of seat which enables him to get the most out of his horse, and this has led all first-rate foreign horsemen, whether English, French, Italian, Belgian, or Portuguese, to abandon the old academical position for the modern elastic seat which permits the rider to deal with obstacles in perfect accord with the movements of his horse – in other words, to play an active and not a passive part in the performance. [Julio de Oliveira, Captain, Instructor of Equitation at the Portuguese Military Riding School]

Ladies at the Races (1900)

If the old stager were asked which of the social developments struck him the most forcibly, his answer could scarcely fail to be the everyday attendance of ladies. That ladies have assisted at races in the past, and even taken actual part in them on rare occasions, the history of the Turf informs us. The presence of gaily dressed ladies at Ascot and Goodwood affords a spectacle of no novelty whatever, but Ascot and Goodwood are social functions of high order and reputation. At Newmarket, where racing pure and simple is the programme, and where no string band charms the ear or delicacy-laden table panders to the palate, the feminine spectator was not such a great while since a scarce phenomenon, to be counted upon the fingers. This was in the days previous to the erection of the stand, a comparatively modern affair, and in the absence of any such shelter it was, on by no means rare occasions, no light thing to face the elements. (Newmarket has always been the slowest to adopt measures that tend to the greater convenience of visitors, perhaps by way of gentle reminder that 'The play's the thing', and that if good racing is provided on the finest of all racecourses, people should be perfectly satisfied.) The present season is the first in which provision has been made in the reserved inclosure (Tattersall's) for ladies in the shape of special seating accommodation. Previously the bare boards, covered with the dust from the soles of thousands of boots, was all there was to sit upon. Newmarket could not doubt subsist very comfortably without the handful of ladies who frequent

Tattersall's, and the incident is, therefore, noticeable as evidence of the mysterious force which compels all of us to march with the times.

Light Cavalry (1870)

The crushing weight of the accoutrements, etc., of even our light cavalry is a subject which constantly comes up for examination when any spasm of uneasiness or excitement causes us to distrust our military organisation, and just as constantly is dropped and forgotten whenever the excitement is past. Ever since the Crimean war this question has been discussed and shelved alternately, at intervals of a year to two, without any practical result. Perhaps in no part of the world has it so much interest for us as in India. There light, active cavalry, composed of men of the Ghoorkah stamp, and mounted on wiry, hardy little Arab-bred horses, are indispensable, and of these we ought to have a very large number, so that in case of any future mutiny (a by no means improbable contingency) we could command as much ubiquitousness and endurance as it is in the nature of any cavalry in the world to furnish.

Long Jump (1953)

The record long distance jump by a horse occurred during a showjumping competition held at Barcelona in 1951; Colonel Lopez Dell Hierro, riding Amado Mio, cleared 8.30 m over a water jump. A steeplechaser named The Chandler it is stated cleared 39 ft at Warwick on 22 March 1847.

The Lonsdale Drive (1891)

On 11 March 1891, Lord Lonsdale drove a single horse, a pair, a four-in-hand team, and a pair, postillion fashion, in 55 minutes 30 seconds on the Brighton road between Redhill and Crawley. The original wager with Lord Shrewsbury was £100, but there was no contest, as Lord Shrewsbury and his horses did not turn up. Lord Lonsdale therefore 'walked over'. The course was 5 miles, and this was covered once by each yoke. The ground was covered with half melted snow, and the going very heavy.

Lost Scent

Hounds lose the scent of a headed fox not because of any change in the scent given off by the fox, but because the extraneous cause of

MESSRS. THRUPP

INVITE attention to their improved Four-wheeled DOG-CART PHAETONS, now
now in so much request, from the superior safety and capacity of a vehicle on four wheels. The
prices will be found moderate for Dog-Carts, built to order, or selected from the superior stock, in
different sizes and colors, kept at 269, OXFORD STREET; where may also be seen Messrs. Thrupp's
newly-invented SHAMROCK DOG-CART, for small horses in England, India, or Australia.

the fox 'being headed' has intervened to capture, divert or destroy
the hounds' power of smelling. For instance, their attention to, and
powers of, smelling can be captured by the stronger scent of a flock
of sheep or of a vixen crossing the line; they can be diverted by the
disturbance of motor-cars, railway trains or human beings; and they
can be lost as the consequence of the fox passing along a watercourse
or wetted sunken road. Similar phenomena can be observed in
hunting with harriers, and can be reproduced in the training of
police dogs by means of drags damped with human sweat.

Moifaa

Moifaa, the 1904 Grand National winner, was a brown gelding by
Natator out of Denbigh. He was bred in New Zealand and bought
for £500 by Mr Spencer Gollan after winning three 'chases in New
Zealand. Mr Gollan was a wealthy sheep farmer and bloodstock
breeder in New Zealand, who raced in England. He sent Moifaa to
Hickey at Epsom, who had been a steeplechase jockey in New
Zealand. After a year in this country he ran 8 times, but his only
success was in the Grand National at the price of 25 to 1. He carried
10 st 7 lb. Moifaa had an adventurous career, being shipwrecked in
transit to England, and swimming ashore. Mr Gollan lost his life in
1934 by being run over by a bus in London. After the 1904 Grand
National, Moifaa was sold to King Edward VII, for whom he ran in
the 1905 Grand National. He was ridden by Lord Kitchener in the
Coronation procession of King George V in 1911.

The Nabob by The Nob (1860)

The Nabob, by The Nob, dam Hester by Camel.

Scrutator's Prejudices

'Scrutator' was Mr K. W. Horlock, who began keeping foxhounds in the year 1822. In the course of his career he hunted about Christian Malford, now in the Duke of Beaufort's country, and subsequently, on the resignation of Mr Warde, had the Craven hounds, of which he was master during Mr Assheton Smith's earlier years at Tedworth. Mr Horlock was the author of *Horses and Hounds*, *The Science of Foxhunting*, *Lessons on Hunting and Sporting*, besides several novels. Mr Horlock was well informed on everything concerning hunting, but was occasionally prejudiced in his views.

Social Goodwood (1892)

Ninety years ago, Goodwood had made its mark as a social function – that is to say, when the meeting was only 2 years old – as we find the reporter of a Chichester paper waxing very eloquent over the Duke of Richmond's new departure. 'To the efforts of equestrian skill,' we are told, 'is to be added the princely and almost unprecedented munificence of the noble founder of the Goodwood Races, in providing the newly erected stand, with a collation which might be entitled a general refrigerium; for the access was as easy as the reception was elegant and hospitable.' This newly erected stand, however, the magnificence of which so struck the eulogistic Chichester correspondent, turns out to have been only a small wooden building with a thatched roof; a poor substitute, according to our modern ideas, for the large and convenient erections now deemed necessary on every racecourse of any pretensions. In lieu of the luncheons now spread beneath the shade of the trees on the lawn, the earlier patrons of Goodwood managed with a sandwich, a crust of bread, a piece of cheese, with a glass of old October; while the ladies of the party sustained themselves with cake, fruit, and cowslip wine – a menu at which the racing woman of today would turn up her pretty nose.

Stirrup Cup and Jumping-Powder

The usual stirrup cup is port and the usual food, fruit-cake. You can count on up to 10 glasses from each bottle according to the size of the glasses. So you will need a dozen bottles at least because the portion of teetotallers is invariably offset by the 'jumping-powder' addicts.

Stout Boots for Hunting (1900)

Our own preference is for a moderately stout boot, not watertight; but this is a matter of opinion. You can scarcely have a boot which is at the same time stout and light. There is no particular kind to recommend, but it must be a boot which, whether made to measure or purchased ready-made, fits the foot and is not too small. If you use leggings at all, those made of box cloth are perhaps the coolest; but why not wear knickerbockers and stockings? You would perhaps find shoes more comfortable than boots.

Turf Handicaps (1900)

The difficulty of the handicapper is one which the Jockey Club is likely to have always with it, because so long as there are handicaps, so long will owners of a certain class make it their business to throw as much dust into the eyes of the handicappers as they can. The successful concealment of a horse's true form has long been considered as the most envied of racing fine arts with a section, and that not an inconsiderable one, of frequenters of the turf.

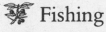 # Fishing

Benione

Benione, said in *The Compleat Angler* to be used for keeping otters off salmon waters, is an old and obsolete name for benzion, and the mention of this in the book seems to refer to the brittle, resinous product obtained from the tropical tree *Styrax benzoin*, now known as gum benjamin.

Cocks' Necks

A simple way to preserve gamecock necks for fly-tying is to rub the skin of the necks thoroughly with powdered alum and allow them to dry. Pack loosely with a few moth balls and keep them cool.

Colour of Rod (1855)

As to the colour of the rod, we do not consider this of itself to be unimportant; but, probably, one of the tints which most resembles that of the sticks and branches the fish are in the habit of seeing agitated by the wind on the banks of the river would be the least likely to excite their suspicion.

Coloured Prawns for Bait

The salmon-fisher's shrimp is normally a small prawn, but the true shrimp can be treated in the same way. For a more attractive colour boil before preserving; they can then be preserved in salt and will keep for several months. Put a layer of salt on a cloth; cover the prawns with salt and roll up the cloth. After 24–48 hours take out the prawns and pack in a bottle with fresh, dry salt. Another way is to put them in a jar containing a solution of glycerine and water in equal quantities, to which a little formalin (40% aqueous solution of formaldehyde) is added. Boil the prawns before treating them thus, and insert a length of fine but stiff wire into each prawn in order to straighten it out.

Creosote and Lobster Pots

The smell of creosote on a lobster pot will have dissipated sufficiently within 6 months, if the pot is in the open or in a well ventilated place, for it not to deter a crab or lobster. The pot could be used after a few days in sea water. But, as the fumes (smell) of creosote disappear, the preservative strength goes too. An organic solvent which is more penetrative would be better, being less smelly and longer lasting in effect from brush application.

Dabchicks and Fishing

Dabchicks feed mainly subaqueously. Their food varies considerably and includes fish of several species. They take small trout and will sometimes feed on the exposed ova of trout and salmon. In this, they harm trout fisheries, but, by eating such creatures as bullheads, they do good, too. Dabchicks are part of the pattern of river nature and a few pairs here and there should be tolerated. If they become a nuisance to fishermen, then some control is desirable. Do not kill off any creature simply because of some known damage it does. Often the good far exceeds the harm, and generally a fair balance arises.

Dapping with Live Insects

Hooks with a spring attachment for tethering live insects for dapping are made, but it is actually a very simple matter to make some yourself. Take an ordinary hook and some very fine spring steel wire. Spin the wire about 3 laps around the centre part of the hook shank, leaving the two ends of the wire standing up together, about ¼ in on the back of the hook. Use a little solder to keep the spring stays in the right position. The two ends of the wire can then be levered apart with a needle to allow the insertion of the bait between them. The spring tension will then act to grip the insect and hold it correctly. You can turn the ends of the spring wire to form nebs which will act to retain the grip.

Flashing Line (1953)

We are advised by the makers that it is indeed quite practical and possible to use silver nitrate to remove the glossiness or flash from nylon monofilament fishing lines by dipping them in a solution of the salt. An alternative method of staining is to dip the nylon line in strong tea.

Fly-fishing for Pensioners

Fly-fishing is a sport or pastime you can follow chiefly in the warmer (spring/summer) months of the year, and apart from any catch benefits it is a pleasant way of being in touch with the natural environment, relaxing to the senses, and should prove enjoyable rather than maddening to one of your years, for some time, mobility and fitness permitting. There are broadly 2 kinds of fly-fishing: dry-fly and wet-fly. Dry-fishing is probably the more interesting, more fun and easier than thought by many people. One fly-fisherman holds that the most important piece of equipment is a pin, to clean the eyes of flies of dirt, varnish etc., and facilitate threading and tying.

Fly-rod Woods (1855)

We consider that ash makes the best butt, the upper joints hickory, and the top bamboo. Some prefer having both the intermediate joints and the top of lance-wood, which is excellently adapted for the purpose, being, when not cross-grained, quite as strong as hickory, and possessing a most elastic spring. The objection to it consists in its being a great deal heavier than hickory; and if cut across the grain, as not unfrequently happens, but which is not perceptible through the dark varnish with which the rod is usually coated, it is not only apt but almost certain to splinter; and although when free from this defect it is well enough adapted to the lower part of the top joint, it is not so well suited to the extreme end as bamboo, as it will not bear being reduced to so small a size without greatly diminished strength and, even if free from cross-grain, is still apt to break in splinters with a heavy strain upon it. The best way to prevent this consequence is to take a turn or two of silk around the joint at intervals of about an inch asunder, from one end of the joint to the other, which, being well varnished over, will prevent the splintering in a great degree, and will add considerably to the strength and durability of the joint.

Foreshore Fishing (1916)

By Magna Charta and the statutes of Henry III, which confined its provisions, all tidal water vests in the Crown, and as such is free fishery for all subjects, saving exceptional cases where there is distinct proof that the Crown transferred its foreshore tidal rights to a subject prior to Magna Charta (as in the recent case of Fitzhardinge and Pascall).

Grow Your Own Worms

To breed worms in large numbers for fishing, you should obtain a large quantity of leaf mould and add a small quantity of manure – pig manure is good – boarded in at the sides like the leaf mould heaps in gardens, to use as a nursery. Then obtain as many 'gilt-tail' worms (also called cockspurs) as possible, by rooting about among decaying vegetable matter in a garden, and allow them to breed. After a few months, sift the mould taking out the full-grown ones and allowing the young to grow on. Replace any worms with the typical 'girdle' on them as these will lay eggs shortly. 'Brandlings' (the worms with the yellow rings all down their bodies) can be bred in manure, but will also increase reasonably in leaf mould if there is a percentage of pig manure with it.

Kinks in a Line

If your nylon spinning line is kinking despite using an anti-kink vane, a ball-bearing swivel would help if you are not using one. A reversible spin devon, or a pair of left- and right-hand devons will overcome this difficulty in future. To unkink the line, let it run off into fairly fast water without anything on the end and the kink will rapidly twist out. If this fails the line can be trailed through grass, which should take the twist out of it.

Knuckle in a Fly Line

If your oil-dressed silk fly line was bruised when it was crushed between a rock and a nail in your shoe, it may be advisable to cut it and splice it together. Scrape 2 in of each end (3 in for a salmon line) free of dressing and unravel ½ in of each with a needle. Paint the scraped, but not the unravelled parts thinly with a solution of cobbler's wax, and when tacky lay the two ends together so that the unravelled tufts can be worked with the fingers round the beginning of the waxed part of the other piece of line. Tie together temporarily and then whip with silk. Finish with a thin coating of cobbler's wax solution and when dry dust with talcum powder. However, you will not want to cut the line if it can be avoided. You might try giving the 'knuckle' 1 or 2 dressings with cobbler's wax, a small piece at a time, in methylated spirits till it is the thickness of cream.

'Otters' (1916)

The use of 'otters' is vetoed by statute and by by-laws under statutes for practical salmon waters and lakes. But we are not aware of any veto against their use from the sea shore on open ocean waters if the surface of the sea should be sufficiently smooth to admit of the attempt.

Paternoster (1860)

A paternoster is about a yard of gut with a bullet at the bottom and 2 or 3 hooks at intervals of some 10 in; these hooks you bait with minnows or worms. It is dropped into the water, the bullet finds the bottom and the line is held tight. A bite is felt immediately. It can be cast to some distance and gradually worked home, so that every inch of water can be fished with it.

Pickled Sprats as Salmon Bait

A 2% solution of formaline (made up from the commercial 40% formaldehyde) is often used for pickling sprats. Change into a fresh solution after 48 hours, as the first lot gets very cloudy. For dyeing the sprats a golden colour use a solution of 1.75 Acriflavine. Keep immersed for a week. Wash the baits well before dyeing after removal from the formaline.

Preserving a Sea-fishing Line

A good method to preserve a line from the action of salt water is to wind the line in a coil and steep it in a mixture of 1 part melted Vaseline to 2 parts of mutton fat, though the proportions are not very important. This will penetrate right through the line, and though it may be a little sticky at first it will improve with use. The stickiness can be overcome to a great extent by rubbing down the line with flannel. The line should be dried immediately after use, and if it is not to be used for any length of time it should first be washed in fresh water.

Record Pike (1953)

We very much doubt if an authentic figure has ever been kept. The record for the British Isles, however, is a fish of 53 lb caught on Lough Conn in Ireland in 1920. Pike on the Continent attain much greater weights, and fish of 80 lb and 90 lb are sometimes offered for sale in the fish markets of Vienna and elsewhere. Dr Gesznik of Linz is quoted by J. F. Hampton as saying that he had the word of an Austrian officer that he was present at Bregenz in the autumn of 1862 when a pike of some 145 lb was taken.

Sticky Line

We would recommend you to make powdered whitening into a paste with a little water. Soak the line in it for 3 or 4 days, then stretch it out to dry in the shade. When dry, rub it down with a soft flannel and polish with chamois leather.

Stuffed Fish (1854)

We cannot point out any establishment where 'stuffed specimens of all our river-fish' can be inspected. It would, certainly, answer the purpose to fit up a room or two for such an exhibition.

Tangled Line (1923)

The other evening, while I was helping a beginner to learn to throw a fly, he managed to get his cast into a glorious tangle. Sitting down to try to straighten things out I happened to bring the cast over our white supper paper, and found that I could see every strand of gut though it was dark, and we were soon right again. Some of your readers whose sight is not what it once was may be glad of this tip when changing a fly late in the day. [Cecil Holmes, Didmarton Rectory, Badminton]

Three Men in a Boat

A normal Thames-type punt, about 18 ft long, would be suitable for 3 men fishing a trout lake. But a resin-glass craft is better, as virtually no maintenance is needed. The long-term saving compensates the fact that resin-glass hulls are slightly more expensive than wood. A firm in Holland makes an unsinkable dinghy-type hull designed for fishermen, as it incorporates a fish well. It is about 13 ft long, and accommodates 3 or 4 people. It is safer, as it has more freeboard than a punt.

Trout Flies (1900)

Almost any feathers can be worked up into flies of some kind or other, but you will be well advised to use those recommended by 'Athenian' and not trust to any chance cock, hen, pigeon or goose that comes along.

Varnish for a Rod (1855)

Varnish is not only essential to preserve the wood and keep it from warping, but also to preserve the ring ties, the silk of which soon wears out when there is any lack of varnish over it; and a pennyworth or so of copal varnish, laid on carefully with a camel-hair brush, will last a rod throughout the whole season. But the best coating by far is the French polish, which, although a long and tedious process in the first instance, is lasting almost beyond belief, as a proof of which, a favourite old rod of ours, which has been in constant use and considerably knocked about for the last 16 years or more, has never had anything but its original coating during the whole of that period, the surface being perfectly smooth, without even a perceptible scratch upon any part of it.

Welsh Flies (1855)

The red fly is very beautifully dressed by most village Welsh anglers. They carefully breed poultry having the proper hackles, which should be blood-red, with black root about half its length. The body, coppery peacock's herl, or that of the ostrich, for variety. Sewin and salmon-peel, throughout Wales, rise well at the coch-y-bouddhu, when ribbed or tipped with fine gold thread. Those anglers who can't reconcile themselves to the use of a single fly will find the following to be a killing dropper. Hackle, freckled dun, reddish or copper coloured at the edges. The bird producing this feather, I also never observed among English poultry. Get the body made with a mixture of fur, having yellow tips, from the hare's ear, mixed with yellow wool. Rib or tip as usual. These two, with about half a score besides, dressed smaller, compose a jury of flies, which, to adopt old Izaak's phraseology, shall condemn every trout in our Welsh rivers, whether he swim in water salt or fresh. The coch-y-bouddhu is called Marlow-buzz by Saxon fishermen. Here follows a list of insect imitations, which generally kill well throughout the Principality, north and south. Sand fly, towards sunset, in hot weather; red dropper, any summer duns, alder, willow, grannam, iron blue, and stone fly, the latter for dusk. The flies more peculiarly local are – makerel; one winged with two small feathers tipped reddish, taken from the outside of a cock-sparrow's wing, and mole's fur body; an imitation of the horse-stinger, made from a hackle of a young cock-partridge's back, with simple hare's ear body. These flies, *coeteris paribus*, will not disappoint him who tries them there.

Wet and Dry Flies for Beginners

Dry flies are for the most part fuzzy, so that they float on the surface, whereas wet flies are sparse so that they will pierce the water surface tension and sink. The dry fly is used to imitate aquatic flies which have risen to the surface and are floating before flying; the 'spent' state of the same type of flies after they have shed their eggs into the water and are lying on the surface dead or dying; and terrestrial flies blown on to the water. Wet flies represent the underwater stage of various flies and the numerous small creatures living in water.

Worms for Fish

The most useful worms are lobworms (for big fish), marshworms and brandlings. Lobworms are most easily procured at night on lawns after rain or when there is plenty of dew. With an electric torch, walk slowly up and down the lawn. The worms will be visible on the grass. Pick them up and drop them into a container. Some dexterity is necessary in seizing them as they are very quick to withdraw into their holes. Marshworms like heaps of moist leaf mould or other garden rubbish. They are rather large, of a clear red colour and much appreciated by most fish. Brandlings live in ripe manure heaps, and are popular with most coarse fish. For trout, opinions differ, but they are often taken well. A big worm, the blackhead, is liked by tench, barbel and trout, and is useful for salmon, as it is very strong and wiry and works actively on a hook. It can be dug up from heavy soil. Worms can be scoured in damp moss for a few days if it is desired. This improves their colour and toughens them. For general keeping, use a small tub filled with leaf mould and pieces of old sacking. Keep fairly moist, with a layer of moss on top. If worms are put with a few sprigs of saxifrage or florists' moss they will scour very quickly and will become extremely lively.

Sports, Games and Pastimes
OUTDOOR
Beagles Abroad

Probably whenever there is a hound, a man, and a suitable quarry, there you will find a pack of beagles. There used, for example, to be one – it may still exist – in Ceylon. But the only foreign country in which it is possible to find an official list of beagle packs is in America. According to Mr Richard V. N. Gambrill writing in *Harehunters All*, 'There are really two sports known as Beagling in the United States. One is in following the regular packs which are kept and hunted just like an English pack. These are hunted almost entirely on hare. In addition, there are thousands of men all over the country who keep 2 or 3 beagles and use them for shooting purposes. One or 2 beagles will drive a rabbit at a pace which will bring her around in a circle to the guns, and that is about the most satisfactory way to shoot them. . . . These shooting men . . . are very fond of running their hounds in Field Trials.' Where the beagling is comparable, it is as popular in America as in Great Britain and Ireland.

Ben Nevis Race (1955)

This race is an annual running race. From old photographs, it is obvious that in the old days some of the contestants had walking sticks with them and presumably they walked part of the way. Any race since 1899, when some form of record has been kept, always rules that they shall reach the top and back by the quickest possible method, which obviously means running at some time. The fastest recorded time for this annual running race appears to be 1 hour 47 minutes 4 seconds by B. Kearney in 1954. It is estimated that an average person would take about 3–3½ hours going up, and about 1½–2 hours on the descent. An experienced walker, however, would no doubt do it in about 2 hours up and 1 hour down. It is pretty good going for anyone to complete the trip in under 3–3½ hours.

Bicycle and Tricycle (1900)

A curious development of latter-day bicycling was to be seen at Molesey lock last Sunday. A bicyclist of considerable inefficiency was taken in tow by a motor tricyclist – apparently a professional who met him at Molesey by appointment. We say of considerable inefficiency, because the bicyclist seemed unaware that the result of tying the towline to one end of the handlebar instead of to the middle would be an almost inevitable smash. When this had been adjusted and a start made the pace attained by the pair was quite considerable, something over 20 miles an hour. The bicycle was, of course, fitted with a free wheel. The rider of the motor tricycle in conversation stated that he made a practice of towing bicyclists and had recently taken one for a run of 200 miles in the day.

Home-made Catapult

The wooden handle and crotch should be cut from a forked hazel stem of suitable dimensions, or preferably blackthorn, though box or hickory can also be used. The necessary elastic of square section can be obtained at a games shop selling materials for model aeroplane building; and the stone holder can be of a small piece of flexible but tough leather – an old shoe tongue is often suitable.

Mick the Miller

The intelligence and speed of this great tracker have never been matched. He won the greyhound Derby in 1929 and 1930 and only just failed to win on a third occasion. Trained by an Irish priest, he was sold after winning a heat in the 1929 Derby for £800 and any prize won by him in the Derby. Soon after his great win, when he covered the 525-yard course in 29.96 seconds, he was sold for £2,000 and won the same event the following year for his new owner in 30.24 seconds. Altogether 'Mick' won nearly £10,000 in prize money and probably earned the equivalent sum when at stud. During his 13 years he became as famous as any sporting celebrity and, after his death, his body was embalmed and placed in the Natural History Museum.

Julius Caesar Plays for England (1861)

The band of cricketing heroes who challenge Australia, and intend visiting them at the close of the home season, consists of Julius

Caesar, Caffyn, Daft, Griffith, Jackson, Mortlock, Stephenson (Surrey), Stephenson (Yorkshire), R. C. Tinley, Willsher, and either Carpenter or Hayward.

Death at Cricket (1892)

Several instances are recorded in *The English Game of Cricket*, the most noteworthy one being that of George Summers, who received so severe a blow from a ball, while playing for Notts against the M.C.C. in 1870, that he died a few days afterwards.

History of Lord's

The first Lord's ground consisted of 10 acres on the site of Dorset Square, where Thomas Lord held an agricultural tenancy under the Portman family. The first match played on it was that between 5 of the White Conduit Club and 6 picked men against All England on 20 June 1787. Lord was compelled to leave his first ground and took over a field which he had to quit after 3 years on the construction of the Regent's Canal. He then opened the St John's Wood ground in Marylebone, which became the headquarters of the Marylebone Club (established in 1787) and the game. The ground was announced as ready for play in April 1814. Lord made his fortune and retired; later Mr William Ward purchased the lease of the ground to save it from the builders. Mr J. H. Dark bought the unexpired term from him. He considerably improved Lord's and in 1838 erected the tennis court, spending over £4,000, and in 1850 added a racket court. In 1853 Mr Dark had about 50 years of his lease to run.

Overhead Wires

[I play cricket on a pitch which has overhead wires running across. Could you tell me the correct way of dealing with the situation when the ball touches the wires?]

This seems to be a case where it would be more satisfactory to accept any consequence from the presence of the overhead cables as an unavoidable 'rub of the green' than to put upon the umpire the onus of calling 'dead ball' whenever the ball might be deflected in its flight. It might well be an arguable point as to when the ball was actually deflected, and it would obviously be unsatisfactory to rule out any ball which touched the wires. The only ruling that has any bearing on the case is that 'if no boundaries have been arranged, a striker can be caught off a tree, hedge or building'. It is essential, however, that the point should be agreed upon between the captains before play begins.

Reconstruction of Cricket (1919)

I should like to make a suggestion which as far as I know has not been put forward lately, and it is one that would: (a) put a premium on hitting the ball in the middle of the bat; (b) encourage the bowler who makes the ball turn on a good wicket; (c) assist towards the finishing of games; (d) tend to enliven the game, as the ball can be hit harder. Each of the foregoing points applies to all cricket, not to first class only. My suggestion is to *narrow the bat* from 4¼ in wide (which, after all, is only an arbitrary width) *down to* 3¾ in. Having had a bat made to this width and batted with it, I can speak from experience how delightful it is to use and how easy to wield it. [E. C. Lee]

Shrewsbury *v.* Birmingham (1853)

A match was played, or, rather, a hopeless attempt to play was made on Monday and Tuesday, the 20th and 21st ult. The sun rose on Monday morning without a speck to dull his jolly face; but since 5 o'clock in the afternoon of that ill-omened day, we have had nothing to do but whistle 'Begone, dull care', and pray for a change of wind. We have had rain, rain, rain, alternating between a Scotch mist and a Jamaica thunderstorm, with an occasional pleasant interlude of a regular straight up-and-down English soaker: a hailstorm variety would be a positive relief. In the early part of Monday, some excellent cricket was shown; but the bowling of such steady-to-the-wicket workmen as Buttriss and Armitage accounts for the smallness of the scores. Caution is all very well, but too much of it is tiresome to all – field and spectators; it is certain that if a man has the nerve to go out a step, open his shoulders well, raise himself on tip-toe, and make a slogging hit or two, he will break the heart, and spoil the machine-like accuracy, of any bowler.

University Cricket (1919)

It is all very well to say that, in a great many cases, parents do not care a straw for a man's academic achievements so long as he gains his 'blue' and makes 'the right sort of friends'. But the day is coming (as is patent to all earnest thinkers) when such vital questions as the employment of young men's time at a most critical period of their training can no longer be left to the whim of irresponsible parents, but is a matter of public concern in which the interests of the nation are involved. To allow and even encourage a man to waste the 7 best hours of each weekday over the pomposities of a game whose native excellencies are being stifled in an atmosphere of exaggerated competitions is to lose all sense of educational prospective and to disregard the great potentialities of university life in the development of young English manhood. The game, with all its variety and all its attractiveness, becomes dull and unprofitable once it is made a separate end rather than a means of recreation.

The Eton Wall Game

The Eton wall game owes it origins to the presence of a high wall, about 120 yards long, enclosing part of the college grounds along the road from Windsor to Slough. The area of play comprises a strip of ground about 6 yards wide running along the wall. At each end is an area known as 'calx', equivalent to the area behind the goal lines in Rugby football. One end is called 'good calx', the other end 'bad calx'. Good calx has a wall running at right angles to the long wall and a door in it is the goal. Bad calx is open and part of an elm tree is the goal. The teams are 11-a-side. Five players on each side form down against the long wall in a bully, or scrummage; the remaining players take up positions outside the bully. The ball is put into the bully at the start of the game and whenever it goes out of the area of play; the object is to work it along the wall with the feet into calx. When the ball has been forced into calx the attacking side strive to gain a 'shy', which is accomplished by a player lifting the ball with his feet against the wall and touching it there. The ball may then be 'shied' at goal. In scoring, a goal outweighs any number of shies.

Five Ten

The game known as 'five ten' seems to have died out after the First World War and no reference to it has been found for some years. However, a revised form was introduced some years ago under the name of 'Padda Tennis'. It takes up space a little over half the size of a tennis court.

Golf for Old Men

Golf, although it cannot be said to suffer from any lack of rules and regulations or to be wanting in exponents of the first class, still holds out a friendly hand to the player who finds the standard of excellence at lawn tennis or at croquet something too lofty for his taste. Golf is pre-eminently the old man's recreation; and in saying this we are paying it the highest compliment conceivable. For the game is one that appeals almost equally to the competitor for championship honours and to the most arrant duffer who ever handled a club. The reason for this is obvious enough; it lies in the fact that the best and the worst players can be brought to play together with an equal chance of success. Probably no game that was ever devised has so effective and simple a method of handicapping.

The Horse Shoe Game

This game is played by 2 or 4 players. Two pitching boxes, 6 ft square, are established with a central steel stake in each, 1 in in diameter, 14 in out of the ground, each inclined to the opposite pitching box at 3 in. The stakes are placed 40 ft apart for men, 30 ft for women and juveniles. When there are 2 players, both pitch 2 shoes each from 1 box, and then walk to the opposite box and pitch from it. Score is kept as follows: 1 point for each shoe closer than an opponent's to the stake with shoe 6 in or closer to stake; 3 points for each ringer, encircling the stake; 4 points for a ringer and closest shoe. In singles the first to reach 50, in doubles the first to reach 21, is the winner.

The English Long-bow

The long-bow was 5 ft long, and the shaft a yard long. Shot by an expert Welsh archer, it is said the shaft would penetrate an oak board 4 in thick at a favourable distance. Military accounts say that the arrow would normally pierce a well seasoned board an inch thick when fired at 'a favourable distance', which appears to have been as close as possible. Of course, much depended not only on the bow but on the strength and skill of the archer. No table of distances or penetrating powers is known, but odd bits of information come from various sources. Some authorities question the distances and degrees of accuracy claimed for the long-bow in some of the old accounts. Carew, the Cornish historian, said the archers of the county at the end of the military use of the bow could shoot well up to 480 yards, and with the strength to pierce the usual armour of the day. But the aim was to use the bow at as close quarters as possible. The bow lingered on long after the introduction of fire arms, as it could be used half a dozen times or more while a musket was being loaded.

Manly Pursuits (1861)

I am one of those who have throughout life advocated, and, as far as in my power lay, encouraged every kind of manly and athletic exercise peculiar to our country; for I am certain that as long as men are the sole agents, let the nature of the contest be which it may, whether in the prize ring or the wrestling ring, whether on the waters of the Thames, on Lord's Cricket-ground, or the village green, the result is the same – the development of strength and endurance, and as promoting a manly feeling among all classes, whether they are only spectators or active participators in the struggle. Let the opponents of prize-fighting pause for a while, and coolly reflect whether it is just now expedient to interfere with any single one of our national manly sports. The fact may not be apparent to those 'gentlemen of England who live at home at ease', but men like myself, who live abroad, cannot shut our eyes to the fact of the growing jealousy with which Great Britain and all her doings are regarded by foreigners of every class, and I do not believe there is a single nation in Europe but would rejoice at the downfall of old England. They may not say as much, but this I am confident is their feeling; and the day is perhaps not so very far distant when England may have to hold her own in another great struggle – and depend upon it then the battle will not be fought with the pen, and the chief actors in the scene will have to be chosen from among far different men than those who are continually decrying our national manly sports. [An Old Bushman, Sweden]

Motoring in Winter (1919)

On frost-bound roads steel-studded tyres are the most liable to skid, and you would certainly be better with the cross rubber treads. None, however, can be called safe under such conditions.

Outdoor Recreation for the Fair Sex (1860)

Gentlemen are gallant, but why should that prevent a woman's being able to load and fire a gun or a rifle, and to shoot either at game or at an enemy? I see no occasion for a woman's leaving England to fight, but why should she not be found doing her best in the defence of her country? Why should she be excluded from using her rifle behind a hedge? And where will she ever appear to greater advantage than by her husband's side in an action loading his rifle, or firing her own? I do not see why a woman is not to fish, or, in fact, to join in any healthy, useful out-of-door amusement, as long as she fulfils all her home duties. I only hope that, should an occasion ever present itself of defending England, I (with many others) may be found 'the right woman in the right place.' [A riflewoman]

[*Editor's note: This letter was one of several in some passionate correspon-*

dence about whether or not it was 'ladylike' to participate in certain outdoor pursuits other than a gentle walk 'out on a clear road for 2 or 3 miles, and home again,' or a 'ride round the neighbourhood, by the roads, for an hour or two, and back again,' or even a chance to fish 'after the hook is baited for us, placed where a fish is likely to be caught, but we are neither to see the bait we know to be there, nor the fish killed we know was intended to die and for which we have been angling.' Several women wrote about their love of sport and their determination to be actively involved in fishing, skating, shooting, riding to hounds and similar pursuits.]

Players and Spectators (1900)

The distinguishing mark of the Briton – a mark which he is apt to think differentiates him favourably from his less strenuous neighbours on the Continent – has always been his love of games. We may take our pleasures sadly, as the envious have alleged, but there is no denying our healthy love of open-air exercise. But it cannot be denied that every year more and more descend from active participation to the passive relaxation of a seat in one of the stands. The declension seems to us somewhat ignoble. Professionalism is no new thing, but it has developed amazingly of late years, and with the development of professionalism has come an inclination to take our games perhaps a thought too seriously. Primarily a game should be regarded as a means of amusement and healthy recreation for all; it should certainly not be elevated or degraded to a spectacle and a matter of business. The Eastern potentate at a ball asked with surprise why we did not hire our dancers to perform before us instead of putting ourselves to the trouble of going through the performance in our own persons. It is to be feared that in a good many of our games we are no longer liable to this comforting reproach. It is too late now to rescue football and cricket from the taint of professionalism, but it might be worth while to consider seriously the ethics of the bystander. The man who spends his days in watching other people play a match is apt to hold a high opinion of himself as a sportsman, a connoisseur, and a supporter of all that is best in the tradition of the country. As a fact, he is indirectly hiring a company of professionals (assisted occasionally by a few amateurs) in precisely the same manner as though he had taken a stall at a theatre, although not so expensively. We confess to a suspicion that it would be better for his descendants, and for the country in general, if he were to employ his hours of leisure in cultivating somewhat more actively those qualities of eye and nerve and endurance that have always been the boast of this nation in the past.

Professionals and Officers (1900)

The recipients of money prizes would become professionals, and all who raced with them would incur the same disqualification. Officers, however, may race each other exclusively for prizes (not money) at the meeting without becoming professional.

Rowing (1892)

It is impossible to answer your questions off hand without measuring the distances. Approximately the L.R.C. flagstaff is barely, and the Bishop's Creek rather more than, ¼ mile, Craven Steps ½ mile, the Mile Tree 1 mile, the Distillery 1½ miles, Hammersmith Bridge 1¾ miles, Chiswick Ferry 2½ miles, Barnes Bridge 3¾ miles – less the distance short started – say, 75 yards.

Rugby Fixtures for the Schools (1966)

The 15 school matches which King's College School played last term (and 18 matches in all) were certainly an exceptional number and we believe it was a record for this season, as far as the leading schools are concerned. However, there were other schools, not so well known as K.C.S., which played as many or more matches. We notice that a school called Forest G.S. played 21, of which they won 10, drew 1 and lost 10. Windsor G.S. played 18 and Henley G.S. 17. Probably the most remarkable record was that of Okehampton G.S. They had 21 fixtures on their list, but 3 were cancelled owing to waterlogged grounds or other causes. So they played 18 (17 against schools) and won them all. For the current term they have arranged a further 12.

Sailing to Paris (1887)

You may occasionally get up to Paris with 7 ft draught, but you could not get through to the Rhine with more than 4 ft 9 in.

Disembarking (1887)

The Council of the Y.R.A. has decided that it is admissible, in the event of a boat getting ashore, for the crew to get out and assist in floating her, providing of course that they return to the boat; but a 'corinthian' or gentleman passenger can, under Y.R.A. rules, join or leave a yacht when he pleases.

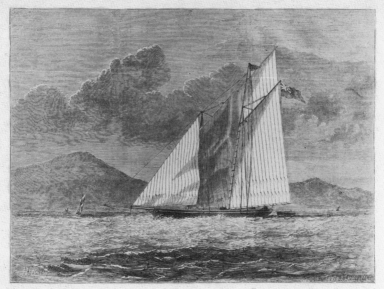

A schooner yacht

Corinthian (1900)

The term, which in yacht parlance is synonymous with amateur, was commonly applied to the patrons of sports half a century ago. The name was adopted in consequence of the similarity between the fashionable young men of Corinth, who emulated the feats of athletes, etc., and their modern prototypes. In this sense the word is used by Shakespeare, I.Hen.IV.,ii.4.

A Fair Day's Work (1892)

(1) Generally now a 'fair day's work' is whatever the artisan chooses to give his employer. (2) In the north, about 12 ft (lineal) per hour would be expected; in the south, probably 10 ft. In your case it should be at least 15 ft. (3) Waged 9d. to 10d. per hour.
[*Editor's note: This question was answered under the general heading of YACHTING. . . .*]

Paid Hands (1892)

A paid hand must not leave a yacht after the first gun has been fired, nor after the blue peter has been hoisted, except in the case of injury such as you refer to.

Sheathing a Yacht

Both processes (fibreglass and nylon) are expensive. It would be foolhardy to use either on a large old wreck. Nylon is usually the more expensive process and is difficult to apply. It is hard to obtain a good finish and it should really be applied professionally to obtain the best use of it. Fibreglass is easier for the amateur. The thickness needed depends on the size, as it is not so flexible. To sheath a boat of under 18 ft a single thickness should suffice, but over 18 ft use double thickness. Fibreglass has the great advantage that the thickness can be varied depending on the strength required. The finish can be better than nylon and there is a large choice of materials. The open-weave type of fibreglass is not suitable for this work. Equally the very close weave is difficult to impregnate.

Shrovetide Sport (1898)

For almost time out of mind, sport and pastime have been connected with Shrove Tuesday. It is a well-known fact that, in the early days of the Turf, horse races were held upon various public holidays in different parts of the kingdom in preference to other days, and Chester was one of the places which took the lead in this direction: it was the custom for the company of saddlers belonging to Chester to present to the drapers a wooden ball decked with flowers, and placed upon the point of a lance, the ceremony being performed on the Roodee; but in 1539 or 1540 the ball was changed into a bell of silver, worth 3s.6d. or more, to be awarded to him who should run 'the best and furthest on horseback' on Shrove Tuesday. Ball games have ever been popular in England, and on Shrove Tuesday the London schoolboys were accustomed to adjourn to the fields immediately after dinner, to play at the celebrated game of ball, each party of boys carrying their own ball, so it would not appear as though on these occasions one school contended against another. In connection with football, too, does Chester once more come to the fore: for many years, the shoe-makers, thinking with pardonable pride that there was nothing like leather, were in the habit of presenting one ball of leather, called a 'foote-ball', to the drapers and with this said ball people played between the Roodee and the Common Hall. So many windows, however, appear to have been smashed, and so much general inconvenience caused, that the ball was changed into silver trophies, and foot races were held instead of football. There was also a close connection between Shrove Tuesday and cock-fighting. Then there was the barbarous custom of throwing at cocks which were tied to a stake, and this custom caused a foreigner to remark, 'The English eat a certain cake on Shrove Tuesday, upon which they immediately run mad and kill, by throwing, ever so many cocks.' This custom, curiously enough, prevailed in St Mary's, the chief of the Scilly Isles, and after the throwing at cocks was over, the boys had a custom of throwing stones in the evening against the doors of private houses. A somewhat similar custom, known as 'Lent Crocking', obtained on Shrove Tuesday in Dorsetshire. The 'tug of war', now a very common sort of competition, would appear to have been in the first instance connected with Shrove Tuesday: according to tradition a division of opinion at the siege of Ludlow by Henry VI when two parties in the town, one supporting the pretensions of the Duke of York, the other wishing to give admission to the King, led to an annual controversy which at last came to be settled on Shrove Tuesday and it appears to have taken the form of a tug of war.

Skating Jumps

All these jumps (axel, loop, lutz, salchow) may be started on either foot and be performed double and in some cases triple. Rfo = right forward outside, Rfi = right forward inside, Rbo = right back outside, Rbi = right back inside. Axel: Start Rfo edge, $1\frac{1}{2}$ revolutions in the air, landing on Lbo (or starting Lfo). Loop: R or Lbo, 1 revolution in the air, landing on the same edge backward. Lutz: Rbo, spot with left toe, jumping with body rotating in 'counter' direction, landing on the 'spotting' foot Lbo. Salchow: Rbi jump in direction of a 'three turn', landing Lbo.

Late Skating (1860)

In the year 1854 or 1855 skating was carried on as late as the first week in March, when the long frost broke up.

Swimming Action (1900)

There must be something wrong with the leg action. Hurrying over a short course is calculated to do no good. Professional instruction, which can be obtained at most London baths, is the best remedy. The instructions in the *Badminton Library* are worthy of attention, but only from practice under good tuition can any considerable improvement be expected. You should be able to develop both speed and staying power to a considerable extent.

INDOOR
Billiards Break (1916)

The break by Tom Reece was 499,135 (including 249,552 cannons). It was made at the saloon of Messrs Burroughes and Watts, Soho-square, from 3 June to 6 July 1907. The actual time occupied was 85 hours 49 minutes.

Boxing (1860)

As for the sport or exercise of boxing, there is much to be said in its favour, and very little against it. We do not mean to say that the spectacle of two men pommelling each other is one which a delicate lady would care to behold; but there are many other very necessary matters which are not proper objects for the eyes of ladies. The world being as it is, many occasions present themselves to every one when the power of putting down the bully or assisting the weak would be very pleasant. It is good to wield skilfully the weapons with which Nature has provided us. However, we would have it understood that we have consistenly set our faces against prize-fighting, not so much from a belief that *the exercise* is an improper one, or that the practice is necessarily pernicious, as from a knowledge of the exceedingly immoral state into which the Ring has of late years fallen.

Ink to Water (1860)

Procure a large glass, fill it with filtered water (it looks clearer), and in the water place a goldfish, then place in the water a lining of black oil-skin, as near the sides of the glass as you can; the glass of water then presents an appearance of a glass of ink; procure a small ladle, as much in form and appearance as a small toddy-ladle as possible; the handle of the ladle must be hollow, and an opening left near the bowl to let the fluid out; there must also be a small vent-hole near the top of the handle; the hollow handle fill with ink; place a small piece of wax on the vent-hole. 'Before me,' says the conjuror, 'is a large tumbler of ink. Observe, I take a ladle-full of ink from the glass.' He dips the ladle in the water and removes the wax from the vent-hole, which is easily slipped off with the nail; the ink runs from the handle into the bowl of the ladle; the performer immediately pours the ink into a white plate, which he holds in the other hand. 'You perceive, ladies and gentlemen, this glass contains ink. I shall cover it with a handkerchief, wave my magic wand around it; lift the handkerchief; observe, the ink has changed into beautiful transparent water, with a fairy fish gambolling therein.' When the conjuror lifts the handkerchief from the glass, he takes care, also, to lift with the handkerchief the lining of black oil-skin.

Odds in Cards (1923)

The holding of a hand containing all the 13 Hearts is a very unusual and remarkable occurrence. The odds against a 1-suit hand being dealt to a given player in a given deal are 158,753,389,899 to 1. Two cases of the occurrence were recorded some 40 years ago in the *Westminster Papers*.

Selfmate (1954)

Selfmates are a form of problem which was devised quite a long time ago when the supply of original ideas for problems seemed to be getting exhausted. It certainly gives the composer considerable additional field for his individuality. The object is, instead of mating your opponent, to force him to mate you. Thus it often happens that the position viewed from the angle of the ordinary problem looks strange. White may even have a mate on the move, which, of course, is the one move he must avoid. If you study one of the selfmates in *THE FIELD* and work out the solution given in the following week, in the light of what I have said, you will soon become proficient.

 Travel

Angola (1900)

The natives are harmless, but very lazy, and there is often great difficulty in getting porters. The usual mode of travelling into the interior is in 'tepoias' (hammocks slung on a palm rib). Angola is a long way behind the world in the matter of roads, and the native single file path still predominates. In the vicinity of St Paul de Loando you could use a horse, but they are seldom to be purchased in Angola, and are generally brought from the Cape Verde islands. We cannot give you the name of any sportsman now living who has travelled through Loando but by writing to Mr A. H. Baynes, 19, Furnival-street, Holborn, you might probably hear of some missionary who has done so.

Living in the Channel Islands (1892)

They are certainly better suited for residence to a person who has lived in the West Indies than most parts of England. Food and clothing are no cheaper in Jersey than they are in England; but the rents are lower, the taxes practically *nil*, wines, spirits, and tobacco very cheap, and a good house, suitable for a small family, would be rented at from £40 to £50 a year. Fruit and vegetable growing is carried on successfully, but the price of land varies so much, that anything we might tell you would be of little service.

Chicago (1892)

It is possible to get to Chicago for £12.

Fiji (1900)

The climate of Fiji as a whole is agreeable and healthy, and considering its proximity to the equator, is not nearly so hot as might be expected, the sun's heat being lessened by the sea breezes. For 9 months in the year the climate is delightful, and free from diseases, though during the hot season dysentery attacks those who live carelessly.

Hungarian Travel (1887)

The language of the rulers of the country is Hungarian, that of the peasants Roumanian; German is understood by most officials. French, like English, is a fashionable language among the aristocracy, and useful in that way, but unknown generally. The journey from London to Vienna occupies 36 hours; the fares are, first class, £10.2s.6d.; second class, £7.14s.; and the fares from Vienna to Budapest are, first class, £1.10s.; second class, £1; the journey occupies 7 hours.

Malaga (1900)

Malaga is one of the best winter resorts in Europe for patients requiring a warm, dry, tonic climate. The sanitary condition is not satisfactory.

Bicycling in Portugal (1900)

September would be a good month for a bicycling tour in Portugal, central and northern Spain. You would not find anglophobia prevalent, but you should be very careful when meeting vehicles or animals in country districts, or you may cause accidents and ill-feeling. The roads in Spain and Portugal vary in quality, as in other countries, but many of them are good, and quite suitable for bicycling.

Siam (1900)

The climate of Siam is not generally healthy, especially in the south, but it is quite possible for Europeans to live in Bangkok all the year round without immediate danger to health, although long residence without periodic changes of climate greatly enervates even the strongest. Necessaries such as rice, chickens, vegetables, fruit, etc., are cheap, especially outside Bangkok, but stores and any European luxuries are expensive. A broad distinction as regards cost of living must be made between Bangkok and the country, the cost of living in Bangkok is much dearer than in the country where provisions are cheaper but much more difficult to obtain. On the whole, the cost of living is much the same as in India. There are about 1,000 Europeans and Americans in Siam, quite one half of whom are in Bangkok. We do not know of any person who could give you instruction in Siamese.

Interpreters in Turkey (1854)

We have now a Terjuman (*Anglice*, dragoman), a clever little fellow, who speaks perfectly 10 languages. I am learning Turkish under his auspices, and can already make myself understood among our friends of the fez. The construction of the verbe is most singular; for example, there are two future tenses, one signifying the determination, 'I will do it'; the other expressing 'At present such is my intention'. On a first hearing the language sounds remarkably like gibberish; but when the ear becomes more accustomed to it, it is not unpleasing. [One of our infantrymen at Redout Kaley, Georgia]

A Sapper's Attempt at Turkish (1854)

The following is a specimen of the conversation heard between a linguist sapper and a Turkish driver: 'Arabajee, caval soo, yok; haidee Balaklava Adjutant Ivett; chabook Johnny no forget haidee, chabook; buono, yes, understandy.'

A Miscellany

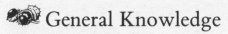 General Knowledge

Belle Tout Lighthouse

The Belle Tout Lighthouse on Beachy Head probably came into being through the activities of Jonathan Darby, parson of the Eastdean churches as far back as 1715. He was much distressed by the shipping casualties, and set to work to hollow out a cave in the rocks between Birling Gap and the site used later for the Belle Tout. The present old Belle Tout Lighthouse was built in 1831, on the second cliff westward from Eastbourne. It is at a height of about 500 ft above the sea and for some years served a useful purpose in guiding shipping. In the course of time, however, it became obsolete and it was decided to build a new lighthouse rising from the sea, at the foot of the headland. The spot is now chiefly interesting as the landing place of the cable from France.

Binocular Figures

The figures on binoculars show the power or magnifications given by the lenses, and field of view covered. The first figure – 7x, 8x, 9x, 10x etc. – indicates the power of magnification. A binocular of 7x is one that magnifies the object being viewed 7 times. The second figure – it usually ranges from 30–50 – gives in millimetres the diameter of the objective lens, which is the large one farthest from the eye. It broadly indicates the field of view. The larger the diameter, the greater the field of view, but the higher the magnifying power the smaller the field of view.

Bridle Paths (1953)

Bridle paths may only be used for their original purpose, namely the passage of horsemen, the leading of horses, and in certain instances, the driving of stock.

Cheese Lord

The term 'Cheese Lord' in the deeds of 1613 and 1649 relating to property in the Forest of Dean is a misreading. In the old form of writing and printing, 'S' and 'F' looked much alike and the word is not 'Cheese' but 'Cheefe', which was a form of writing 'Chief' at the time and has long since been obsolete. Thus the actual reference in the deeds is to the Chief Lord who held the land under the Feudal System, or as we are more accustomed to see, to the Lord of the Manor.

Use of a Cockade (1900)

It is very doubtful whether you are entitled to the use of a cockade. According to the best authorities you are not; but these points are never really settled, because there can be no prosecutions for infringement of the law.

Definition of a Commoner (1958)

There is no definition of a commoner, except the rather unsatisfactory one of a person who has rights on that particular common. A common is usually an area of land within the boundaries of a manor. Commoners are usually those who live or own land within the area of the manor. Naturally they are usually individuals, but there seems no reason why a company, or even a miners' lodge, if it owns land on the manor, should not have common rights. It is impossible to be dogmatic, because when the common was enclosed it was usually the subject of a local Act of Parliament, and these vary. They may reserve common rights to those who might not otherwise be expected to have them.

Court Jesters

It is probable that court jesters existed from Anglo-Saxon times to the times of the Commonwealth (1640s). The earliest known was Hitard, the fool of Edmund Ironside (*circa* 1016). Other celebrated jesters or fools well known by their names were Goles, the fool of William I, Will Somers, the fool of Henry VIII, and Archie (Armstrong), the fool of James I. The famous Yorick in Shakespeare's *Hamlet* was the jester of the King of Denmark.

Crest Tax (1916)

(a) If your vehicles are put aside unused for the whole of the financial year they are not excisable for that period, and on this basis any crests or arms on their panels are not in use. But (b) if you retain crests on harness, or even on one signet ring, in use, you are as fully liable for duty on armorial bearings as if every item in your plate basket for daily use was crested. (c) If you use your spring cart for other than trade purposes – e.g., to convey you for personal convenience to the station or elsewhere – it becomes excisable. (d) You must pay the annual tax on male servants, even if they quit your service before a year expires, whether they quit for military service or under usual mutual notices between employer and employed. If you replace the absentees you do not pay any extra tax.

John B. Dillon (1855)

Mr John B. Dillon, Barrister-at-Law, one of the 'leaders' in the insurrectionary movement of '48, and not the least among the able but dangerous press contributors of that insane period, has arrived in Dublin from the land of Knownothings, where he has, it seems, been eminently successful in his professional capacity. With creditable good taste, Mr Dillon, since his temporary return to this country, is living in the strictest privacy at the seaside.

Driving Furiously (1853)

James Tracey, a veterinary surgeon, was brought before Mr A'Beckett, charged with furious driving, and injuring a child by running over it with his horse and cart. Charles Kemply, a broker at Dockhead, stated that about half-past 12 o'clock that day he was passing along George-street, Bermondsey, when he saw the prisoner coming towards him in a horse and cart, driving at the rate of 9 miles an hour. He seemed to have no command of the animal, and, before witness could get near it, a child who was passing with some dinner was knocked down, and one of the wheels passed over its legs. Mr Button, a surgeon in George-street, stated that the wheel had passed over one of its legs but had not broken any bone. The prisoner, who said he could not help it, was fined 40s. for furious driving.

Earl's Court

Earl's Court derives its origin from the circumstance of the place so designated having been the site of the court house belonging to the de Veres, Earls of Oxford, who were lords of the manor, and who held their courts there. The hamlet of Earl's Court grew up round the court house and manor house of the de Veres. In the Court Rolls of Earles Court from 1554 to 1850 the name is always written Earles

Court. The old inflection of the possessive case was 'es'. When the 'e' was omitted, as it now always is, the absence of the 'e' was indicted by the apostrophe. The correct modern usage is Earl's Court.

Eggs in Tombs (1865)

The curious position in which the large New Zealand egg was found holds out a very strong hope that many others will shortly come to light. As to the reason of this egg being held up in the hands opposite to the face of the dead, was it not a position of adoration? The egg in many nations, curiously enough, is by common consent a divine emblem. In the East the egg is the symbol of the primitive state of the world, and of the creation of all things. The new year begins at the spring equinox about Easter, the renewal of Nature. A festival was celebrated in the new moon of the month Phamenoth in honour of Osiris, when painted and gilded eggs were exchanged as presents in reference to the beginning of all things. Tyle speaks of the 'Hindoo conception of heaven and earth being formed by the two halves of Brahma's egg'. There is a legend prevailing in the Sandwich Islands, that they were produced by a bird, a frequent emblem of Deity, a medium through which the gods often communicated with men, who laid an egg upon the waters, which afterwards burst and produced the islands. The Turks to this day place ostrich eggs on their graves. The tribes of the interior of Africa do the same. Therefore something more than provision for the way, over and above a viaticum, may have been intended by the interment of the egg with the defunct Maori. May not his future representatives, when sitting on Macaulay's arch, retort the same idea on us, with regard to the sacramental wine cup, placed in the hands of the priests in mediaeval tombs?

Gong Men

There have been 3 'Men with the Gong' at the opening of Rank films – Bombardier Billy Wells, Phil Nieman and, since 1955, Ken Richmond, the British wrestler who won a bronze medal at the 1952 Olympic Games. But not Gunner Moir, as you suggest.

Green Man

The 'Green Man' sign for inns was once very popular. Although the real origin is lost in antiquity, the matter has been very deeply investigated and authorities have come to 2 conclusions. The majority say the Green Man represents the green, wood or wild man, a most popular figure in medieval pageants. Such is described by many old writers, including Machyn, who in his Diary describes the Lord Mayor's Day events of 29 October 1553, when a Green Man figured prominently. Such men were dressed in masses of green leaves. Their primary duty seems to have been to clear the way for processions and to amuse the crowd in the process. For instance, we have an account of Queen Elizabeth's visit to Kenilworth Castle in 1575 when she was met in the forest and welcomed by a man clad in ivy leaves. These Green Men usually carried cudgels or sticks, possibly for the purpose of warning those who did not get out of the way of approaching processions, but quite often used in later proceedings to amuse the crowds by engaging in combat. The 'Wild Man' sign that once marked an inn in the West Riding of Yorkshire was actually another version of the Green Man. Another theory, probably based on later usage, was that the Green Man was essentially a forester, and some inn signs showed him in forester's dress. Trade tokens of the 17th century showed the Green Man in such costumes rather than in a dress of leaves. Robin Hood was represented in this way in some inn signs, and could be recognised by the figure of Little John at his side. Associated with the Green Man is the Lincoln green of the old ballads.

Hill or Mountain?

The Oxford Dictionary gives 2,000 ft upwards as the height of a mountain in Britain, but we should say above 2,500 ft. Again what is a mountain may be governed by comparative height of the peaks in different countries; for example it might not be considered as such below 7,000 ft in the Alps, 9,000–10,000 ft in the Himalayas or Andes and 8,000 ft in the Caucasus or the Rockies.

Jumping Beans

The Mexican or jumping beans consist of seeds of the species of an American plant genus (*Sebastiania*) which are infested by the larvae or caterpillars of a small moth, *Cydia saltitans*. This moth is closely related to the codling moth *Cydia pomenella*, which infests apples in Europe. The moth lays her eggs on the seeds, and the grubs, which are quite tiny, bore inside. In throwing themselves from one side to another in feeding they cause the seed to move or jump. It is possible that this movement is normally connected with the caterpillars' attempts to detach the seeds from the parent plants and in some manner seek cover in or on the soil. Apparently, the best way to stimulate action is to place the seeds in a warm place, or hold in a warm hand. Later, the caterpillars pupate within the seeds, and the jumping ceases. Finally, the moths emerge through a small hole.

Living on £1 a Week (1892)

Your friend could live very cheaply at some village in Cornwall or in Hanover; but we do not know of any place where a gentleman could live with comfort on £1 a week.

London Hippodrome (1887)

From Dobney's-place, Islington, and Halfpenny Hatch, Lambeth, to Olympia is a wide jump. It was at the two former places that the circus was first established; and it is at Olympia – which, by the way, the advertisement tell us is *not* a circus – that it has been presented in its most modern form. 'Horsemanship', to give the circus the name by which it is still best known in the country, though now so popular, was unknown in England till the end of the last century, though the Romans, while they occupied the southern portion of England, are said to have amused themselves with mimic chariot races in an arena. It has been stated that the Paris Hippodrome, now at Kensington, has never before visited England but in the year 1851 the Great Exhibition set all entertainers thinking how they could best turn the occasion to account, and William Batty took a piece of ground at Kensington, constructed a wooden building capable of holding 14,000 spectators, and called it the Hippodrome. The items of the entertainment were as nearly as possible a counterpart of those presented in the Parisian establishment, whose manager, M. Soullier, was engaged to bring over his men and horses. This London hippodrome was subsequently turned into a sort of outdoor riding school, and the scenes therein enacted supplied John Leech with material for many of his sketches. In later days it came into the hands of the Messrs Blackman, and then the gates, fences, and stables made way for Baron Grant's mansion, which in its turn has been supplanted.

Measuring Horn Length (1915)

In 'Answers to Correspondents', 11 September 1915, we stated in reply to your question that 'the length of horn should be measured along the outside curve,' assuming that the expression 'outside and inside curves' would be familiar to most sportsmen. But as apparently we have not made our meaning clear, we may quote the directions usually given for horn measurements, and state that 'the dimensions (taken in inches) are length of horn *measured along the curve behind* from base to tip of longest tine; circumference between bay and tray; and greatest width between the horns.'

Ouse and Thames

'Ouze', or in its usual spelling 'Ouse', is the name of several English rivers. The word is merely a variation of isis, esk and uisg, all of which mean water. 'Thames' is derived from the Latin *Thamesis*, meaning the broad isis. It is, therefore, quite likely that the word 'ouse' was used in a general way for any stream.

Oysters for Poor Men (1956)

It must, indeed, have been many years ago when oysters were described as a poor man's food. But it is, perhaps, significant that the deliberate culture of oysters as we know it today is of comparatively recent innovation. The Romans knew the art of oyster culture and appreciated the bivalves as an epicurean dish. But oyster culture lapsed after their time, and since the shallows of the sea and estuaries where the oysters bred were more or less clean and favourable, it may well be that oysters were more common and looked upon as a poor man's food in districts where they were plentiful. The localities in which oysters will breed are limited, and the saying can have had only limited currency. A related saying is that mussels are a poor man's oyster. Nowadays, the culture of oysters is carried out artificially, and the revival of epicurean interest makes them very much a rich man's food. The only time when the poor man would have had a chance would be when the oysters bred freely and naturally.

Property Prices (1860)

The Cracrop estate, of 1162 acres in extent, was sold by auction last week, at Carlisle, and brought £22,300, about 31 years' purchase according to the present rental. Hornby Castle and Manor, in North Lancashire, the property of the late Mr Pudsey Dawson, has, it is announced, become the property of Mr John Foster, of Cliffe Hill, near Halifax, for the sum of £205,000. The estate consists of the honour and manor of Hornby, the borough of Hornby, the manor of Tatham, and about 3,500 acres of land; the livings of Hornby, Tatham, and Lowgill; the right of sporting over upwards of 24,000 acres of land, and of fishing over 7 miles or more of the river Lune, and the whole length of its tributary streams – the Wenning, Hindburn, and Roeburn.

New Road Code (1930)

If 'etiquette' appears to monopolise more than its fair proportion of space in Mr Norrison's Code of the Highway, it must be remembered that there are now many punishable offences which formerly constituted only a breach of politeness and common sense. The non-motoring public will, however, be making a great mistake if they dismiss the code as no concern of theirs. Its provisions apply equally to all users of the road: indeed, the most important sections may be said to be those applying to cyclists, horse-driven vehicles and persons in charge of animals. It is of the most vital importance, for instance, that everyone should know that, in future, all animals, ridden, led, or driven, must keep to the left, or near side, of the road, except when overtaking. Hitherto, of course, they have kept to the right, facing oncoming traffic. Use should be made of grass or other verges where these exist, and, when approaching a corner, drivers of flocks or herds should send someone on in advance to warn approaching traffic. Before crossing the road or changing direction, those in charge of animals must await a favourable opportunity and show their intention 'by some appropriate signal'. But why should not the carrying of a lamp or lantern by the drover or shepherd be made compulsory? Nothing is quite so invisible as a black horse or bullock on a wet night. Cyclists should not hold on to a motor vehicle, even when it is stationary, where traffic is held up, but get to the kerb and dismount. Another section of the code that should prove fruitful of controversy is that relating to the use of signals. That everyone should get to know what the signals mean is mere common sense, but the suggestion that pedestrians should give signals themselves is a little alarming. One has visions of an old lady wildly signalling in the middle of the road with traffic piling up on either side in a state of hopeless confusion. Finally we would draw attention to a piece of advice addressed to all users of the road, that cannot be too frequently or too strongly stressed: 'Keep on guard against the errors of others. Never take a risk in the hope or expectation that everyone else will do what is necessary to avoid the consequences of your rashness.'

Rule of the Road (1887)

The rule of the road is only laid down to regulate traffic and prevent confusion. A hard and fast adherence to it, in all cases, would sometimes be wrong. If a man can avoid an accident by going to his wrong side, he must do so; otherwise he will be deprived of right to obtain damages in case of injury to himself or property. In meeting or overtaking a groom in charge of 2 horses, it is proper to take that side which will leave the led horse farthest from you. This is well known to, and generally done by every one conversant with riding and driving. To do otherwise is to put yourself in the wrong in the case of accidents.

Specific Gravity of Cork and Human (1892)

The specific gravity of cork varies considerably; you could easily ascertain that of any particular specimen as compared with water by the usual means. Water is, in round numbers, 800 times heavier than air, a cubic foot of water nearly weighing 1000 oz, or 16 lb, and a cubic foot of air 1¼ oz. The human body and water are of nearly equal specific gravity, as is proved by a man floating quietly on his back.

Soothsayer (1887)

A certain soothsayer is said to have prophesied before his royal master that something was going to happen, though, when it came to the point, he could not be induced to state what the something might be. From that historical augur the modern race of tipsters must have taken their cue. For weeks past some of the fraternity have advertised that the Lincolnshire Handicap would be won, not by the favourite, but by an outsider. This delightfully vague prophecy has been fulfilled to the letter. The gains of the tipsters can only be estimated.

Tiger Boys (1900)

The term 'tiger', as applied to a boy acting as carriage groom, is now seldom heard. When the cabriolet was a common vehicle, it was customary for a small boy to stand on the platform behind. The word tiger is said to have arisen from the stripes on the waistcoat, which was commonly worn.

Restoration of a New Wife (1853)

A curious application was made to Mr Hall, just before the closing of the Bow-street court, on Tuesday. A young man, respectably dressed, stated that he was married on Monday morning at Islington Church, and he had scarcely got out of the church when his bride threw her wedding-ring into his face, declared she would not have him, and returned home to her friends. What was he to do? Could he not have a summons to compel her to live with him? Mr Hall

An Ungallant Epigram (1854)

When Eve brougt *woe* to all mankind,
　　Old Adam called her *woman*,
But when she *woo'd* with love so kind,
　　He then pronounced it *wooman*;
But now with folly and with pride
　　Their husbands' pockets trimming,
The ladies are so full of *whims*
　　The people call them *whimen*.

regretted that he had no control over the young lady, and feared the applicant could hardly go into the ecclesiastical court for the restitution of conjugal rights. The application was certainly a novel one. Men came to the court every day to try to get rid of their wives, and there had been two such appeals to him that very afternoon; but, unfortunately, they never had a man imploring to have his wife restored to him.

Welsh Motto (1861)

[In your impression of the 2st ult., 'Firefly', in replying to 'Clwyd's' rendering of the Welsh motto *Heb dduw, heb ddim, a dduw, a digon*, says 'it is the motto of one or two old Welsh families'. Will 'Firefly' or any of your other readers oblige by saying what old Welsh families use the motto, and what arms they bear? I have heard that both in Wales and Ireland families have from time immemorial used arms and mottoes that have not been registered. R. Palmer Williams]

One of the letters we received in answer to 'Clwyd's' question stated it to be the motto of the Merediths, of Pentrebychan, Denbighshire; another mentioned it as occurring over the fireplace in the entrance-hall at Gloddeath, near Conway, a seat of the Mostyn family. We believe one or two others were also mentioned, but cannot now find the letters.

White Horse and Blowing Stone

The Blowing Stone used to stand on or near the Uffington White Horse but now it stands in a garden in the village of Kingston Lisle, in the Vale of the White Horse. When the horse was being scoured in the late 1940s, it was discovered that the foreman who was standing on a hillside a ¼ mile away could make the workmen on the horse hear when he was speaking in his normal voice. The site was acting as a whispering gallery. So, when the stone was situated in its position on or near the horse, the booming noise that it makes when the wind blows would have been regarded as the authentic voice of the horse.

'Whyre'

The word 'Whyr' is an old dialect word used as a call for driving sheep. In view of your locality near Swindon, this seems the more likely derivation of the name of your house than old Welsh.

In Times of War

[Editor's note: from the very first issue of THE FIELD *in 1853, and for nearly a century thereafter, the British seemed to be fighting someone somewhere in the world. Leading articles and reports from the front were always an important feature of a publication read by exactly the kind of men who either were, had been or would like to be officers in the armed forces. Frequently, thoughts of war inevitably spilled on to the pages of 'Answers to Correspondents' and gave a flavour of the times.]*

Call-up Papers (1916)

If you have either Army form B.2505-A. or E.2512-A., you might take it you are at liberty, but if not you may be called upon again.

The statement made was to the effect that those rejected, unless they possess the forms mentioned, will be required to undergo a further examination. Those certified as medically unfit on account of organic disease will be registered, and those rejected on account of eyesight or some slight physical defects will be attested and passed to the Army Reserve. They will then be utilised as they may be required. Due notice will, it is understood, be given to those necessary to be examined again. You cannot leave this country without a passport (although there is plenty of land available in the colonies if you can get out there) and whether one will be granted to you will depend largely on your position in relation to the facts set out in the first part of this answer.

Improved Crutches (1916)

The single-pole crutch is characterised as an abomination, productive of crutch palsy, and the Wantage adjustable crutch was an outcome of Dr Loveday's efforts to devise a comfortable support for his patients, to prevent or cure crutch palsy. The point where it

The Wantage crutches, showing the adjustable hand-pieces

scores over other makes is in the handpiece, which is 4 in wide, affording a good grip, and is made to adjust to the length of the arms, so that the weight of the body is borne by the arms and not supported under the armpits. Again, where padded heads are employed they become hard, and shock is felt which, it is stated, even springs do not dispose of. With the Wantage crutch a flexible chrome leather strap provides an excellent soft cushion for the armpit, gives a full inch of spring movement, does not lose its resilience with use, and effectively prevents road shock. For hospitals a pair of crutches with 7 extension pieces are provided for 12s.6d. and they give practically 7 pairs of crutches in one.

Plates for Heroes (1916)

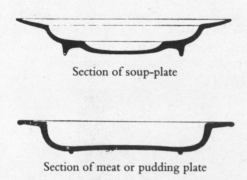

Section of soup-plate

Section of meat or pudding plate

A couple of plates have been devised which seem to be of use to such of our sailors and soldiers as are deprived of the use of one arm. One is a soup-plate with a depth in the centre, from which the last 2 or 3 spoonsful of soup can be easily removed. The other is a plate for solid food which has vertical sides and an overhanging rim. Against this pieces of meat and pudding can be pushed without any risk of their toppling over the edge of the plate. For convenience of commerce it has been suggested that the plates be named, and 'Unimanus' has been suggested (cf. Livy 35.21 and 41.21) but it seems simpler and shorter to call them *manchot* plates.

Russians at Batoum (1854)

Batoum and Teflis in the north, and Erzeroum and Ararat to the south, are the 4 points of the square, while Kars stands in the centre of them; the whole, as to position, may be compared to the pips on the 5 of clubs. If the Russians defeat Guyon they will soon be in

Kars, and Batoum also. English men-of-war steamers ought already to be at Batoum, but . . .

Your Own Chauffeur and Gardener (1916)

Where there's a will there's a way. Men are now acting as their own chauffeurs, who before the war thought they were too old to learn to drive a car. Others who had hardly handled a spade in their lives are now manfully digging over their kitchen gardens, and finding it not unexciting though laborious work. There is a piquancy about coming across stray potatoes in patches which purpost to have been thoroughly explored long ago. When a man by force of circumstances becomes his own gardener, he realises a good many essential truths, one of which is that the proverbial slowness of the professional is due quite as much to the stubborn character of Mother Earth as to the restful proclivities of the sons of Adam. Orderly rows of vegetables represent a great deal of solid and patient labour, and some of us are learning this lesson for the first time now that we realise that the rows of vegetables are part of the country's economic strength.

Index